Horizons

Mathematics 6

Book 2

Authors:
Cindi Mitchell & Lori Fowler

Editor:
Alan Christopherson

Graphic Design:
Jennifer Davis *Kyle Bennett*
Chris Burkholder *JoAnn Cumming* *Lauren Durain*
Keith Piccolo *Brian Ring* *Laura Miller*

AOP

804 N. 2nd Ave. E. Rock Rapids, IA 51246-1759 800-622-3070 www.aop.com

This book is dedicated;
To my Lord and Savior, Jesus Christ;
to my husband, Chet Fowler; and
to all of those people who faithfully prayed for me
after my serious automobile accident
which occurred during the writing of this book.
Lori Fowler

Media Credits:
Page 53: © Marvid, iStock; **page 53:** © Sibiryanka, iStock; **page 61:** © AlexLMX, iStock, Thinkstock

Horizons Mathematics 6, Book 2

804 N. 2nd Ave. E., Rock Rapids, IA 51246-1759

Printed in the United States of America
978-0-7403-0010-3

Multiplying Fractions

Michael had $\frac{1}{2}$ a cake to share among his friends. They ate $\frac{1}{2}$ of the remaining cake. What part of the whole cake did Michael and his friends eat?

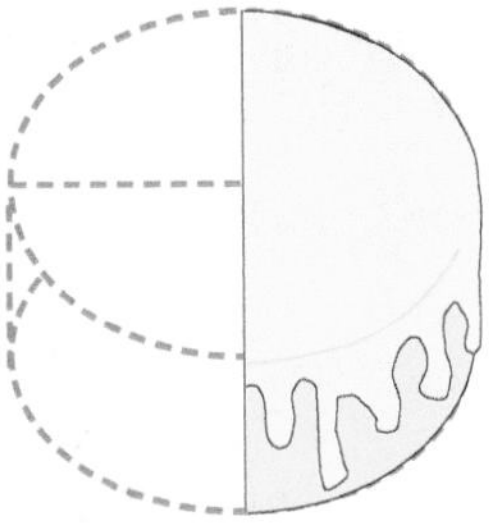

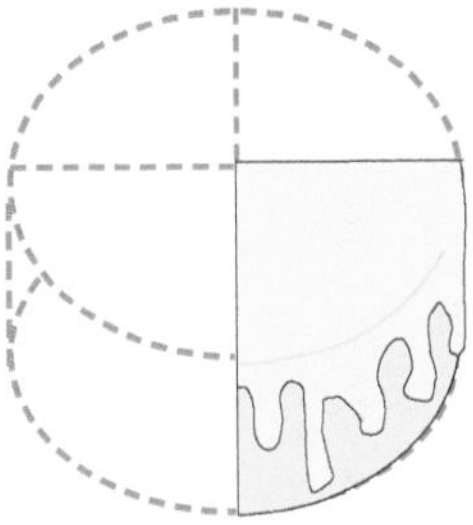

They ate $\frac{1}{4}$ of the entire cake.

We want to find $\frac{1}{2}$ of $\frac{1}{2}$, so we multiply.

STEP 1:
Multiply the numerators.

$\frac{1}{2} \times \frac{1}{2} = \frac{1}{?}$

STEP 2:
Multiply the denominators.

$\frac{1}{2} \times \frac{1}{2} = \frac{1}{4}$

(1) Multiply. Reduce to the lowest terms.

$\frac{7}{8} \times \frac{1}{8} =$ $\frac{4}{5} \times \frac{1}{2} =$ $\frac{1}{9} \times \frac{2}{5} =$ $\frac{3}{7} \times \frac{1}{4} =$

$\frac{4}{6} \times \frac{1}{3} =$ $\frac{1}{3} \times \frac{4}{12} =$ $\frac{7}{15} \times \frac{1}{2} =$ $\frac{3}{8} \times \frac{9}{10} =$

2 **Solve and interpret any remainders.**

The Bearley's need 1,290 tiles to cover a floor and a splash area. The tiles are sold in boxes of 25 tiles each. How many boxes should they buy?

Coach Brian needs has 229 players in his T-Ball league. Each player is to be given a Loganville T-Ball League patch. If the patches come in packages of 15, how many packages does Coach Brian need to buy?

Latrobe First Baptist needs to mail 8 boxes of supplies to their missionaries in Africa. If the church has $425 to spend on shipping, and each box will cost approximately $65, how many of the 8 boxes can they ship with $425?

Each cabin at Youth Camp houses 12 students. If there are 69 girls going to camp and 43 boys going to camp, how many cabins will be needed for all the students? (Remember, girls and boys cannot share a cabin).

3 **Find the quotient.**

$0.5\overline{)3.20}$ $.82\overline{)2.952}$ $62.5\overline{)4.3125}$ $3.8\overline{)2.1280}$

4 **Convert the following numbers from base 2 into base 10.**

2^4	2^3	2^2	2^1	$2^0 = 1$
1	1	0	1	1 =
	1	1	1	1 =
	1	0	0	1 =
			1	1 =
1	0	1	1	0 =
1	1	1	1	1 =

5 **Count the change. Use the fewest coins and bills possible.**
Write the total amount due.

Price	Paid	Change Due
Example: $1.55	$5.00	3 dollars, 2 dimes, 1 quarter = $3.45
$3.14	$5.00	
$8.29	$10.00	
$12.30	$15.00	
$38.75	$40.00	
$12.19	$20.00	

6 **Label each time zone.**
Draw the correct time on the clock face in each time zone.

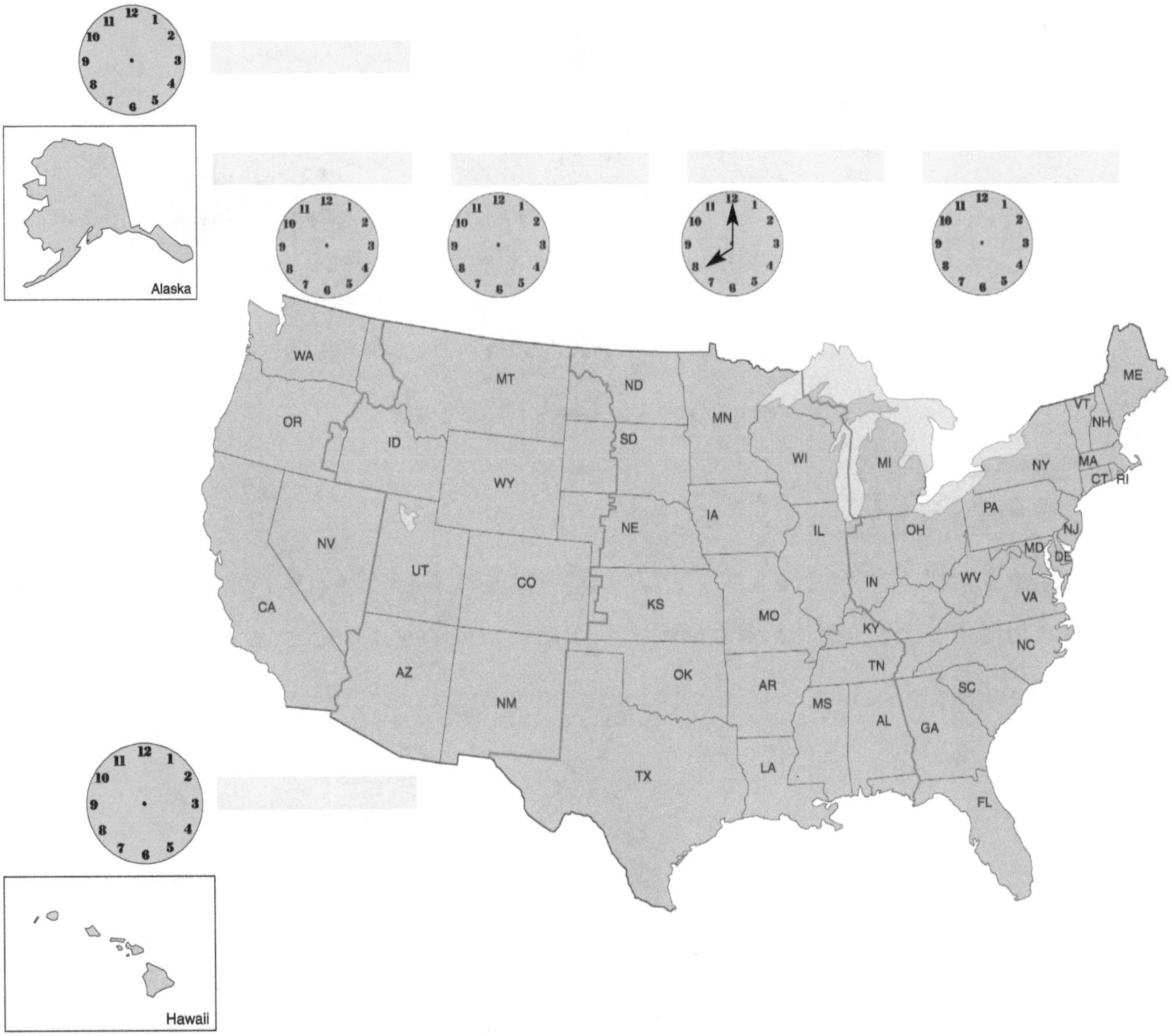

Multiply a Fraction by a Whole Number

Clara collected data about the 15 children in her preschool class. She discovered that $\frac{3}{5}$ of the children have a pet at home. How many children in the class have a pet?

To find the fraction of a number we multiply:

What is $\frac{3}{5}$ of 15? **OR** **$\frac{3}{5}$ of 15 =**

When you see the word "of" in a mathematical equation, it means to multiply. Rewrite the equation and substitute a multiplication sign where the word "of" is written.

$\frac{3}{5}$ of 15 = 9 OR $\frac{3}{5} \times \frac{15}{1} = \frac{45}{5} = 9$

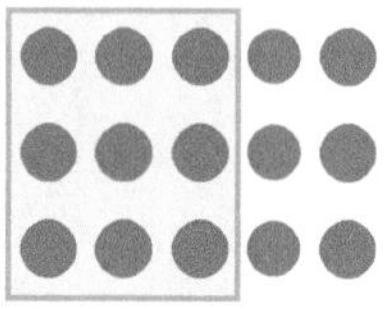

9 of the students in Clara's class have pets.

Clara also discovered $\frac{1}{3}$ of the students with pets have cats as pets.

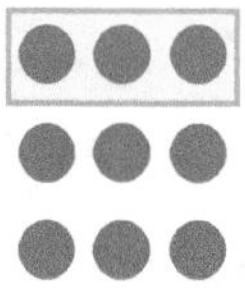

How many students have cats?

$\frac{1}{3}$ of 9 = 3 OR $\frac{1}{3} \times \frac{9}{1} = 3$

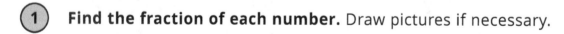

1 **Find the fraction of each number.** Draw pictures if necessary.

$\frac{1}{2}$ of 16

$\frac{1}{4}$ of 12

$\frac{1}{4}$ of 20

$\frac{2}{3}$ of 9

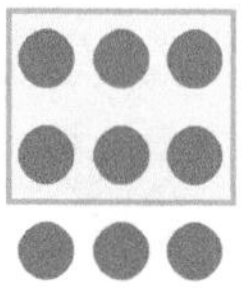

$\frac{1}{10}$ of 50

$\frac{2}{3}$ of 24

(2) Multiply. Rename to lowest terms.

$\frac{23}{25} \times \frac{2}{10} =$ $\frac{9}{18} \times \frac{4}{8} =$ $\frac{7}{20} \times \frac{5}{8} =$

$\frac{56}{90} \times \frac{45}{50} =$ $\frac{6}{8} \times \frac{2}{3} =$ $\frac{15}{16} \times \frac{4}{3} =$

---

(3) Solve and interpret any remainders.

The caterer made 250 mini quiches for the preschool brunch. If each person will eat 3 quiches, how many people will be fed?

A giant watermelon, weighing 30 pounds was cut into 20 equal slices. How much did each slice weigh?

How many boards 48 inches long can be cut from a board 168 inches long?

In your monthly budget you have allowed $175 for gasoline. If it takes approximately $21 to fill up your tank, how many times can you fill up in a month?

(4) Divide.

2.095 ÷ 5 = 18.78 ÷ 6 = 17.334 ÷ .54 = 28.35 ÷ 5 =

482.4 ÷ 4.02 = .0072 ÷ 8 = .658 ÷ 7 = 9.54 ÷ 6 =

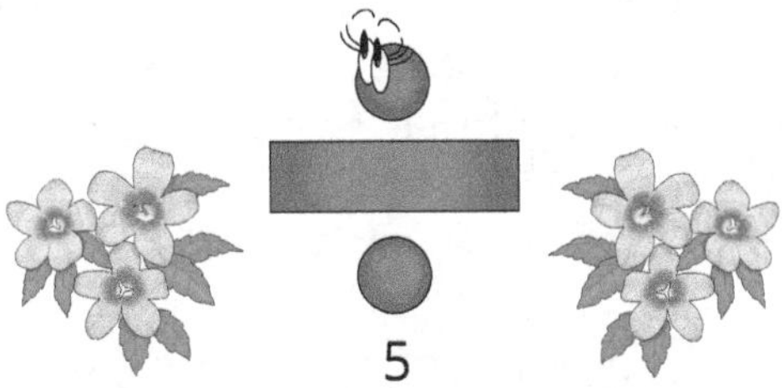

5 **Convert each base 10 number to its base 2 equivalent.**

56 = 63 = 9 = 23 =

6 **Round each decimal number to the nearest hundredth in order to find your path through the maze.**

10.239 =_____ 56.982 =_____ 0.367 =_____

0.085 =_____ 42.006 =_____ 19.732 =_____

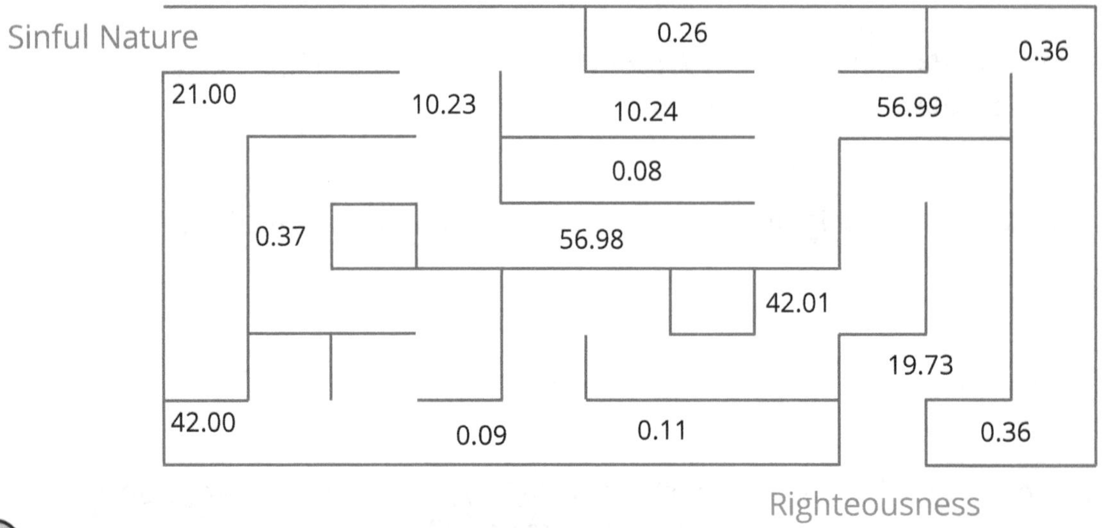

7 **Write the amount of change due from each transaction.** Use the fewest coins and bills possible.

Eileen purchased a set of tires for her car at a cost of $397.65. If she gave the cashier $500.00, how much change is she due?

Mr. Tomko used $295.00 to purchase a miter saw and $58.95 to purchase a new drill. How much change will he receive if he gives the cashier four one hundred dollar bills?

Kathy purchased a pair of shoes. She paid the cashier with a $100.00 dollar bill. If she received a ten dollar bill and a quarter in change, how much did the shoes cost?

Mrs. Ross spent $146.25 at the grocery store. She then spent $35.65 at the grocery store's pharmacy. If she left the house with 3 one hundred dollar bills, how much cash does she now have? List what bills she has in her wallet if the cashier gave her the correct change.

Area

Don is recarpeting a large family room. If the room measures $5\frac{1}{2}$ yards long and $5\frac{3}{4}$ yards wide, how much carpet will Don need?

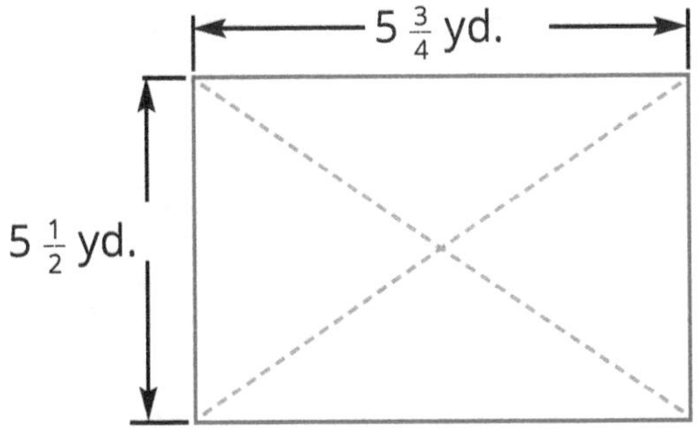

When first looking at this problem, one might round the measurements shown and calculate that Don will need at least 36 square yards of carpet. But what if Don needs an exact answer?

$$5\frac{1}{2} \times 5\frac{3}{4} =$$

To multiply mixed numbers, we must first write them as improper fractions, then multiply.

$$5\frac{1}{2} \times 5\frac{3}{4} = \frac{11}{2} \times \frac{23}{4}$$

$$\frac{11}{2} \times \frac{23}{4} = \frac{253}{8} = 31\frac{5}{8} \text{ square yards}$$

Don will need exactly $31\frac{5}{8}$ yards of carpet.

1 **Multiply.**

$2\frac{1}{2} \times 3\frac{1}{4} =$

$5\frac{1}{5} \times 4\frac{1}{4} =$

$3\frac{4}{5} \times 2\frac{2}{8} =$

$8 \times 2\frac{3}{4} =$

$9\frac{5}{6} \times 10\frac{7}{8} =$

$5\frac{1}{4} \times 3\frac{5}{8} =$

(2) Find the product.

$\frac{4}{5} \times 8 =$

$15 \times \frac{1}{3} =$

$\frac{2}{3} \times 12 =$

$\frac{5}{10} \times 100 =$

$\frac{7}{8} \times 35 =$

$\frac{1}{8} \times 40 =$

$\frac{1}{5} \times 200 =$

$\frac{2}{3} \times 300 =$

(3) Solve and interpret any remainders.

Andy's computer printer prints 500 lines per minute. How many lines does it print each second?

Dan budgets $60.00 for lunch money. This money should last him for 2 weeks of work (Mon. – Fri.). If he spends $5.00 each day on lunch, how much money should he have left over at the end of 2 weeks?

Lloydsville Christian Academy has 59 5th grade students. If each class should have only 15 students, how many 5th grade classes will there be?

Lloydsville Christian Academy's monthly financial statement showed that $1,918 was made selling coupon books. If each book cost $12 is this total correct?

(4) Find the sum.

62.5 + 2.65 + .1849 + .005 =

.43 + .002 + 15.07 =

0.82 + .0672 + 146.25 =

32 + 0.651 + .02 + 3.15 =

2.63 + .125 + 2.1243 =

How to determine the percentage.

Bob's Motor Company had 60 automobiles left to sell. It sold 10% of them at a discounted price. How many cars were sold at a discounted rate?

You are really asked to determine: What is 10% of 60?
Remember: the word "of" signals multiplication (x) when used in a mathematical equation. 10% x 60 =

Change the % to a decimal: .10 x 60 = 6

6 cars were sold at a discounted price.

(5) **Complete the chart by finding the amount of each discount.**
Hint: Round any change to the nearest penny.

ITEM	PRICE	10% DISCOUNT
automobile	$27,973.00	
toaster	$ 89.99	
sofa	$ 798.99	
refrigerator	$ 1495.26	

(6) **Order each decimal number from the largest to the smallest in order to reveal a message.**

51.023	.0986	0.0035	9.086	513.002	79.26
E	E	R	R	D	I
139.32	79.60	78.47			
E	L	V			

___ ___ ___ ___ ___ ___ ___ ___ ___

Psalm 56:13

Multiply Fractions

Whenever you are working with fractions, you are expected to give answers in lowest terms, or in reduced form. Simplifying by using the cross-out method can make the process of reducing, renaming into lowest terms, less difficult. When simplifying through the cross-simplification method, you examine the numerators and denominators which are diagonal from each other. Look at the examples provided below:

$\frac{\cancel{20}^{1}}{30} \times \frac{10}{\cancel{40}_{2}} =$

20 and 40 are both divisible by 20.
Divide by 20 and this will simplify them.

$\frac{\cancel{20}^{1}}{\cancel{30}_{3}} \times \frac{\cancel{10}^{1}}{\cancel{40}_{2}} =$

30 and 10 are both divisible by 10.
Divide by 10 and this will also simplify them.

If worked the original way you would have to simplify a very large fraction. Notice that the cross-simplification method avoids the large numbers.

$\frac{20}{30} \times \frac{10}{40} = \frac{200}{1200} = \frac{1}{6}$ $\quad$ $\frac{1}{3} \times \frac{1}{2} = \frac{1}{6}$

Look at these additional examples. This first example does not use the cross-simplification method. Notice the large numbers which you have to work with. They are shown in green. Also notice the additional renaming which is required of the answer.

$4\frac{4}{7} \times \frac{3}{4} =$ $\quad$ $\frac{32}{7} \times \frac{3}{4} = \frac{96}{28} = 3\frac{12}{28} = 3\frac{3}{7}$

Now look at the second example below which uses the cross-simplification method. Notice the large numbers and additional renaming of the answer has been eliminated through this easy process.

$4\frac{4}{7} \times \frac{3}{4} =$ $\quad$ $\frac{\cancel{32}^{8}}{7} \times \frac{3}{\cancel{4}_{1}} = \frac{24}{7} = 3\frac{3}{7}$

(1) Use cross-simplification and multiply.

$5\frac{1}{3} \times 1\frac{1}{4} =$ $\qquad$ $2\frac{1}{4} \times 12\frac{1}{3} =$ $\qquad$ $2\frac{1}{4} \times 6\frac{2}{3} =$

$\frac{15}{20} \times \frac{2}{5} =$ $\qquad$ $\frac{3}{5} \times \frac{10}{7} =$ $\qquad$ $\frac{3}{6} \times \frac{1}{3} =$

2 **Multiply.**

$6 \times \frac{4}{5} =$ $4\frac{1}{2} \times 5\frac{6}{7} =$ $2 \times \frac{8}{9} =$ $7\frac{1}{5} \times \frac{1}{2} =$

$5\frac{4}{7} \times \frac{3}{5} =$ $\frac{1}{6} \times \frac{1}{2} =$ $\frac{1}{3} \times \frac{3}{10} =$ $\frac{6}{12} \times 4\frac{1}{2} =$

3 **Solve.**

Mrs. Kuhn receives a 10% discount each time she buys fabrics at The Textile Mill. Below is a chart which shows her January orders.
How much money will she save on each order?

Hint: When calculating discounts, round to the nearest tenth (penny).

Week in January	Total Order	Amount of Discount (10%)
Week 1	\$5,697.25	
Week 2	\$ 378.98	
Week 3	\$ 476.29	
Week 4	\$3,091.73	

4 **Write <, >, or =.**

0.264 ◇ 0.337 485.625 ◇ 485.0625 61.82 ◇ 61.79

931.8 ◇ 931.800 58.026 ◇ 57.026 6723. ◇ 6.723

5 **Solve by using the information in the chart.**

Hint: Remember, you are calculating the amount of the discount.
Round each decimal to the nearest penny.

Jerry's Bait & Tackle
Clearance Sale

Fishing Rods	$\frac{1}{2}$ off	Fishing Line	$\frac{1}{2}$ off
Fishing Reels	$\frac{1}{3}$ off	Tackle Boxes	$\frac{1}{4}$ off
Plastic Worms	$\frac{3}{4}$ off	Lures	$\frac{1}{3}$ off

Al purchased two fishing rods: one marked $65.00 and one marked $55.00. He also purchased a tackle box for $25.00. How much did he spend after receiving the sale discounts on these items?

David bought 5 packs of plastic worms and two rolls of fishing line. If the regular price of the worms was $1.25 per pack and the regular price of the line was $2.50, how much did David spend?

James has $125.00 to spend at the store. He wants to purchase a new rod marked $56.00 and new reel marked $155.00. Does he have enough money to purchase these items once the discounts have been taken?

Len wants to purchase four (4) lures at a regular cost of $3.00 each. If he has $10.00, can he purchase all four lures once the discounts have been calculated?

6 **Solve.**

Sally's Boutique is marking down all the summer merchandise to make room for the new fall clothes. Everything is already marked with a sale price and Sally is now discounting everything by an additional 10%, what will the new prices be?
Fill in the new price chart shown below.

Sally's Boutique

All dresses	$40.00
All dress shorts	$25.00
All blouses	$15.00
All earrings	$2.00 pr.
All belts	$5.00 ea.

Sally's Boutique

All dresses	
All dress shorts	
All blouses	
All earrings	
All belts	

7 **Order the following decimal numbers from the smallest to the largest.**

56.395	65.293	56.095	65.329
101.110	101.011	101.010	100.010
254.636	245.636	223.654	254.363

Reciprocals

Two numbers whose product is 1 are reciprocals of each other.
Look at the example below:

$\frac{4}{5} \times \frac{5}{4} = \frac{1}{1} = 1$ $\frac{4}{5}$ and $\frac{5}{4}$ are reciprocals.

In looking at this example, you will notice that the numerators and denominators of these two fractions have been exchanged. In short, you may switch the numerator and denominator of a fraction to find the reciprocal.
Look at this additional example:

$\frac{3}{4}$ Exchange the numerator and denominator to find the reciprocal. $\frac{4}{3}$ is the reciprocal.

Now multiply the two fractions to see if they equal 1. True reciprocals will always equal 1.

$$\frac{3}{4} \times \frac{4}{3} = \frac{12}{12} = 1$$

To find the reciprocal of $1\frac{1}{5}$, you must first write $1\frac{1}{5}$ as an improper fraction.

$$1\frac{1}{5} = \frac{6}{5}$$

The reciprocal of $\frac{6}{5}$ is $\frac{5}{6}$

Multiply $\frac{6}{5} \times \frac{5}{6} = \frac{30}{30} = 1$

1 **Write the reciprocal of each fraction.**

$\frac{12}{100}$ $\frac{45}{65}$ $\frac{2}{4}$ $\frac{10}{19}$ $\frac{7}{8}$ $\frac{4}{5}$

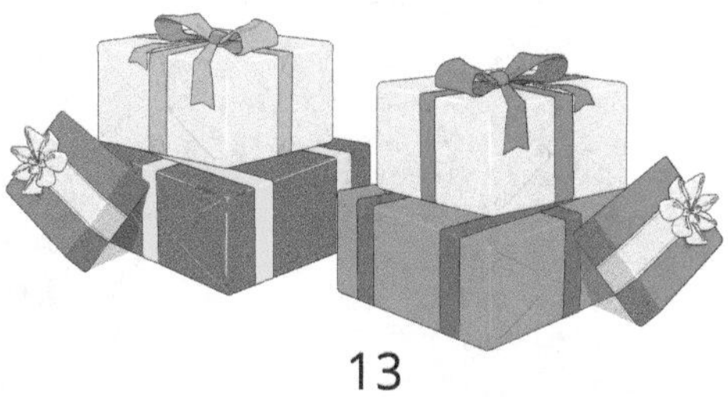

2 **Solve using cross-simplification.**

$\frac{5}{8} \times \frac{4}{7} =$ $\frac{3}{8} \times \frac{16}{27} =$ $\frac{2}{3} \times \frac{1}{4} =$ $\frac{3}{10} \times \frac{5}{6} =$

$\frac{2}{3} \times \frac{3}{5} =$ $\frac{14}{19} \times \frac{1}{2} =$ $\frac{16}{21} \times \frac{7}{8} =$ $\frac{6}{7} \times \frac{7}{9} =$

3 **Match the problem with the correct answer.**

$1\frac{2}{5} \times 2\frac{6}{7} =$	$27\frac{5}{8}$
$4\frac{1}{3} \times 3\frac{6}{8} =$	4
$7\frac{2}{5} \times 2\frac{1}{7} =$	7
$3\frac{1}{4} \times 8\frac{1}{2} =$	$16\frac{1}{4}$
$2\frac{3}{8} \times 2\frac{2}{3} =$	$6\frac{1}{3}$
$4\frac{2}{3} \times 1\frac{4}{8} =$	$15\frac{6}{7}$

4 **Fill in the missing number.**

$\frac{1}{2} \times$ ___ $= 12$ $\frac{1}{4} \times$ ___ $= 5$ $\frac{2}{3} \times$ ___ $= 6$

___ $\times 30 = 10$ ___ $\times 100 = 50$ ___ $\times 100 = 75$

5 **Solve.**

0.278 − 0.021 = 195.033 − 23.21 = 56.98 − 25.43 =

41.08 − 1.559 = 2.706 − 0.291 = 8.061 − 2.639 =

6 **Fill in the missing number and the corresponding letter to decode the hidden message.**

```
  14.00?  __ = O     436.89  __ = I     3.?6  __ = H     11?.03  __ = L
+  7.118           +266.0?            +0.19            +286.18
  21.122            702.92             3.95             397.21

  0.4?4  __ = S     2?.86  __ = N     7.7?5  __ = E
+0.748            +  4.89           +3.289
  1.172             34.75            11.054
```

__ __ __ __ __ __ __ __

7 4 1 3 9 6 2 2

Ephesians 4:22-24

7 **Solve for *n*.**

$582 + n = 777$

$2{,}621 + n = 3{,}125$

$3{,}413 + n = 8{,}562$

$1{,}934 + n = 2{,}597$

$643 + n = 925$

$8{,}621 + n = 17{,}789$

Division of Fractions

Gayle has two chocolate bars and wants to use these bars to make a chocolate pie. If each pie calls for $\frac{2}{3}$ of a chocolate bar, how many pies can Gayle make?

Gayle needs to find out how many two-thirds there are in 2. She needs to divide 2 by $\frac{2}{3}$. To divide a fraction, we multiply by it's reciprocal.

$$2 \div \frac{2}{3} = 2 \times \frac{3}{2} = \frac{2}{1} \times \frac{3}{2} = \frac{6}{2} = 3$$

By looking at the diagrams, and by looking at the problem, one can plainly see that there are three $\frac{2}{3}$ in the 2 chocolate bars. Gayle can make three pies.

Look at the following example:
If you have 4 apples pies, how many people can you serve if each person gets a $\frac{1}{4}$ slice of pie?

Hint: How many $\frac{1}{2}$'s are there in 4 pies?

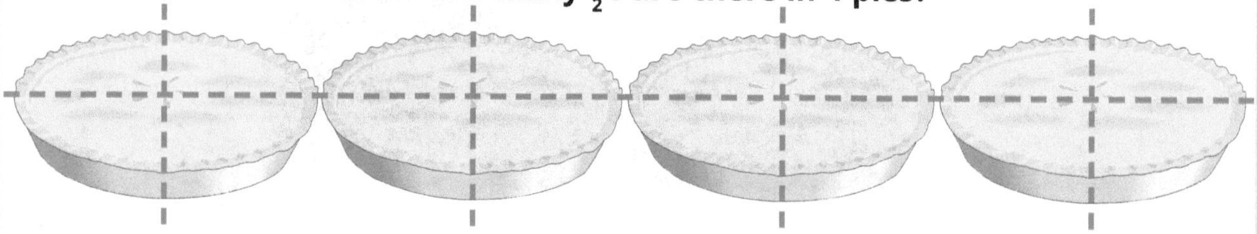

$$4 \div \frac{1}{4} = 4 \times \frac{4}{1} = \frac{16}{1} = 16$$

16 people can be served from the 4 pies.

(1) **Solve.** Draw pictures if necessary.

$4 \div \frac{1}{2} =$ $\qquad$ $3 \div \frac{1}{3} =$ $\qquad$ $12 \div \frac{1}{4} =$ $\qquad$ $23 \div \frac{1}{6} =$

$24 \div \frac{1}{8} =$ $\qquad$ $3 \div \frac{1}{2} =$ $\qquad$ $8 \div \frac{4}{5} =$ $\qquad$ $1 \div \frac{1}{4} =$

(2) Shade the reciprocals of the fractions shown.

$\frac{45}{98}$ $\frac{63}{78}$ $\frac{25}{45}$ $\frac{12}{72}$ $\frac{125}{255}$ $\frac{11}{33}$

$\frac{65}{100}$ $\frac{98}{133}$ $\frac{245}{698}$ $\frac{14}{55}$ $\frac{143}{156}$ $\frac{74}{85}$

$\frac{64}{100}$	$\frac{133}{98}$	$\frac{25}{45}$	$\frac{97}{132}$	$\frac{245}{398}$	$\frac{72}{12}$	$\frac{25}{45}$
$\frac{45}{25}$	$\frac{55}{14}$	$\frac{156}{143}$	$\frac{252}{43}$	$\frac{85}{74}$	$\frac{255}{125}$	$\frac{98}{45}$
$\frac{896}{33}$	$\frac{100}{65}$	$\frac{101}{46}$	$\frac{13}{65}$	$\frac{73}{12}$	$\frac{698}{245}$	$\frac{45}{98}$
$\frac{11}{33}$	$\frac{33}{11}$	$\frac{65}{100}$	$\frac{142}{155}$	$\frac{121}{85}$	$\frac{78}{63}$	$\frac{65}{100}$

(3) Multiply. Use cross-simplification to find the answer in lowest terms.

$\frac{5}{16} \times 20\frac{3}{10} =$ $8\frac{2}{5} \times 6\frac{11}{12} =$ $3\frac{2}{3} \times 2\frac{10}{15} =$

$2\frac{1}{2} \times 12\frac{6}{7} =$ $15\frac{3}{5} \times 9\frac{1}{3} =$ $2\frac{4}{5} \times 1\frac{1}{2} =$

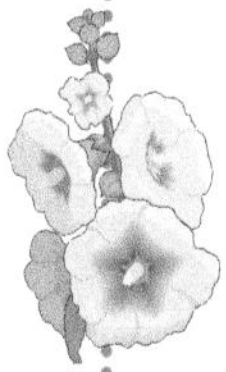

(4) Find the difference.

Help Christen find her way to church. Find each difference. Then add the answers to determine which path she needs to take. The correct path has a sum of 485.261.

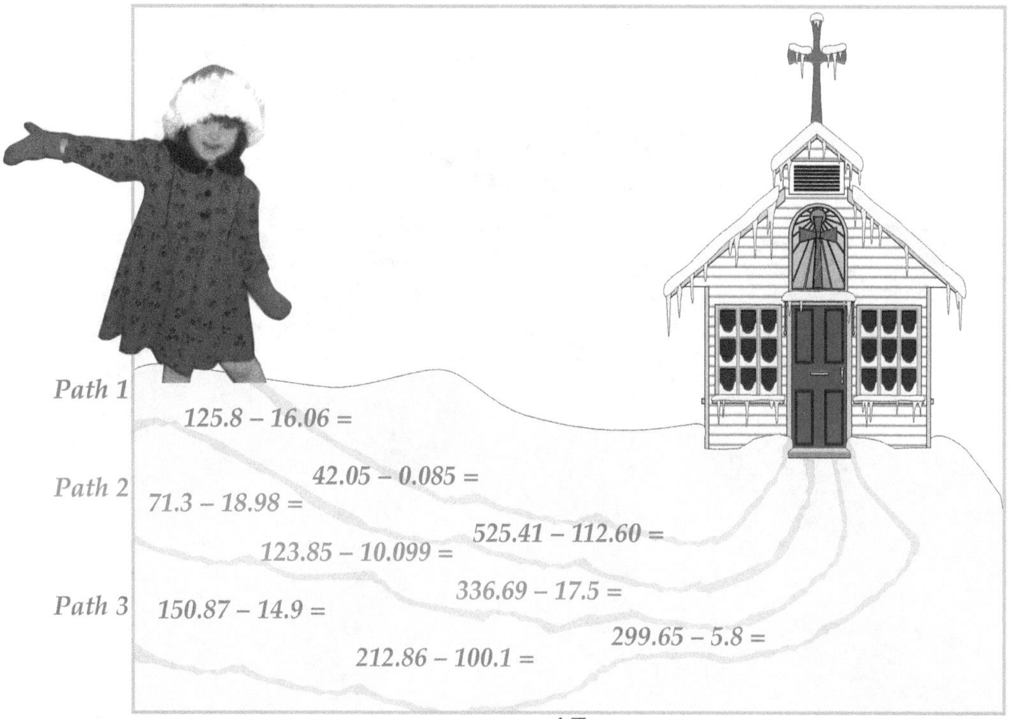

5 **Find the missing numbers.**

$$\begin{array}{r} 38.9 \\ -\ ?.25 \\ \hline 29.65 \end{array}$$

$$\begin{array}{r} 39.65 \\ -\ 5.? \\ \hline 33.85 \end{array}$$

$$\begin{array}{r} 2?.41 \\ -\ 12.63 \\ \hline 12.78 \end{array}$$

$$\begin{array}{r} 50.87 \\ -\ 14.?9 \\ \hline 36.78 \end{array}$$

$$\begin{array}{r} ?9.65 \\ -\ 36.9 \\ \hline 42.75 \end{array}$$

$$\begin{array}{r} 100.58 \\ -\ 77.16? \\ \hline 23.414 \end{array}$$

6 **Solve for N.**

$N - 9 = 125$ $N - 15 = 78$ $N - 12 = 1{,}006$

$N - 123 = 452$ $N - 26 = 937$ $N - 306 = 521$

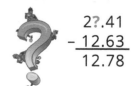

Division of Fractions

Dividing one fraction by another fraction is very similar to the multiplication of a fraction by a whole number. Look at the example below:

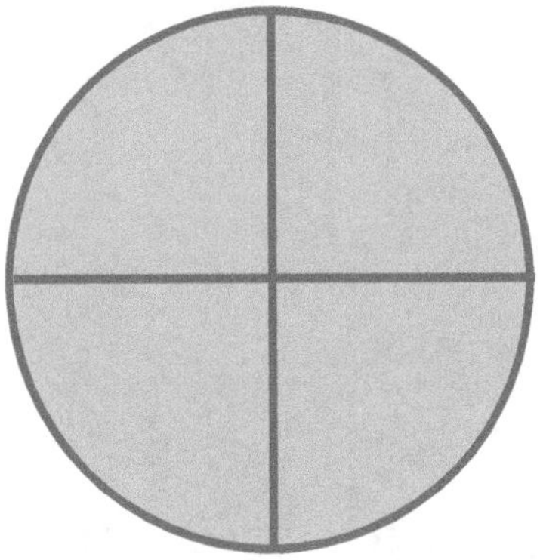

How many fourths are in $\frac{1}{2}$?

$\frac{1}{2} \div \frac{1}{4} =$

Remember to multiply by the reciprocal of the second number:

$\frac{1}{2} \times \frac{4}{1} = \frac{4}{2} = 2$

There are 2 fourths in $\frac{1}{2}$.

How many sixths are in $\frac{2}{3}$?

$\frac{2}{3} \div \frac{1}{6} =$

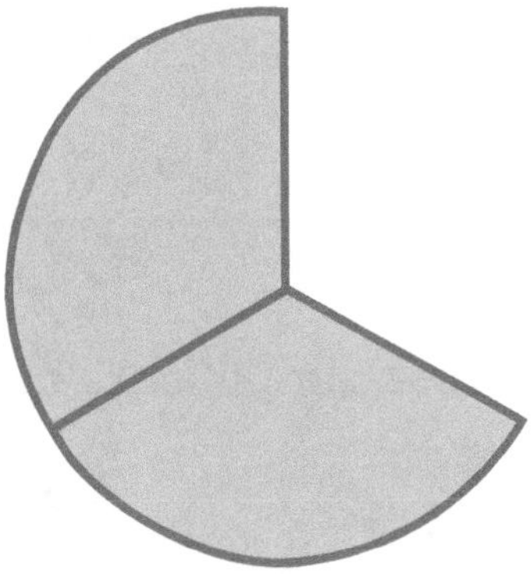

$\frac{2}{3} \times \frac{6}{1} = \frac{12}{3} = 4$

There are 4 sixths in $\frac{2}{3}$.

(1) Divide.

$\frac{1}{4} \div \frac{1}{8} =$ $\frac{1}{2} \div \frac{2}{10} =$ $\frac{3}{4} \div \frac{1}{8} =$ $\frac{2}{3} \div \frac{1}{2} =$

$\frac{20}{25} \div \frac{1}{5} =$ $\frac{18}{30} \div \frac{1}{3} =$ $\frac{2}{3} \div \frac{1}{3} =$ $\frac{8}{12} \div \frac{1}{4} =$

2 **Solve.**

$110 \div \frac{1}{2} =$

$939 \div \frac{1}{3} =$

$854 \div \frac{1}{4} =$

$3{,}416 \div \frac{1}{2} =$

$1{,}212 \div \frac{1}{6} =$

$405 \div \frac{1}{5} =$

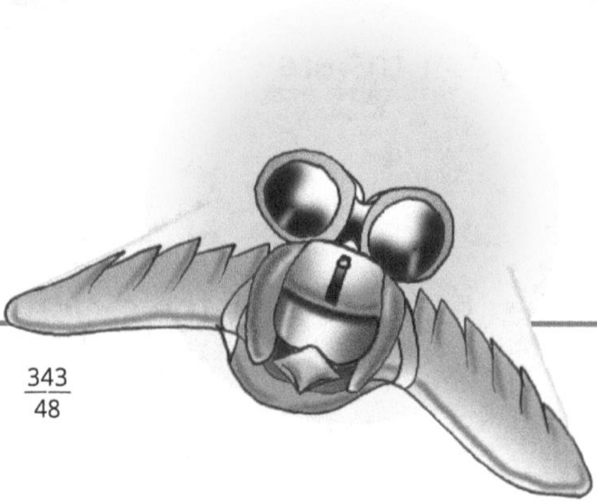

3 **Write the reciprocal.**

$\frac{91}{540}$

$\frac{343}{48}$

$\frac{88}{530}$

$\frac{184}{26}$

$\frac{24}{31}$

$\frac{339}{56}$

4 **Multiply using cross-simplification.**

$\frac{25}{35} \times \frac{10}{15}$

$\frac{65}{100} \times \frac{2}{5} =$

$\frac{78}{99} \times \frac{33}{12} =$

$\frac{125}{225} \times \frac{5}{25} =$

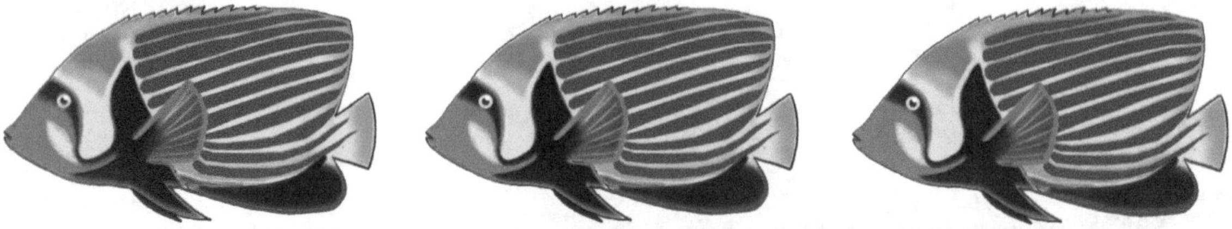

5 **Solve for the missing number.**

$$\begin{array}{r} 5?4 \\ \times\ 60 \\ \hline 33{,}840 \end{array} \qquad \begin{array}{r} 17? \\ \times\ 13 \\ \hline 2{,}288 \end{array} \qquad \begin{array}{r} ?18 \\ \times\ 70 \\ \hline 57{,}260 \end{array}$$

$$\begin{array}{r} 721 \\ \times\ 3?6 \\ \hline 242{,}256 \end{array} \qquad \begin{array}{r} 271 \\ \times\ ?05 \\ \hline 163{,}955 \end{array} \qquad \begin{array}{r} 47 \\ \times\ ? \\ \hline 329 \end{array}$$

6 **Draw the following items:**

A pair of parallel lines

A pair of perpendicular lines

A pair of intersecting lines

7 **Solve for *N*.**

$N \times 24 = 1{,}512$ $\qquad$ $N \times 15 = 1{,}050$ $\qquad$ $N \times 80 = 240$

$N \times 56 = 504$ $\qquad$ $N \times 71 = 1{,}278$ $\qquad$ $N \times 63 = 3{,}402$

Division of Fractions

For lunch Brett, Bryce, and Chet ate half of a pizza. How much pizza did each boy get?

Divide $\frac{1}{2}$ by 3 to find out how much pizza each boy ate.

STEP 1
Write the 3 as a fraction.

$\frac{1}{2} \div 3 =$

$\frac{1}{2} \div \frac{3}{1} =$

STEP 2
Change the problem to a multiplication problem by multiplying the reciprocal of the divisor.

$\frac{1}{2} \div \frac{3}{1} =$

$\frac{1}{2} \times \frac{1}{3} =$

STEP 3
Multiply the numerators. Multiply the denominators.

$\frac{1}{2} \times \frac{1}{3} = \frac{1}{6}$

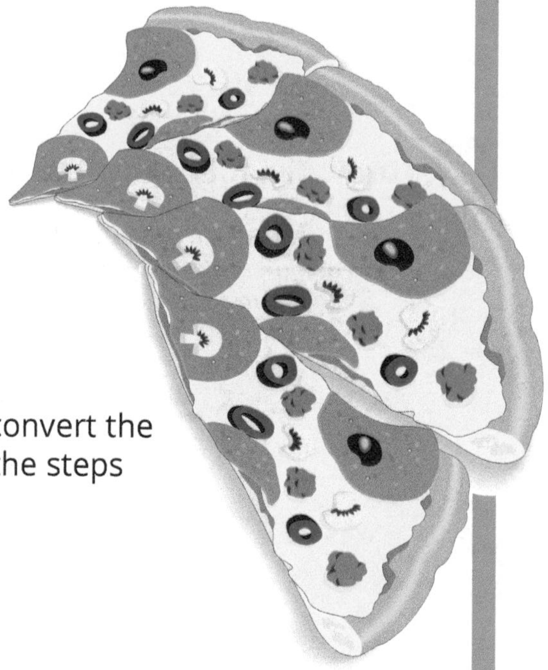

Each boy ate $\frac{1}{6}$ of the pie.

Look at this example:

When dividing a mixed number by a whole number convert the mixed number to an improper fraction. Then follow the steps listed above.

$2\frac{1}{7} \div 6 = \frac{15}{7} \div 6 =$

$\frac{15}{7} \div \frac{6}{1} =$

$\frac{15}{7} \times \frac{1}{6} = \frac{15}{42} = \frac{5}{14}$

1 **Divide and simplify.**

$\frac{1}{10} \div 10 =$	$\frac{1}{4} \div 5 =$	$4\frac{1}{3} \div 3 =$
$\frac{10}{5} \div 3 =$	$\frac{14}{3} \div 2 =$	$4\frac{2}{3} \div 6 =$
$2\frac{1}{8} \div 6 =$	$9\frac{1}{7} \div 4 =$	

2 Match the problem with the correct answer.

$\frac{5}{7} \div 6 =$ $\frac{9}{5} \div 3 =$ $\frac{5}{6} \div 4 =$ $\frac{2}{7} \div 5 =$

Data Bank: $\frac{5}{24}$ $\frac{5}{42}$ $\frac{9}{15}$ $\frac{1}{28}$ $\frac{2}{35}$

3 Find the fraction of each number.

Connect the answers, left to right, and a picture will appear.

$\frac{1}{3}$ of 15	$\frac{2}{5}$ of 10
$\frac{1}{2}$ of 20	$\frac{2}{9}$ of 81
$\frac{2}{3}$ of 30	$\frac{3}{7}$ of 56
$\frac{3}{7}$ of 49	$\frac{1}{9}$ of 27
$\frac{1}{6}$ of 12	$\frac{1}{5}$ of 30
$\frac{3}{4}$ of 100	$\frac{1}{9}$ of 63
$\frac{2}{5}$ of 75	$\frac{2}{10}$ of 70
$\frac{1}{6}$ of 54	$\frac{2}{5}$ of 100
$\frac{2}{3}$ of 18	$\frac{2}{3}$ of 12
$\frac{3}{9}$ of 81	$\frac{1}{3}$ of 150

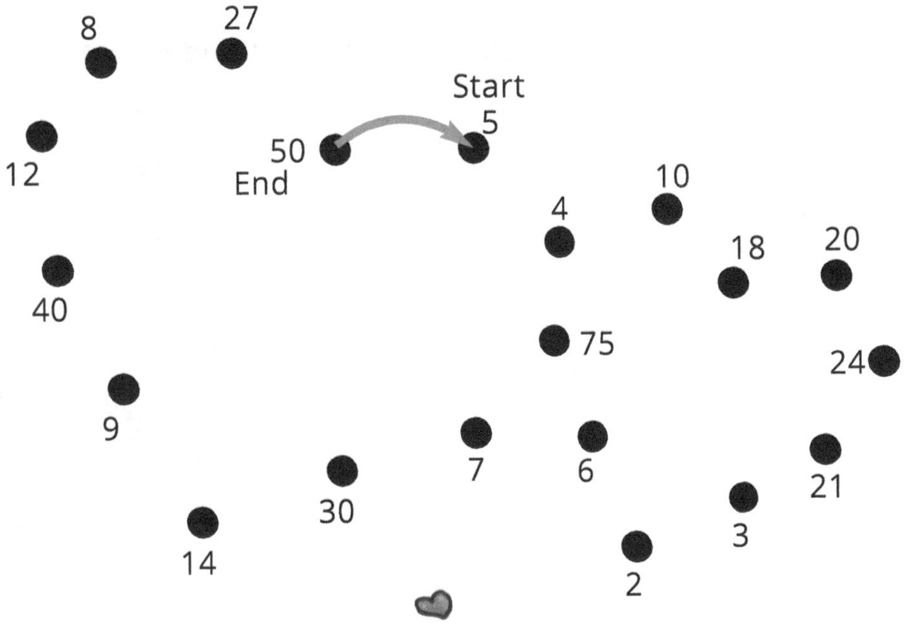

4 Write the reciprocals for each fraction.

$\frac{1}{2}$ $\frac{4}{5}$ $\frac{45}{98}$ $\frac{101}{987}$ $\frac{760}{231}$

$\frac{65}{70}$ $\frac{23}{56}$ $\frac{92}{334}$ $\frac{398}{510}$ $\frac{801}{1010}$

5 **Find the missing number.**

$\begin{array}{r} 271 \text{ R18} \\ 26\overline{)7,?64} \end{array}$	$\begin{array}{r} 128 \text{ R51} \\ 5?\overline{)6,835} \end{array}$	$\begin{array}{r} 206 \\ 39\overline{)8,0?4} \end{array}$	$\begin{array}{r} 35 \text{ R71} \\ ?9\overline{)2,836} \end{array}$
$\begin{array}{r} 40 \text{ R9} \\ 93\overline{)?,729} \end{array}$	$\begin{array}{r} 80 \text{ R16} \\ 42\overline{)3,?76} \end{array}$	$\begin{array}{r} 94 \text{ R61} \\ 8?\overline{)8,239} \end{array}$	$\begin{array}{r} 4,106 \\ 18\overline{)?3,908} \end{array}$

6 **Draw the indicated shape and find the perimeter.** (The shape does not have to be to scale.)

Draw a rectangle with a width of 18 mm and a height of 25 mm. Perimeter =	Draw a 16 cm square. Perimeter =
Draw a 5 cm regular octagon. Perimeter =	Draw a parallelogram with sides of 5 mm and 15 mm. Perimeter =

7 **Solve for N.**

$N \div 63 = 3$ $\qquad$ $N \div 25 = 37$ $\qquad$ $N \div 4 = 267$

$862 \div N = 431$ $\qquad$ $596 \div N = 149$ $\qquad$ $1,554 \div N = 777$

Rounding Fractions

How tall is the stack of papers shown below? According to the ruler, the paper stack is $\frac{5}{8}$ inch, or about $\frac{1}{2}$ inch tall.

It can be helpful to estimate fractions instead of adding fractions to get an exact sum. To estimate a fraction equation, first round each of the addends and then add or subtract.

Compare the numerator and denominator of a fraction in order to know how to round the fraction.

1. Fractions round to zero if the numerator is very small when compared to the denominator:

$\frac{1}{10}$ $\frac{8}{90}$ $\frac{2}{25}$ $\frac{3}{75}$

2. Fractions round to $\frac{1}{2}$ when the denominator is almost twice the amount of the numerator:

$\frac{4}{7}$ $\frac{2}{5}$ $\frac{5}{12}$ $\frac{22}{40}$

3. Fractions round to 1 when the numerator is about the same value as the denominator:

$\frac{6}{7}$ $\frac{9}{10}$ $\frac{17}{20}$ $\frac{98}{100}$

Look at this estimated problem:

$\frac{3}{7} + \frac{5}{12} + \frac{8}{9} =$ (Round each fraction) $\frac{1}{2} + \frac{1}{2} + 1 = 2$

Mixed numbers may be estimated in a similar way:

$2\frac{1}{8} + 3\frac{4}{5} + 5\frac{7}{15} =$

1. Find the sum of the whole numbers:

   $2 + 3 + 5 = 10$

2. Round the fractions and estimate their sum:

   $\frac{1}{8} + \frac{4}{5} + \frac{7}{15} =$ (Round each fraction) $0 + 1 + \frac{1}{2} = 1\frac{1}{2}$

3. Add the whole number sum and the fractional estimation sum:

   $10 + 1\frac{1}{2} = 11\frac{1}{2}$

The estimated sum is $11\frac{1}{2}$.

If estimating fractional products, follow the steps above to round fractions to the nearest 0, $\frac{1}{2}$ or 1. If dealing with a mixed number, round the mixed number to the nearest whole number and then multiply.

$5 \times \frac{11}{23} =$

↓ ↓

$5 \times \frac{1}{2} =$

$\frac{5}{1} \times \frac{1}{2} = \frac{5}{2} = 2\frac{1}{2}$

$3\frac{2}{3} \times \frac{3}{6} =$

↓ ↓

$4 \times \frac{1}{2} =$

$\frac{4}{1} \times \frac{1}{2} = \frac{4}{2} = 2$

1 **Follow the estimation rules to find the sum or product.**

$1\frac{2}{7} \times \frac{4}{9} =$

$10\frac{4}{5} + \frac{8}{9} + 2\frac{5}{6} =$

$\frac{21}{23} + \frac{1}{8} + \frac{3}{7} =$

$9\frac{1}{8} \times \frac{8}{15} =$

$9\frac{6}{13} + 1\frac{1}{10} + \frac{7}{8} =$

$3\frac{2}{10} + 3\frac{2}{13} =$

$3\frac{1}{7} + 2\frac{1}{4} =$

$34\frac{4}{8} + 6\frac{8}{10} + 2\frac{1}{4} =$

$4\frac{1}{3} + 2\frac{3}{4} =$

2 **Solve.** Rename to lowest terms.

$\frac{1}{2} \div 4 =$

$\frac{3}{4} \div 100 =$

$\frac{1}{5} \div 2 =$

$\frac{25}{1000} \div 2 =$

$\frac{15}{16} \div 9 =$

$\frac{4}{8} \div 4 =$

3 **Divide.** Rename to lowest terms.

$\frac{1}{4} \div \frac{3}{8} =$

$\frac{7}{8} \div \frac{1}{3} =$

$\frac{2}{9} \div \frac{1}{4} =$

$\frac{4}{5} \div \frac{1}{12} =$

$\frac{5}{8} \div \frac{2}{12} =$

$\frac{1}{11} \div \frac{8}{7} =$

$\frac{8}{15} \div \frac{1}{2} =$

$\frac{98}{100} \div \frac{1}{4} =$

4 **Calculate the discount.**

Regular price	Fractional amount of discount	Dollar amount of discount
$56.00	$\frac{1}{5}$	
$120.00	$\frac{1}{2}$	
$3500.00	$\frac{1}{2}$	
$16,000.00	$\frac{1}{4}$	
$99.99	$\frac{1}{3}$	

5 **Find the area.** Draw a picture if necessary.

A rectangle with a length of 122 ft. and a width of 75 ft.

A square with a side measurement of 45 meters.

A right triangle with one side measuring 15 mm, and one side measuring 10 mm (neither of these measurements apply to the diagonal side).

The area of a wall measuring 15 feet by 25 feet with a window in the wall measuring 3 feet by 6 feet. (Calculate the area of the wall excluding the window.)

6 **Circle the incorrect problems in order to discover the hidden message.**

7,528 +8,359 15,887 L	1,680 +2,960 4,540 B	5,749 +2,066 7,815 A	14,060 +15,755 19,815 E
3,437 +4,550 7,977 G	2,364 +5,325 7,689 S	2,986 + 465 3,455 O	1,215 + 689 2,004 D
4,514 +2,605 6,519 L	5,005 +6,693 11,698 P	8,193 +1,390 9,833 Y	6,182 +1,279 7,461 M

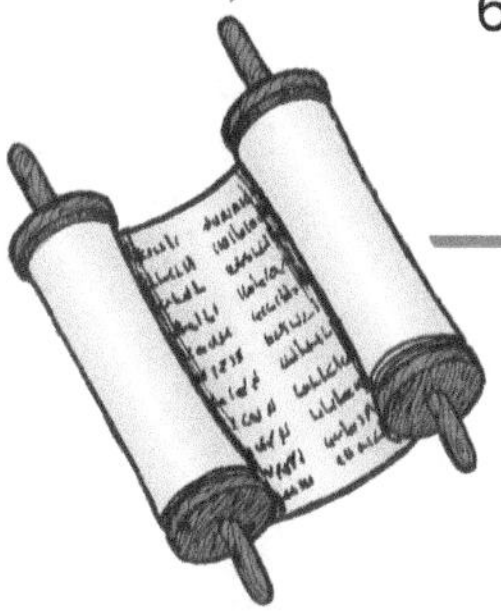

____ ____ ____ ____ ____ ____ ____

1 Timothy 4:7

Fraction Problems

Laurie is making curtains for 4 windows in her new office. Her mother gave her $15\frac{3}{4}$ yards of left over fabric. If Laurie needs $3\frac{2}{3}$ yards of fabric for each window, will she have enough fabric to make curtains for all four windows?

Divide: $15\frac{3}{4} \div 3\frac{2}{3}$

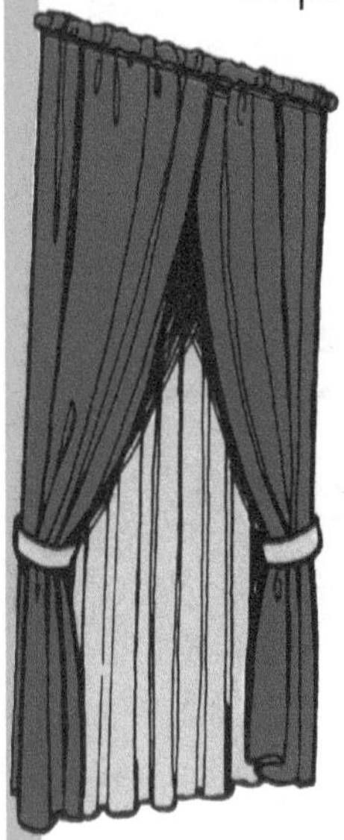

STEP 1

Write each mixed number as improper fractions.

$$15\frac{3}{4} \div 3\frac{2}{3}$$
$$\downarrow \quad \downarrow$$
$$\frac{63}{4} \div \frac{11}{3}$$

STEP 2

Change the problem to a multiplication problem by multiplying the reciprocal of the divisor. Use cross-simplification, if possible.

$$\frac{63}{4} \times \frac{3}{11}$$
$$\downarrow \quad \downarrow$$
$$\frac{63}{4} \times \frac{3}{11}$$

STEP 3

Multiply the numerators.
Multiply the denominators.
Write the answer in proper form.

$$\frac{63}{4} \times \frac{3}{11} = \frac{189}{44} = 4\frac{13}{44}$$

Laurie should have enough fabric to make curtains for all 4 windows because she can make $4\frac{13}{44}$ curtains.

1. **Find the quotient.** Write the answer in lowest terms.

$6\frac{1}{4} \div 1\frac{2}{3} =$

$5\frac{1}{4} \div 1\frac{1}{2} =$

$\frac{3}{4} \div 1\frac{1}{4} =$

$11 \div 2\frac{1}{2} =$

$6\frac{1}{6} \div \frac{1}{6} =$

$2 \div 1\frac{1}{4} =$

2 **Estimate the answers.**

$\frac{7}{8} \times \frac{3}{4} =$

$8\frac{1}{5} \times 9\frac{7}{8} =$

$\frac{12}{10} + 5\frac{3}{4} =$

$10\frac{2}{3} + 9\frac{1}{6} =$

$3\frac{1}{3} - 1\frac{1}{2} =$

$\frac{3}{4} \times 5 =$

3 **Divide.** Write the answer in lowest terms. Shade the fractions that are less than $\frac{1}{2}$. The letters in each shaded box will spell a message.

$\frac{2}{3} \div \frac{2}{2} =$ L	$\frac{1}{7} \div \frac{3}{2} =$ G	$\frac{1}{3} \div 5 =$ R
$\frac{4}{5} \div \frac{7}{6} =$ S	$\frac{4}{7} \div \frac{9}{2} =$ A	$\frac{11}{15} \div \frac{5}{5} =$ N
$\frac{13}{15} \div \frac{7}{2} =$ C	$\frac{2}{3} \div \frac{3}{3} =$ B	$\frac{2}{7} \div \frac{8}{3} =$ E

_______________ *Hebrews 2:6b-8a*

4 **Find the volume in cubic centimeters.**

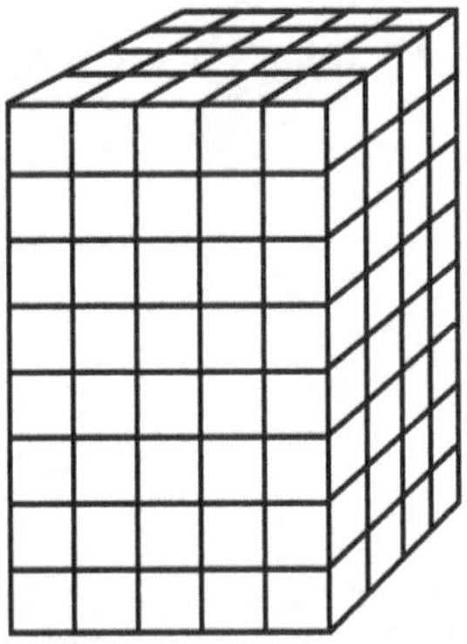

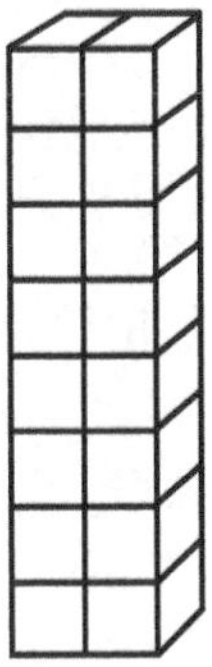

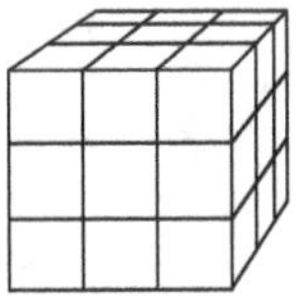

Volume = ________ Volume = ________ Volume = ________

What is **half** the volume of a box with a length of 7 cm, a width of 4 cm and a depth of 5 cm?

A box has a volume of 60 cm^3. If each layer has 15 cubes, how many layers of cubes will fill the box?

This is one layer in a box filled with cubic centimeters.
If there are 6 layers, what is the volume of the box?

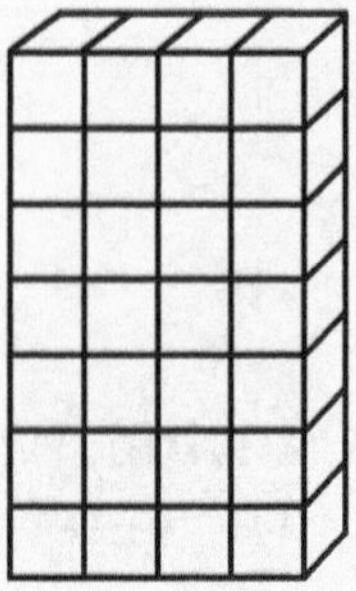

Volume = _______

(5) **Find the missing number.**

______	658,921	______
− 26,232	− ______	− 337,488
13,768	76,891	261,213
192,605	10,054	______
− ______	− ______	− 9,172
126,391	1,457	15,693

(6) **Draw a vertical bar graph to show the following information.**

Children enrolled in Loganville First Baptist Preschool in 2018:

2018 Loganville First Baptist Preschool Enrollment

Toddlers:	5
2-year-olds:	12
3-year-olds:	10
4-year-olds:	11
Kindergarten:	7

1 **Divide to the thousandths. Round the quotient to the hundredths.** 4 pts.

$8\overline{)4}$ $6\overline{)7}$ $7\overline{)11}$ $5\overline{)2}$

2 **Complete each table.** 8 pts.

	× 10
45.9	
8.8	
3.17	
	9.02

	÷ 10
18.9	
3.89	
0.110	
	90.271

3 **Circle the equivalent division problem.** 2 pts.

$47\overline{)9.4}$ $47\overline{)0.94}$ $0.47\overline{)9.4}$ $0.47\overline{)0.094}$

$311\overline{)2799}$ $31.1\overline{)27.99}$ $31.1\overline{)279.9}$ $0.311\overline{)27.99}$

4 **Write the remainder as a whole number with a remainder, fraction, decimal, or rounded whole number.** 6 pts.

1. Amelia has 99 candy canes. If she packages 5 candy canes in each bag, how many bags of candy canes will she have in total?
2. If the perimeter of a pentagon is 58.7 cm, what is the length of each side?
3. Jane brought 5 candy bars to share between 4 people. If the candy bars are divided evenly, how much would each person get?

5 **Graph each set of points. Connect the points in order to create the shape.** 12 pts.

(3,1) (4,1) (4,5) (5,5) (5,7) (4,7) (4,9) (3,9) (3,7) (2,7) (2,5) (3,5) (3,1) **stop**

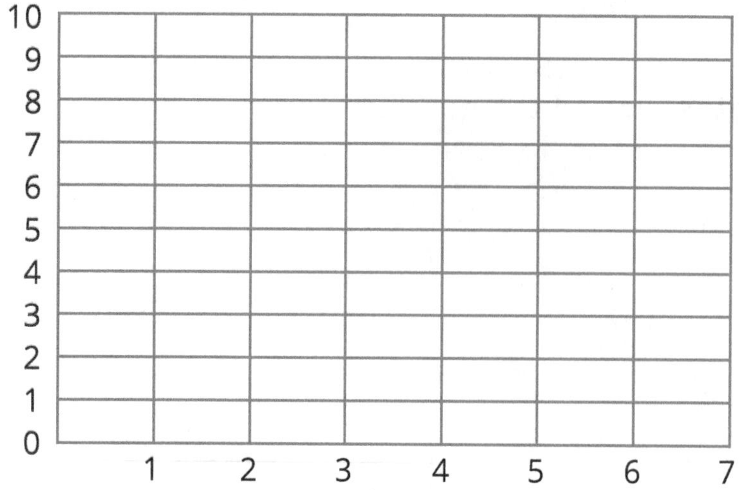

6 **Multiply. Reduce to lowest terms.** 8 pts.

$\frac{7}{9} \times \frac{1}{3} =$ $\frac{2}{5} \times \frac{1}{7} =$ $\frac{7}{9} \times \frac{1}{8} =$ $\frac{3}{7} \times \frac{7}{9} =$

$\frac{4}{11} \times \frac{1}{7} =$ $\frac{1}{5} \times \frac{3}{7} =$ $\frac{7}{12} \times \frac{5}{9} =$ $\frac{1}{2} \times \frac{1}{4} =$

7 **Solve.** 4 pts.

$\frac{2}{3}$ of 12 $\frac{4}{9}$ of 9 $\frac{2}{8}$ of 24 $\frac{4}{8}$ of 10

8 **Multiply. Reduce to lowest terms.** 6 pts.

$4\frac{1}{7} \times 3\frac{1}{2} =$ $7\frac{1}{5} \times 4\frac{1}{2} =$ $3\frac{1}{2} \times 2\frac{2}{3} =$

$4 \times 2\frac{1}{9} =$ $3\frac{5}{6} \times 10 =$ $2\frac{1}{4} \times 3\frac{1}{8} =$

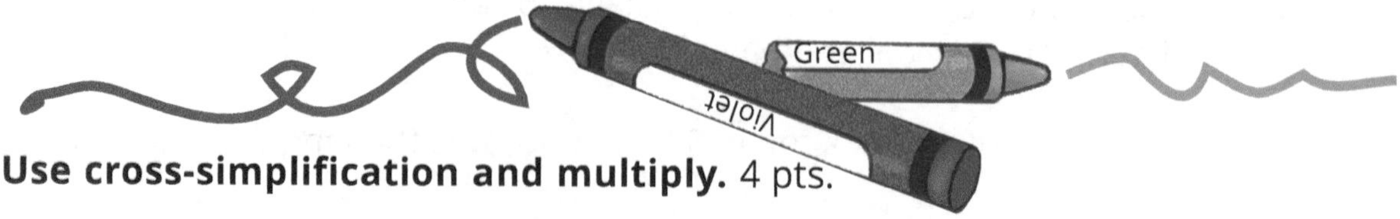

9 **Use cross-simplification and multiply.** 4 pts.

$\frac{15}{30} \times \frac{2}{5} =$ $2\frac{1}{7} \times 1\frac{2}{5} =$ $2\frac{2}{8} \times 4\frac{1}{9} =$ $3\frac{3}{6} \times 6\frac{2}{3} =$

10 **Write the reciprocal of each fraction.** 6 pts.

$\frac{2}{12}$ $\frac{47}{99}$ $\frac{35}{47}$ $\frac{11}{105}$ $\frac{17}{22}$ $\frac{49}{58}$

Customary System of Measurement

We have studied measurement many times. The Customary system of measurement consists of inches, feet, yards, and miles. When looking at the diagram below, the numbered lines indicate the length of the pencil in inches.

The red lines indicate a measurement spacing of $\frac{1}{2}$ of an inch.

The blue lines indicate a measurement spacing of $\frac{1}{4}$ of an inch.

The green lines indicate a measurement spacing of $\frac{1}{8}$ of an inch.

What do you think the brown lines represent?

What unit of measurement would be smaller than $\frac{1}{8}$? The answer is $\frac{1}{16}$ of an inch.

How long does the pencil measure? $2\frac{11}{16}$ inches is the answer.

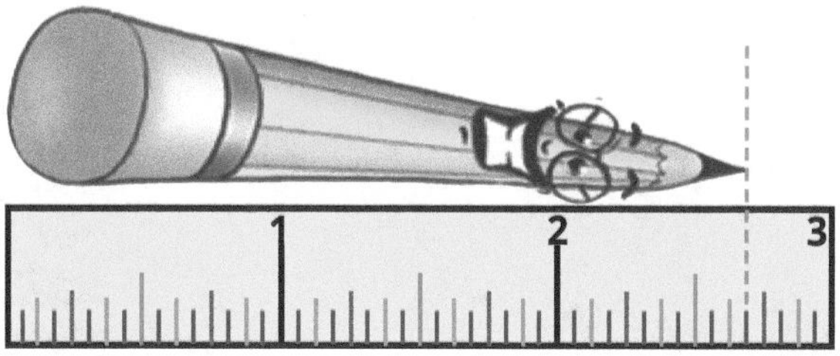

Look at the diagram below.
How long is the pencil shown in this diagram?

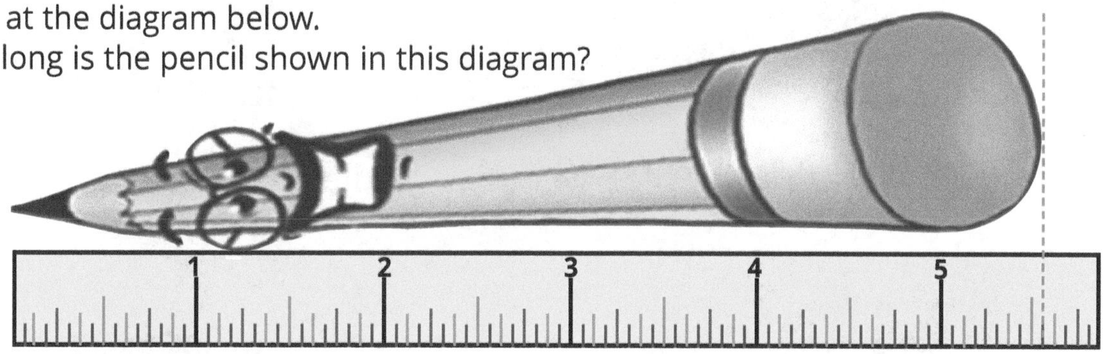

The answer is $5\frac{9}{16}$ inches.

(1) Answer the following measurement questions in sixteenths of an inch.

What is the length of the crayon?
____________ inches long

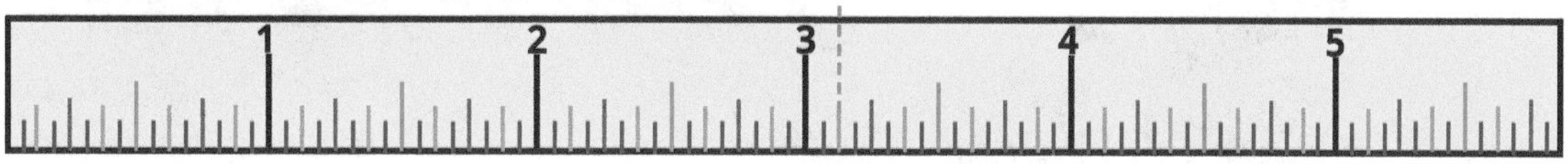

The broken crayon is how long? ______ inches

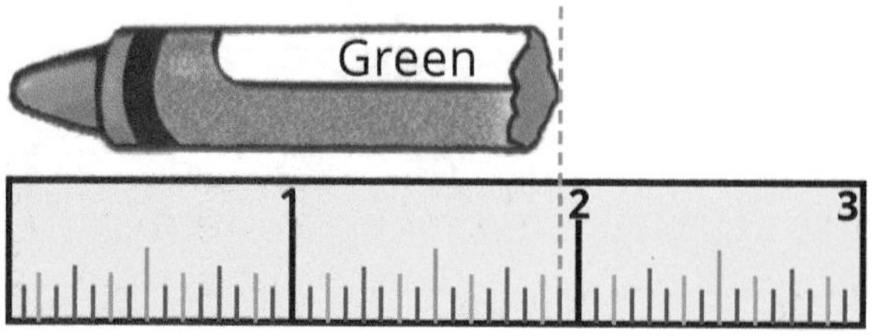

The paper clip measures? ______ inches

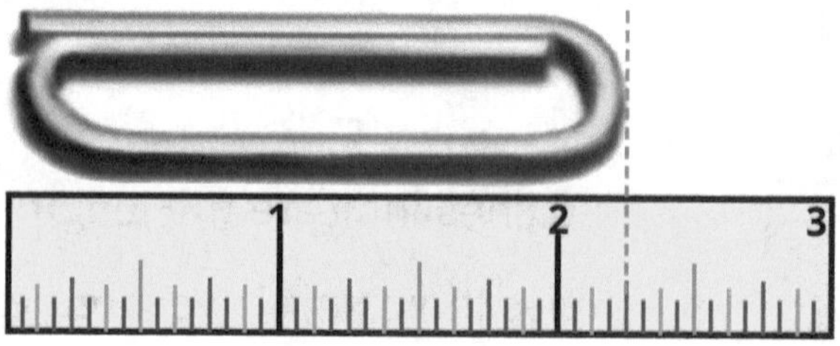

The small key measures? ______ inches

2 **Find the quotient. Write the answer in lowest terms.**

$15\frac{2}{4} \div 1\frac{2}{3} =$

$10\frac{1}{3} \div 1\frac{1}{2} =$

$\frac{3}{4} \div 1\frac{1}{4} =$

$11 \div 2\frac{1}{2} =$

$6\frac{1}{6} \div \frac{1}{6} =$

$2 \div 1\frac{1}{4} =$

3 **Choose the best fractional estimate.**

The glass is ______ full.

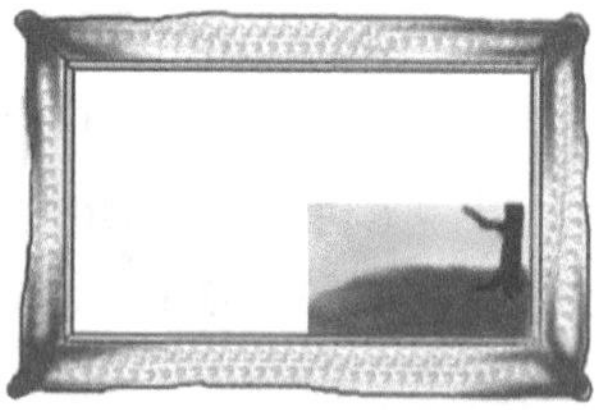

The picture is ______ colored.

The container is ______ empty.

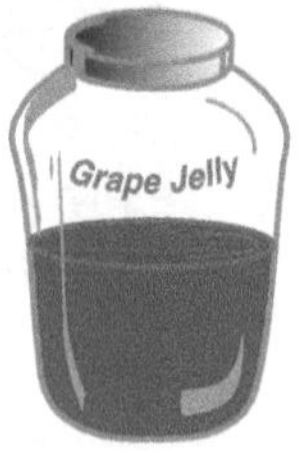

The jar is ______ full of jelly.

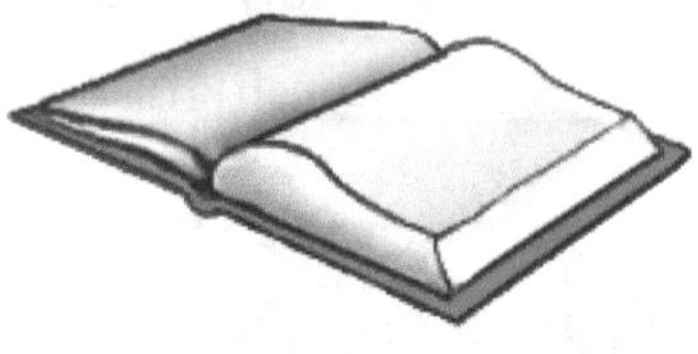

About ______ of the book has been read.

About ______ the yard has been raked.

4 **Solve.**

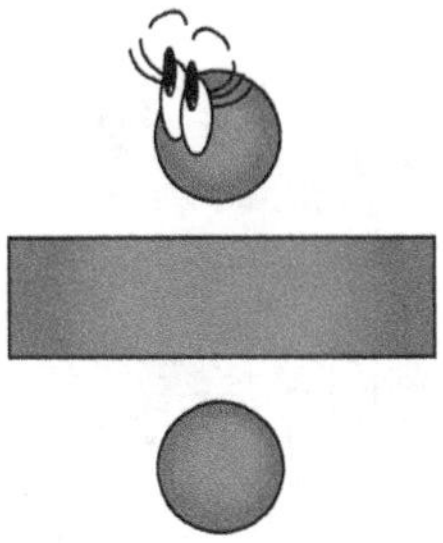

$\frac{3}{4} \div 6 =$ $\frac{2}{3} \div 3 =$ $\frac{1}{2} \div 2 =$ $\frac{7}{8} \div 2 =$

$\frac{9}{10} \div 45 =$ $\frac{3}{5} \div 12 =$ $\frac{8}{16} \div 4 =$ $\frac{3}{5} \div 3 =$

5 **Circle the digit and corresponding letter holding the trillion's place on each number.**

9 8 6 1 1 5 6 4 3 0 9 7 2 0 0
E B L S N P R C O G K D E A F

3 5 7 7 9 0 4 2 4 5 1 6 7 0 0 9
M F G O C S E A B I O D U T S P

Circle the digit and corresponding letter holding the hundred trillions place on each number.

4 4 9 5 7 4 5 0 0 0 2 6 1 0 1 3
R V D T W A S E Q R T L O R E H

2 6 8 8 0 0 1 9 5 4 0 6 2 2 7
E A G R S N M Y I C S U T O L

What word is spelled by the circled letters? ___ ___ ___ ___

Romans 5:5

6 **Draw the indicated shapes.**

Rhombus Parallelogram Square

Rectangle Trapezoid

7 **Complete each factor tree.**

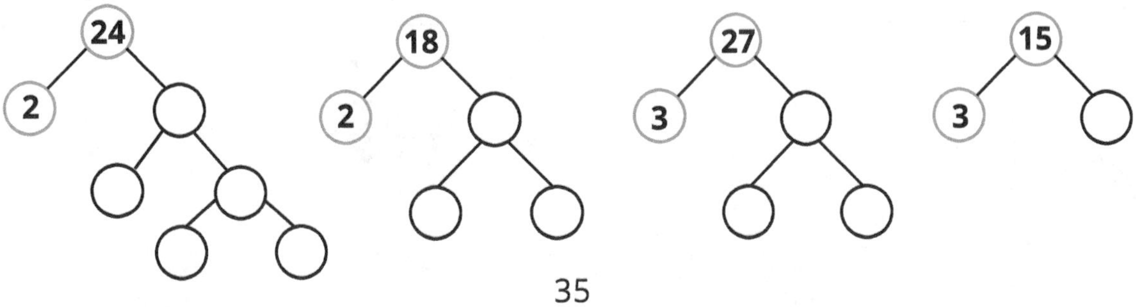

Customary Units of Measurement

Standard (Customary) Units of Measurement	
Length	**Weight**
inch (in)	ounce (oz)
foot (ft)	pound (lb)
yard (yd)	ton (t)
mile (mi)	

Mrs. Chastain works in the local grocery store. She sells lunch meats, cheeses, vegetables, and salads, as well as other items, by weight. It is important for her to understand customary units of weight like ounces, pounds, and tons.
Look at the examples below.

16 ounces = 1 pound	2000 pounds = 1 ton

Swiss Cheese

1 Pound

Potato Salad

8 ounces

Truck

1 ton

Would a cantaloupe weigh 2 ounces, 2 pounds or 2 tons?

Since eight ounces is the weight of the small potato salad container, one pound is the weight of the stack of cheese, and one ton is about the weight of a pickup truck load of cantaloupes, one cantaloupe alone would weigh 2 pounds.

If a customer asked Mrs. Chastain for $\frac{1}{4}$ a pound of lunch meat, how many ounces is this?

16 ounces equals 1 lb, so 4 ounces equals $\frac{1}{4}$ a lb.

1 **Name an item which would weigh approximately:**

10 lb	8 oz	1 T	50 lb	200 lb	5 lb
______	______	______	______	______	______

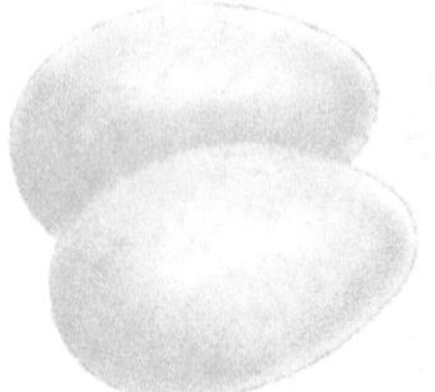

2 **Measure each line shown to the nearest 16th of an inch.**

______ in

______ in

______ in

______ in

3 **Divide.**

$4 \div 3\frac{1}{2} =$ $\quad$ $5\frac{7}{18} \div 1\frac{5}{6} =$ $\quad$ $10 \div 3\frac{1}{2} =$

$25 \div 4\frac{3}{4} =$ $\quad$ $100 \div 10\frac{11}{12} =$ $\quad$ $50 \div 6\frac{1}{3} =$

---

4 **Solve.**

Write a fraction that is close to $\frac{1}{2}$.

Write a fraction that is close to 0.

Write a fraction that is a little less than 1.

Write a fraction that is a little less than $\frac{1}{2}$.

If the numerator and denominator of a fraction are almost the same size, is the fraction closer to $\frac{1}{2}$ or 1?

If the denominator is about twice the size of the numerator is the fraction closer to $\frac{1}{2}$, 0, or 1?

(5) **Solve.**

What is 1 trillion more than 4,561,332,879? ______________________

What is 25 million more than 334,567? ______________________

What is 1 trillion less than 351,008,495,229,314? ______________________

What is 3 hundred million less than 561,220,482,285,882? ______________________

(6) **Find the hidden quadrilaterals in the picture.**

a square ***a rectangle*** ***a trapezoid*** ***a rhombus*** ***a parallelogram***

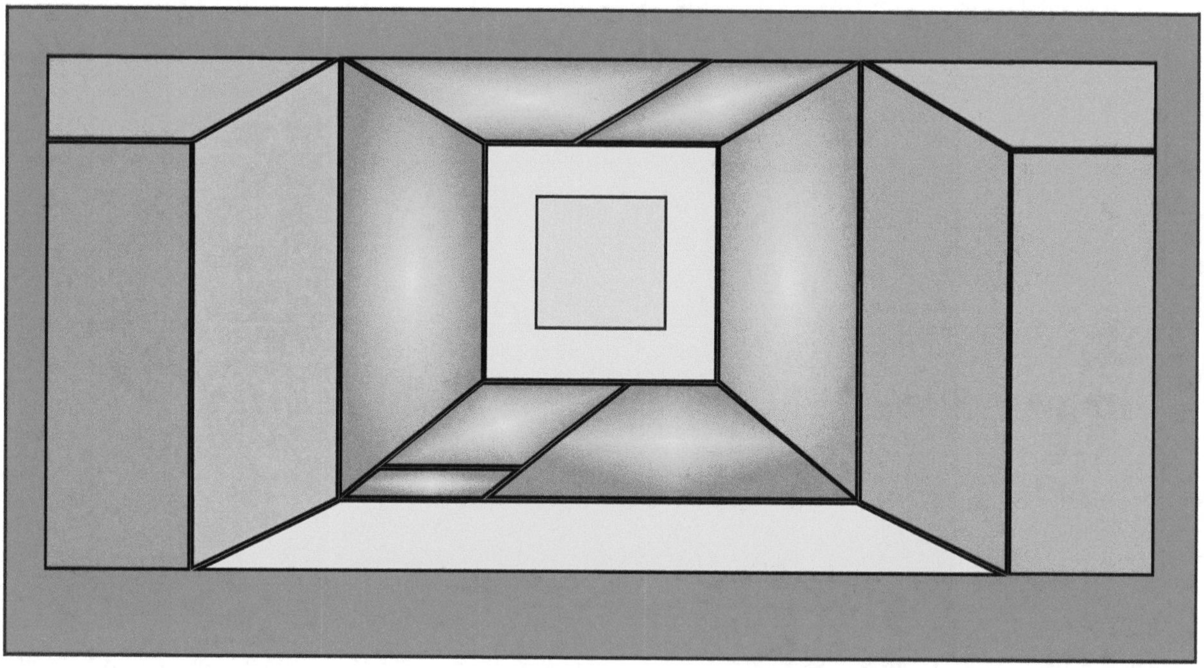

(7) **Shade the prime numbers to reveal a message.**

51	13	93	11	83	73	30	79	90	97
98	23	99	31	57	47	18	67	35	61
46	19	63	89	77	5	15	2	33	19
72	59	82	17	85	19	50	20	7	12
2	3	75	23	71	7	39	21	19	32

Psalm 30:11

Using Liquid Measurement

8 ounces = 1 cup
2 cups = 1 pint
2 pints = 1 quart
4 quarts = 1 gallon
1 tablespoon = $\frac{1}{2}$ fluid oz

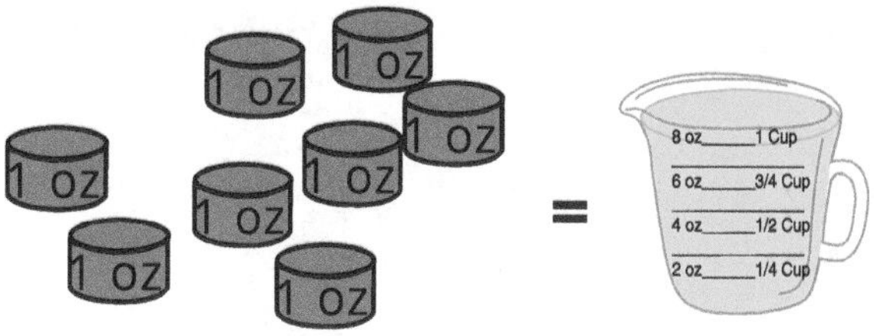

Jenny decided to make some pudding from a powder container. The recipe tells her to mix 1 scoop of the pudding powder with $\frac{1}{2}$ cup of water. Jenny is confused, however, because she does not have a measuring cup or a cup size container. She only has an ounce size container. How many ounces of water equal 1 cup?

If 8 ounces equal 1 cup, then 4 ounces will equal $\frac{1}{2}$ of a cup. Jenny will need to mix 4 ounces of water with one scoop of the pudding powder.

Look at these:

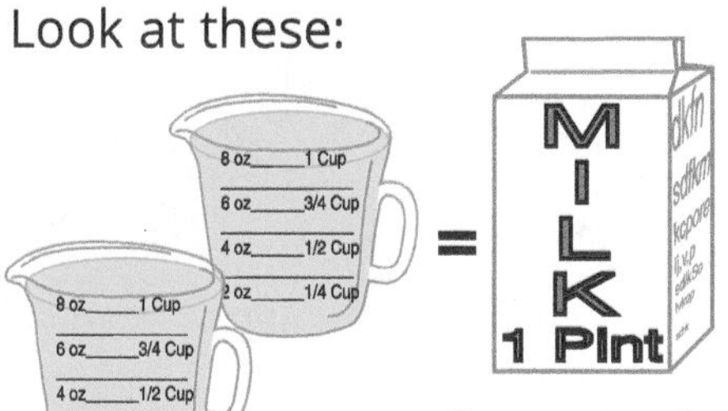

2 cups = 1 pint

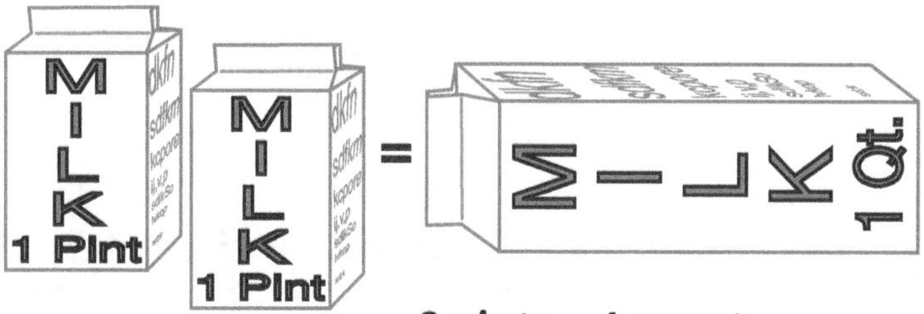

2 pints = 1 quart

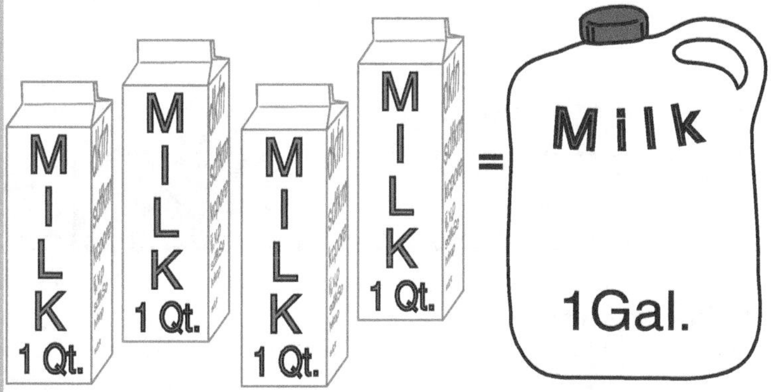

4 quarts = 1 gallon

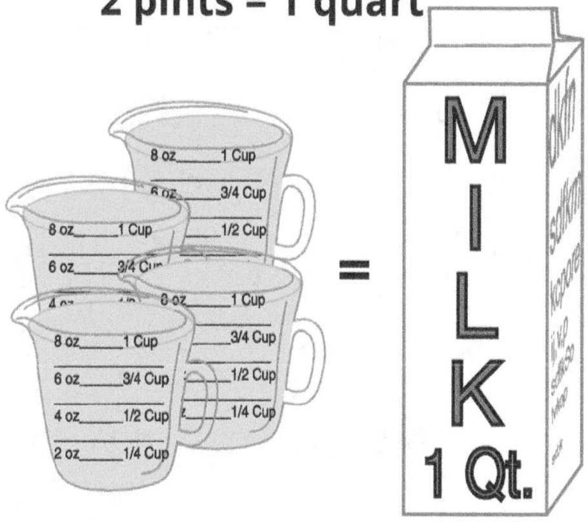

4 cups = 1 quart

1 **Complete.**

$\frac{1}{2}$ qt = _____ pt	4 c = _____ qt	3 qt = _____ pt
$\frac{1}{2}$ pt = _____ c	16 c = _____ gal	8 pt = _____ gal
$\frac{1}{2}$ gal = _____ pt	32 gal = _____ c	8 tbs = _____ c

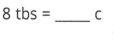

2 **Solve.**

A customer asked David for 2 and a half pounds of ground beef. How many ounces is this?

A stick of butter is $\frac{1}{4}$ of a pound. How many ounces is this?

Which is the better buy per pound, a 5 pound package of ham for $5.75 or a 1 lb package for $1.05?

A 10 lb bag of apples cost $8.99. What is the cost per pound?
Hint: Round to the nearest penny.

The grocery store just received a shipment of potatoes. The potatoes are packaged in 10 lb bags. If the total weight of the potato shipment is 1 T, then how many 10 lb bags are there?

How many ounces are there in a 7 lb bag of pears?

3 **Mark each measurement on the ruler shown.**

Show $4\frac{6}{16}$ on the ruler below.

Show $1\frac{1}{16}$ on the ruler below.

Show $3\frac{5}{16}$ on the ruler below.

Show $2\frac{6}{16}$ on the ruler below.

4 **Match the problem with the correct answer.**

$5\frac{1}{3} \div 1\frac{1}{3} =$	$3\frac{6}{7}$
$3\frac{1}{12} \div 1\frac{1}{3} =$	$3\frac{3}{7}$
$4 \div 1\frac{1}{6} =$	4
$9 \div 2\frac{1}{3} =$	$5\frac{10}{13}$
$12\frac{3}{6} \div 2\frac{1}{6} =$	$2\frac{5}{16}$

5 **Find the sum.**

799,560	498,124	55,091	1,634
+ 173,703	+ 780,544	+ 11,805	+ 3,389

6 **Find the measurement of the missing angle.**

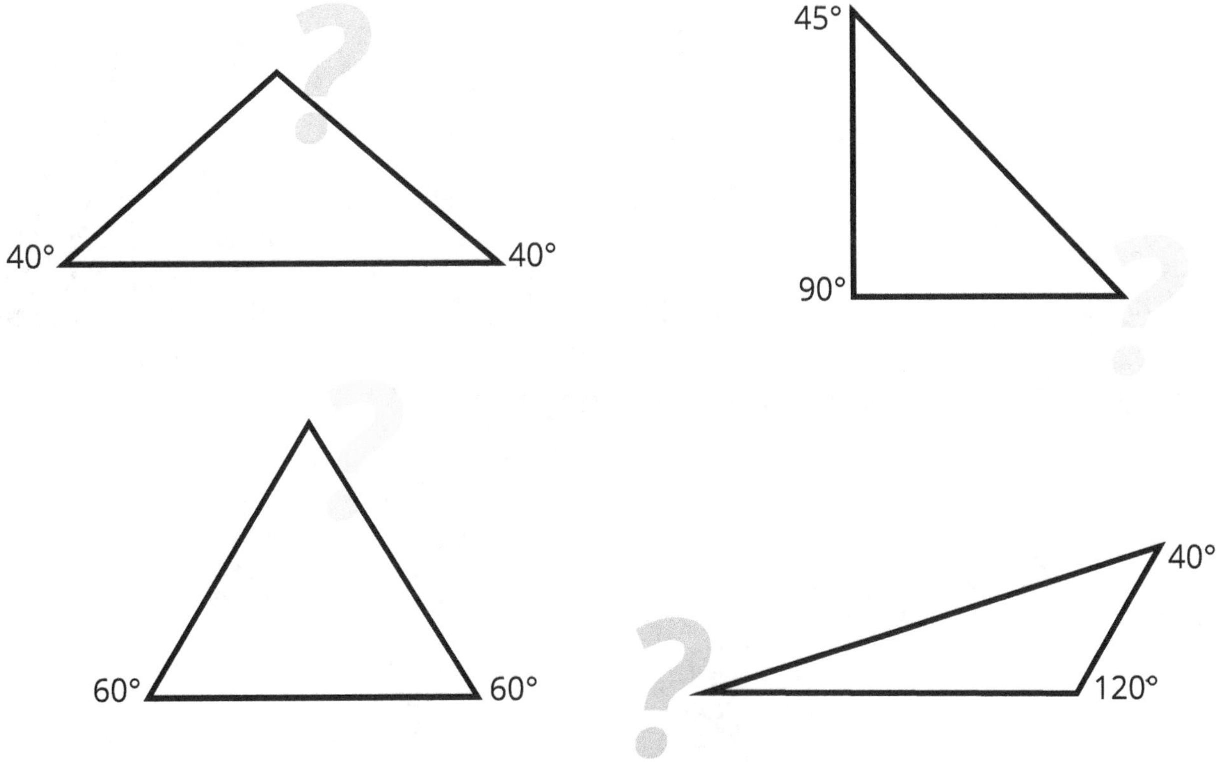

7 **Convert each number into an exponential number.**

$100{,}000 = \_\_\_\_^{?}$

$1{,}000 = \_\_\_\_^{?}$

$343 = 7^{?}$ ____

$16 = 4^{?}$ ____

$81 = 3^{?}$ ____

$3{,}125 = 5^{?}$ ____

Fahrenheit Scale

There are two scales that are commonly used to measure temperature. One scale is the Fahrenheit scale (F°) scale and is part of the Standard (Customary) measurement system. Look at the thermometers below. Several important temperatures are noted. These are important temperatures to memorize and use for reference points when considering Fahrenheit temperatures.

A hot July day in Georgia
95°

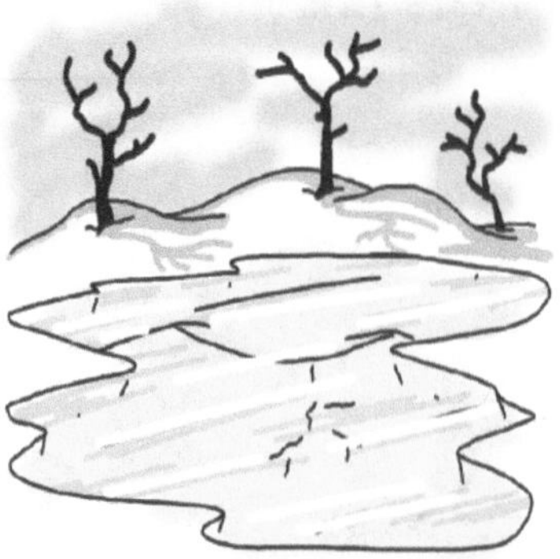

A cold day in Michigan
10°

A child sick with the flu
101°

Look at these other temperature examples:

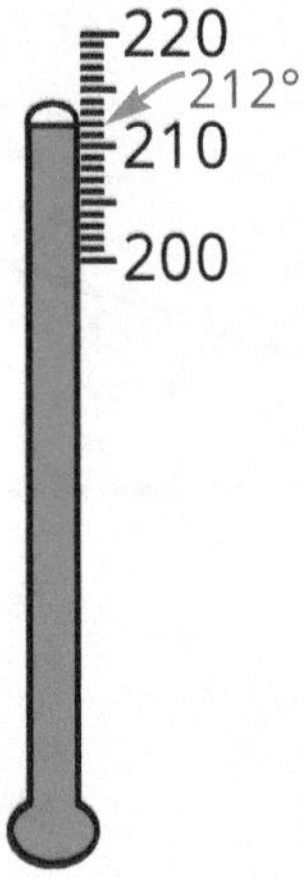

212° water boils

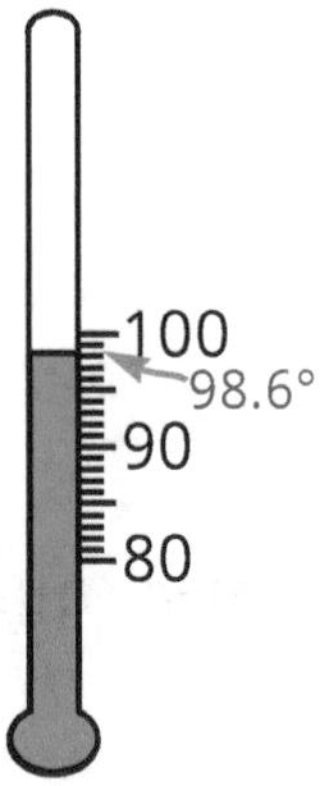

98.6° normal body temperature

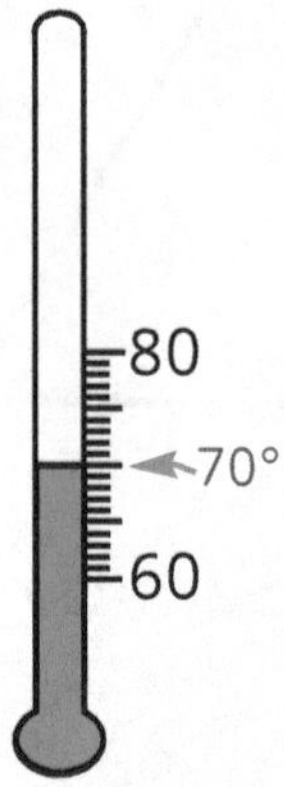

70° comfortable room temperature

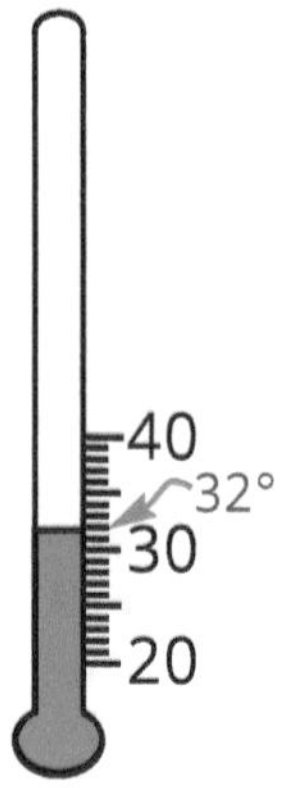

32° water freezes

1 **Match the temperature on the left with the appropriate outside activity on the right.**

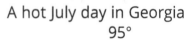

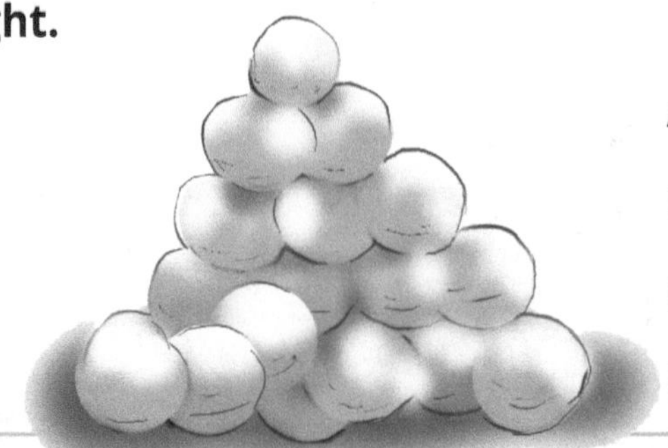

1. 97°
2. 30°
3. 3°
4. 60°

A. building a snowman
B. wear a sweater or light jacket
C. go swimming
D. stay inside to avoid frost bite

② **Complete.**

4 gal = ____ qt

4 pt = ____ gal

6 c = ____ qt

$\frac{1}{2}$ pt = ____ c

16 oz = ____ c

32 tbs = ____ oz

③ **Draw a circle around the best estimate.**

10 oz	5 lb	9 lb	2 oz
100 lb	10 oz	9 tons	1 ton
1 ton	10 tons	9 oz	1 lb

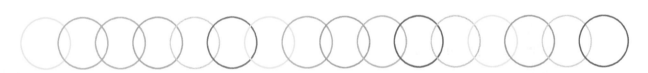

④ **Write the equivalent measurement.**

$\frac{4}{8}$ inch = $\frac{?}{16}$ inch

$\frac{1}{2}$ inch = $\frac{?}{16}$ inch

1 inch = $\frac{?}{16}$ inch

$\frac{12}{16}$ = $\frac{?}{4}$ inch

$1\frac{1}{2}$ inch = $1\frac{?}{16}$ inch

$3\frac{2}{16}$ in = $3\frac{?}{8}$ in

5 **Find the sum.**

3,185	4,361	54,392	50,756	378,093
+ 1,209	+ 5,692	+ 14,208	+ 4,613	+ 104,351

6 **Find the missing angle measurement.**

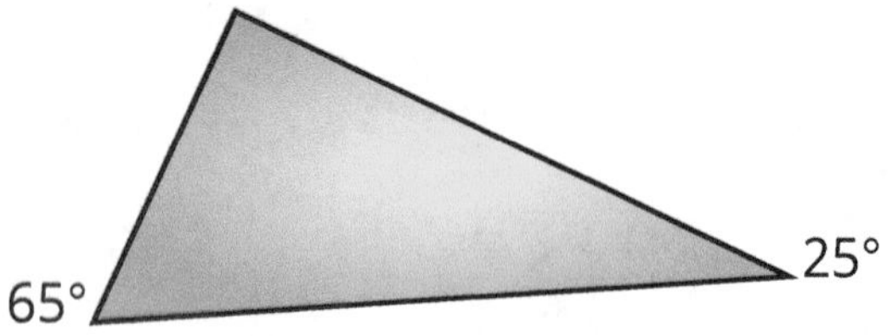

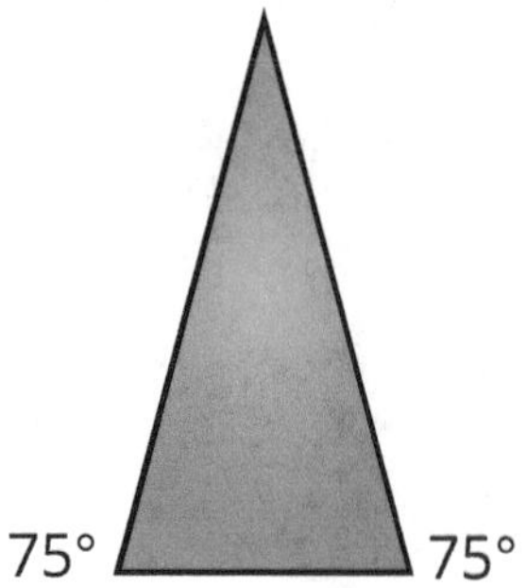

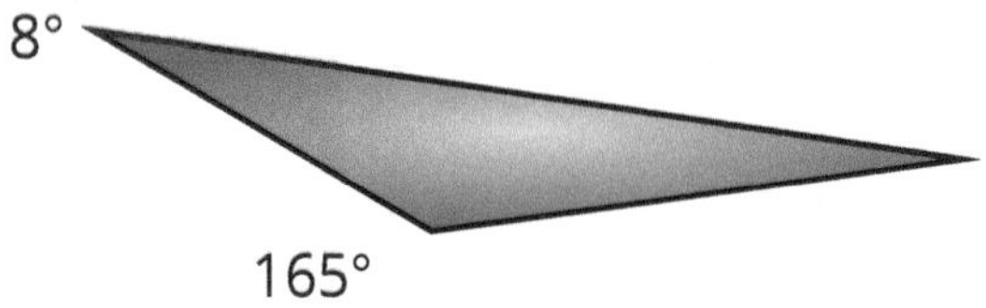

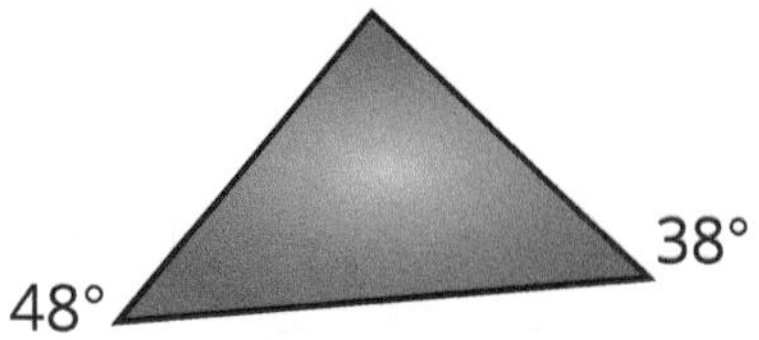

7 **Use your calculator and find the value of each number.**

6^2 ______________________

4^4 ______________________

5^7 ______________________

10^6 ______________________

3^3 ______________________

9^7 ______________________

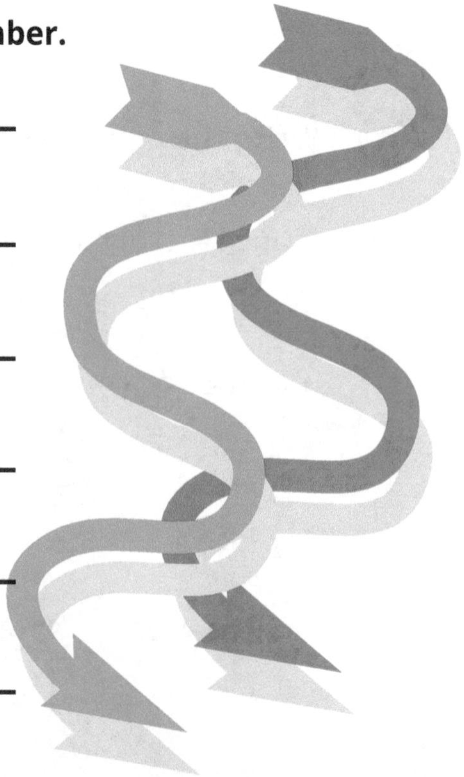

Metric Conversion Charts

Remember the Metric conversion chart. This chart will help you convert Metric amounts more easily.

Kilo	Hecto	Deka	Basic Unit (meter, liter or gram)	deci	centi	milli

(Kilo is the largest measurement prefix and milli is the smallest prefix measurement)

Meter
1000 meters = 1 Kilometer
100 meters = 1 Hectometer
10 meters = 1 Dekameter

Liter
1000 liter = 1 Kiloliter
100 liter = 1 Hectoliter
10 liter = 1 Dekaliter

Gram
1000 grams = 1 Kilogram
100 grams = 1 Hectogram
10 grams = 1 Dekagram

Meter = Basic Unit
0.1 meter = 1 decimeter
0.01 meter = 1 centimeter
0.001 meter = 1 millimeter

Liter = Basic Unit
0.1 liter = 1 deciliter
0.01 liter = 1 centiliter
0.001 liter = 1 milliliter

Gram = Basic Unit
0.1 gram = 1 decigram
0.01 gram = 1 centigram
0.001 gram = 1 milligram

Try another conversion: If we measured a table to be 1580 centimeters long, how many Decameters is this?

Write the number in the conversion chart by placing the last digit "0" in the centimeter box and adding a decimal to the end since we know this is a whole number. Now simply move the decimal to the desired conversion measurement, Decameters. 1580 centimeters (cm) = 1.580 Decameters (Dm)

		1⊙	5	8	0⊙	
Kilo	Hecto	Deka	Basic Unit (meter, liter or gram)	deci	centi	milli

(1) Complete.

Kilo	Hecto	Deka	Basic Unit (meter, liter or gram)	deci	centi	milli

129 mm = ________ cm

3,129 mm = ________ m

1.97 m = ________ mm

19.45 m = ________ cm

6.09 Km = ________ dm

2.53 dm = ________ mm

② Write the temperature on each thermometer.

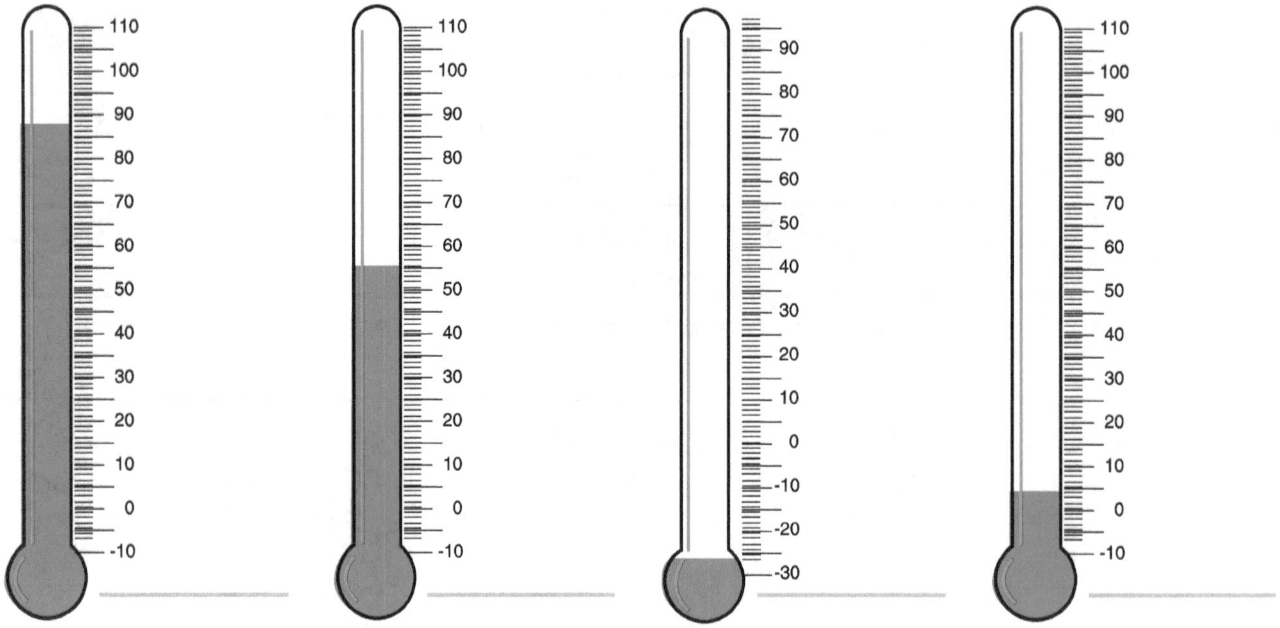

Add 15° to each temperature. Tell the new temperature below and draw the red line on each blank thermometer.

New Temperatures:

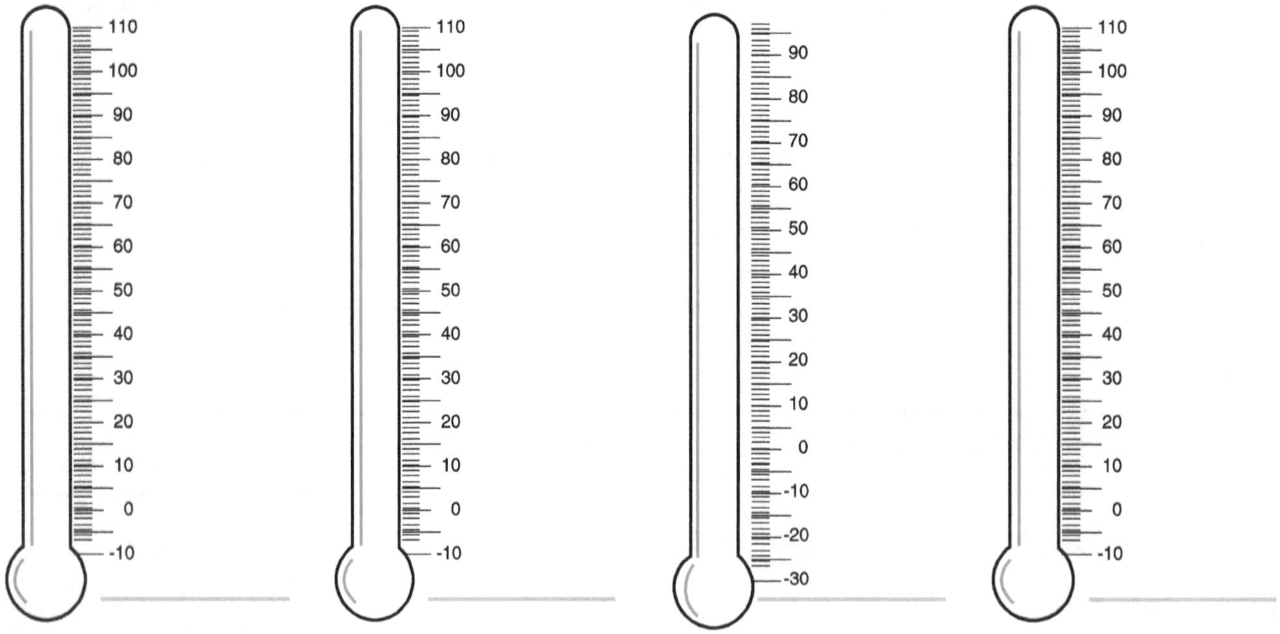

③ Estimate each measure. Circle the best estimate.

a small bowl of soup

1 cup **1 pint** **1 gal**

a jug of milk

1 pt **1 c** **1 gal**

1 can of motor oil

1 cup **1 quart** **1 gal**

medium size jar

1 cup **1 gal** **1 pint**

4 **Complete. Give each measure as ounces.**

3 lb   5 lb   1 ton

5 ton   2 lb 3 oz   7 ton

5 **Find the differences. Complete the crossword.**

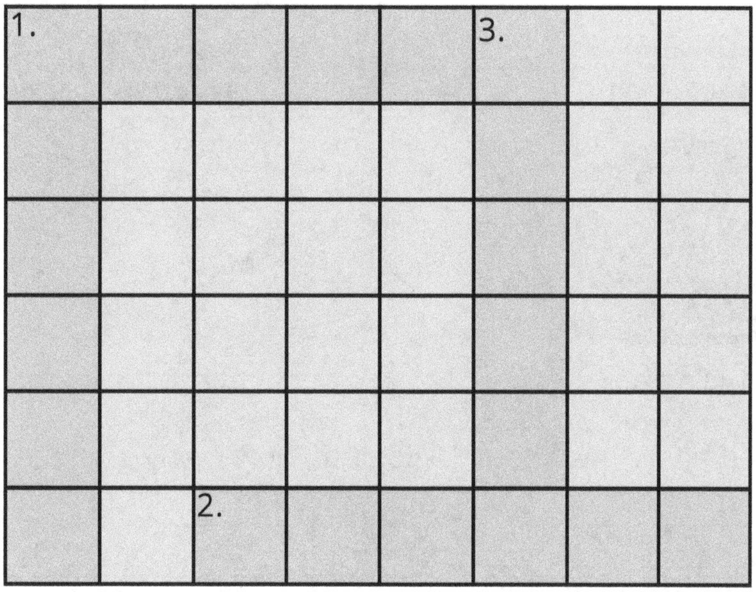

Across

1.
$$\begin{array}{r} 128,903 \\ -21,811 \\ \hline \end{array}$$

2.
$$\begin{array}{r} 781,400 \\ -570,815 \\ \hline \end{array}$$

Down

1.
$$\begin{array}{r} 183,294 \\ -\quad 1,873 \\ \hline \end{array}$$

3.
$$\begin{array}{r} 451,650 \\ -184,045 \\ \hline \end{array}$$

6 **Use your calculator and find the square root of each number.**

144   625   324   400   6,400   1,089

7 **Find the sum.**

$$\begin{array}{r} 5\frac{3}{5} \\ +\ 2\frac{1}{10} \\ \hline \end{array} \qquad \begin{array}{r} 10\frac{2}{3} \\ +\ 12\frac{1}{6} \\ \hline \end{array} \qquad \begin{array}{r} 14\frac{5}{9} \\ +\ 25\frac{1}{2} \\ \hline \end{array} \qquad \begin{array}{r} 9\frac{2}{6} \\ +\ 2\frac{1}{4} \\ \hline \end{array}$$

Metric Units of Measurement

The Metric unit for measuring weight is the gram. A Kilogram is the largest measurement of weight we will discuss. We can still use our Metric conversion chart to convert weight measurements, if necessary.

about 1 gram

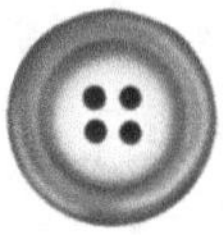

about 1 gram

about 1 kilogram (Kg)

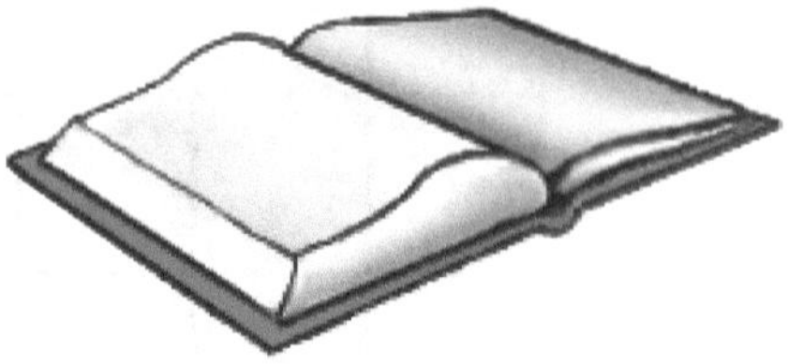

about 1 kilogram (Kg)

If a football weighs about 1 kilogram, how many grams is this?

1.	0	0	0.			
Kilo	Hecto	Deka	Basic Unit (meter, liter or gram)	deci	centi	milli

1 kilogram = 1,000 grams
The football weighs 1,000 grams, or 1 kilogram.

			0.	0	0	2.
Kilo	Hecto	Deka	Basic Unit (meter, liter or gram)	deci	centi	milli

2 mg = 0.002 grams

(1) **Complete.**

Kilo	Hecto	Deka	Basic Unit (meter, liter or gram)	deci	centi	milli

Convert each weight to Kilograms (Kg)

9 g   99 g   820 g

Convert each weight to grams (g)

4 Kg   35 Kg   328 Kg

(2) **Complete.**

1 meter = _______ centimeters

1,000 millimeter = _______ meter

10 millimeters = _______ centimeters

1 Kilometer = _______ meters

25 millimeters = _______ centimeters

9 meters = _______ centimeters

(3) **Draw the temperature on the thermometer.**

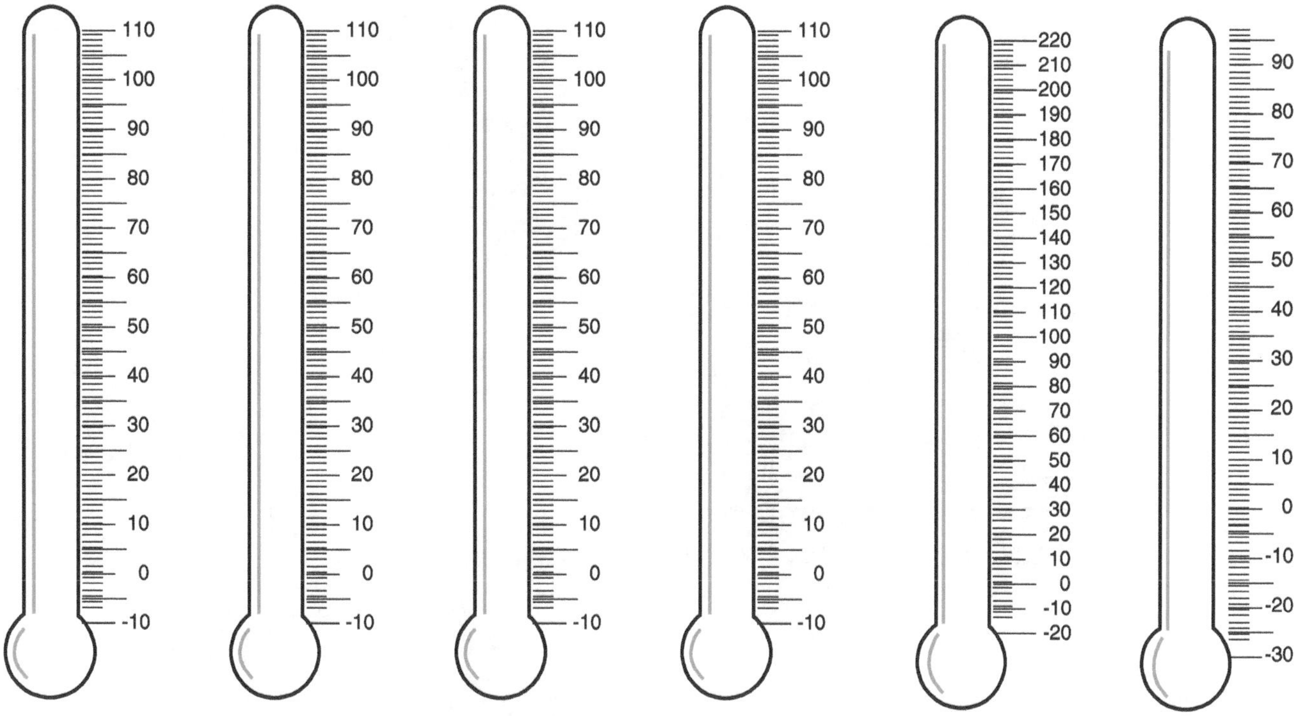

93° 73° the freezing point 52° the boiling point –22°

(4) **Give each measure as gallons, quarts, and pints.**

12 quarts = _______ gals
_______ pts

16 pints = _______ qts
_______ gals

18 quarts = _______ pts
_______ gals

24 pints = _______ qts
_______ gals

35 pints = _______ qts
_______ gals

10 gallons = _______ qts
_______ pts

⑤ Find the missing number.

$\begin{array}{r} \_\_\_\_ \\ -26{,}232 \\ \hline 23{,}768 \end{array}$	$\begin{array}{r} 558{,}922 \\ -\ \_\_\_\_ \\ \hline 76{,}892 \end{array}$	$\begin{array}{r} \_\_\_\_ \\ -237{,}488 \\ \hline 260{,}519 \end{array}$
$\begin{array}{r} 82{,}604 \\ -\ \_\_\_\_ \\ \hline 16{,}391 \end{array}$	$\begin{array}{r} 10{,}054 \\ -\ 2{,}457 \\ \hline \_\_\_\_ \end{array}$	$\begin{array}{r} \_\_\_\_ \\ -\ 8{,}374 \\ \hline 9{,}171 \end{array}$

⑥ Find the sum.

I $3\frac{1}{2} + 4\frac{1}{5} =$

G $2\frac{1}{3} + 6\frac{1}{6} =$

T $15\frac{1}{5} + 4\frac{1}{4} =$

H $8\frac{1}{9} + 7\frac{1}{3} =$

S $1\frac{1}{12} + 4\frac{1}{3} =$

Place the answers in order from the smallest to the largest in order to reveal a message.

___ ___ ___ ___ ___

Hebrews 4:13

⑦ Find the square roots.

6,084	361	16
121	100	1,024

Metric Units of Measurement

The Metric term **Liter** refers to the liquid unit of measurement called capacity. When going to the store to purchase a bottled soft drink most are measured in 2 liter bottles. When dispensing medicine a doctor will sometimes prescribe a certain number of milliliters of medicine be taken. A normal soda can holds approximately 120 ml of liquid. We can still use the Metric conversion chart to convert various liter measurements. 3,400 ml = 3.4 liters

			3.	4	0	0.
Kilo	Hecto	Deka	Basic Unit (meter, liter, or gram)	deci	centi	milli

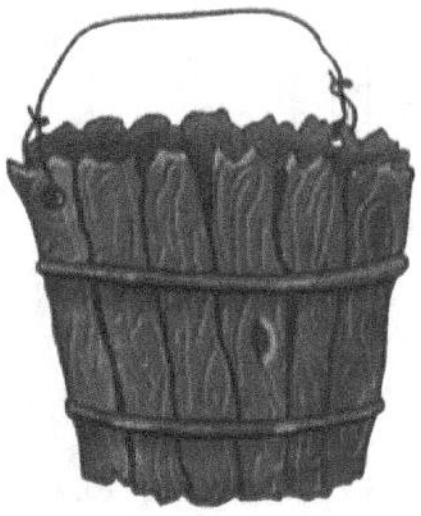

Approximately 8 liters

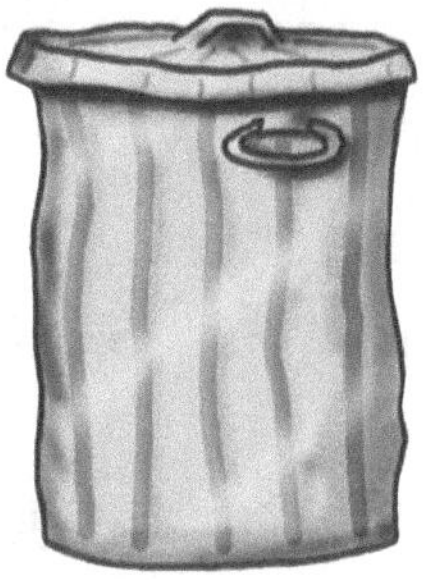

Approximately 170 liters

Approximately 1,000 ml

One milliliter (1 ml) of liquid will fill a cube that is 1 cm long, 1 cm high, and 1 cm wide.

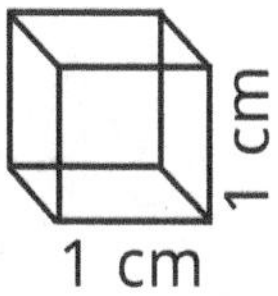

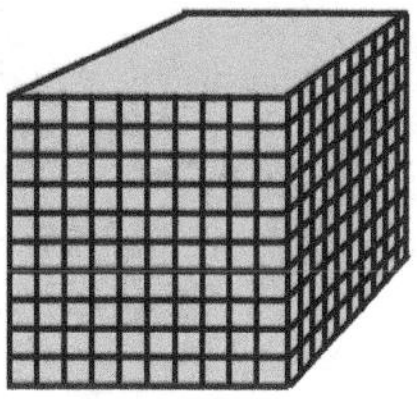

One thousand of these cubes would be 1 liter.
1,000 milliliter (ml) = 1 liter (L)

(1) Complete. (Use the conversion chart if necessary.)

5,000 ml = ________ L   .319 L = ________ ml   15 ml = ________ L

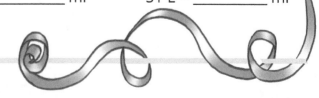

730 ml = ________ L   2 L = ________ ml   51 L = ________ ml

(2) **Write the metric unit of measurement that would fit each item.**

An egg weighs about 50 ______.

A large dog weighs about 50 ______.

A grain of rice weighs about 50 ______.

A feather weighs about 1 ______.

A small kitten weighs about 1 ______.

A small pebble weighs about 1 ______.

(3) **A map is a scale drawing. On this map 1 cm stands for 200 kilometers. Answer the questions using this map and scale of miles.**

How far is it from Yellowstone National Park to Rocky Mountain National Park?

How far is it from Colorado Springs to Idaho Falls?

How far is it from Idaho Falls to Rocky Mountain National Park?

How far is it from Yellowstone National Park to Provo?

How much farther is it from Boise to Colorado Springs than it is from Salt Lake City to Colorado Springs?

What is the distance from Casper to Colorado Springs and then to Provo?

(4) **Write each number in scientific notation.**

3160000 = ______________ 0.998 = ______________

268 million = ______________ 95.5 = ______________

0.00077 = ______________ 865000 = ______________

5 Find each missing number.

Fill in the missing information. Show your work.

$6\frac{1}{5}$	$?\frac{1}{2}$	$8\frac{1}{4}$
$-1\frac{9}{10}$	$-8\frac{3}{4}$	$-2\frac{2}{?}$
$?\frac{3}{10}$	$1\frac{3}{4}$	$5\frac{17}{20}$

$10\frac{?}{?}$	$223\frac{1}{2}$	$19\frac{1}{4}$
$-3\frac{8}{10}$	$-111\frac{?}{?}$	$-?\frac{1}{2}$
$6\frac{3}{10}$	$111\frac{5}{6}$	$17\frac{3}{4}$

6 Find the 10% discount on the following sales items. Write the new sales price on the "price" line. Write the discount amount on the "discount" line.

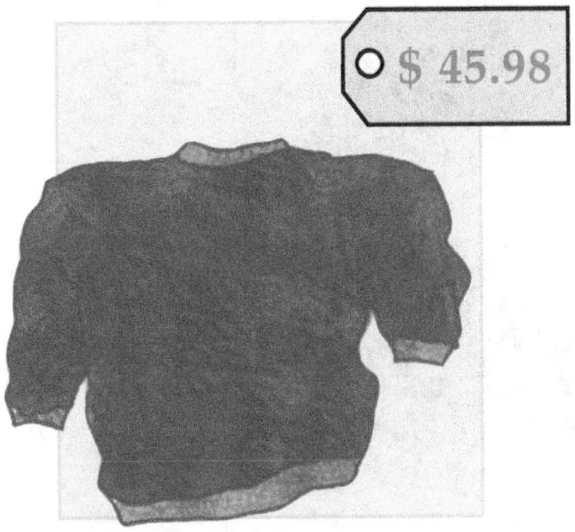

Discount: ____________
Price: ____________

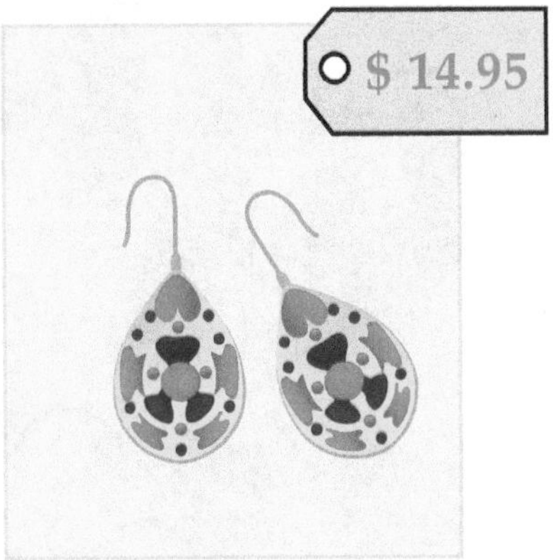

Discount: ____________
Price: ____________

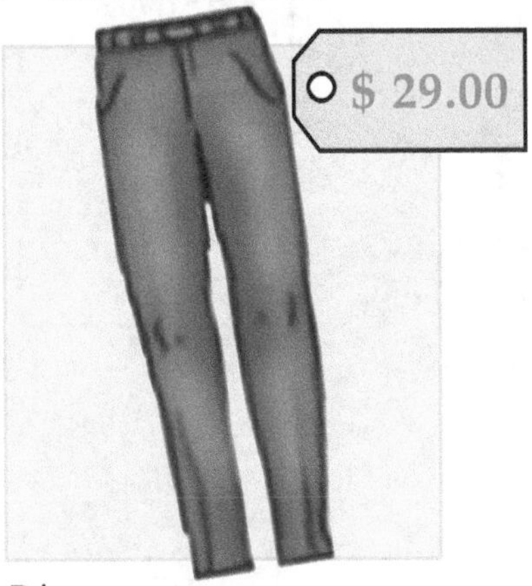

Discount: ____________
Price: ____________

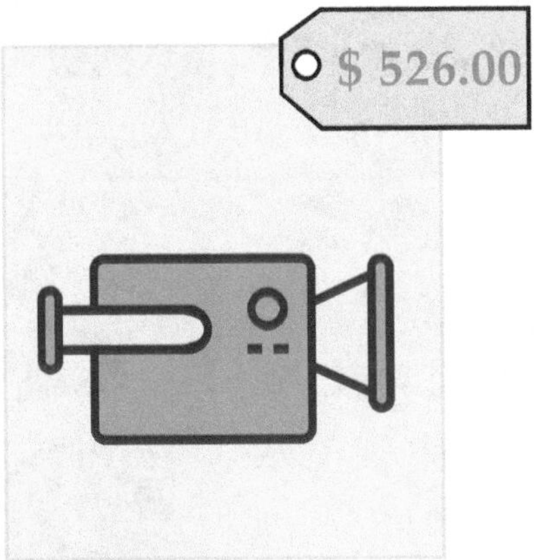

Discount: ____________
Price: ____________

Discount: ____________
Price: ____________

Discount: ____________
Price: ____________

Metric and Customary Units of Measurement

You should recall that Celsius is a Metric unit of measurement for temperature while Fahrenheit is a customary unit of measurement for temperature.

Fahrenheit Scale | Celsius Scale

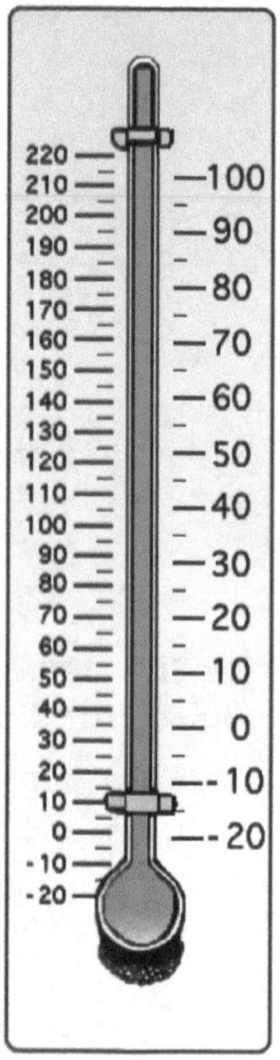

boiling point

37 C is normal body temperature
34 C would be considered a hot day
-5 C would be considered a cold day

freezing point

1 **Write each Celsius temperature shown.**

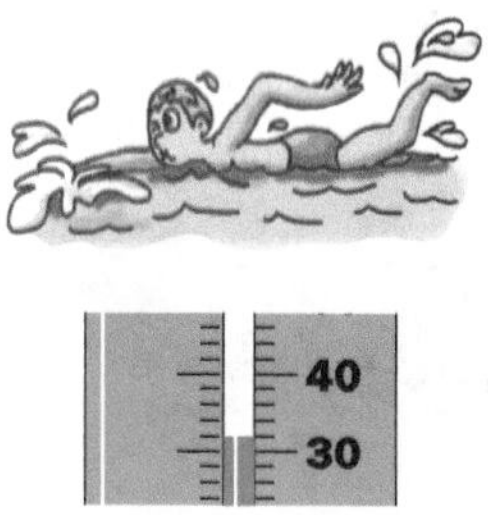

2 **Circle the best answer.**

A tablespoon will hold about:

a. 15 ml   b. 150 ml   c. 1,500 ml

A can of soda contains:

a. 35 ml   b. 3,500 ml   c. 350 ml

Two quarts is about:

a. 20 L   b. 2 L   c. 200 L

A gallon container of paint is about:

a. 40 ml   b. 40 L   c. 4 L

A small glass of orange juice contains about:

a. 150 ml   b. 1,500 ml   c. 5 L

3 **Name an item which would weigh approximately:**

1 gram	1 kilogram	10 kilograms	50 grams
________	________	________	________

4 **Estimate the metric measurement of each.**

How tall is a classroom doorway?

How long is a piece of paper?

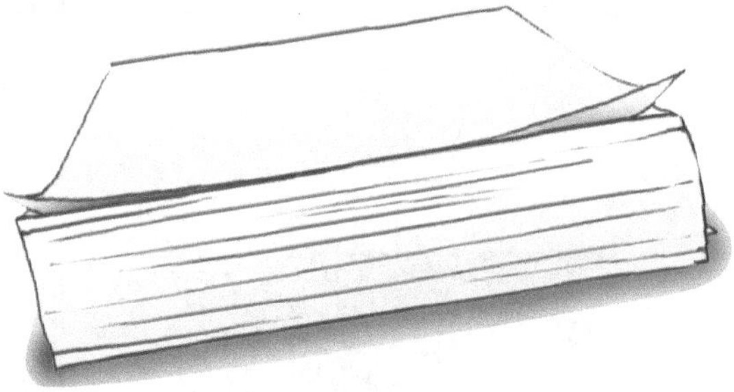

How thick is your math book?

How long is a jumbo paper clip?

What is the height from the floor to the ceiling?

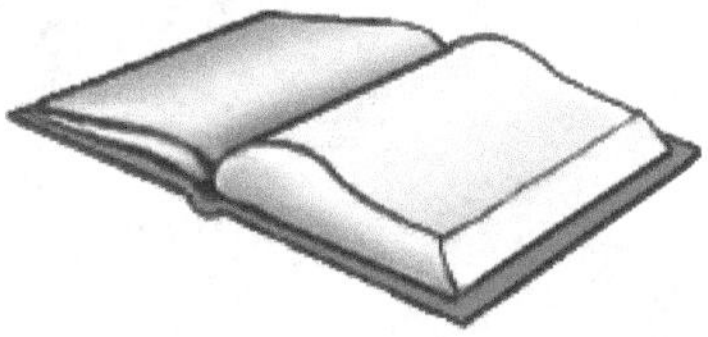

5 **Complete the table.**

Standard Form	Scientific Notation
	10×10^{5}
	5.87×10^{12}
42,000,000	
	7.3×10^{-6}
	10×10^{3}
236,000,000,000	
	4.588×10^{19}
0.000098	

6 **Subtract.**

$39\frac{2}{7} - 5\frac{5}{7}$

$132 - 75\frac{3}{4}$

$48\frac{1}{2} - 19\frac{11}{12}$

$27\frac{2}{3} - 5\frac{4}{5}$

$55\frac{3}{8} - 25\frac{1}{2}$

$225\frac{1}{2} - 195\frac{2}{3}$

7 **Match the item with the 10% discounted price.**

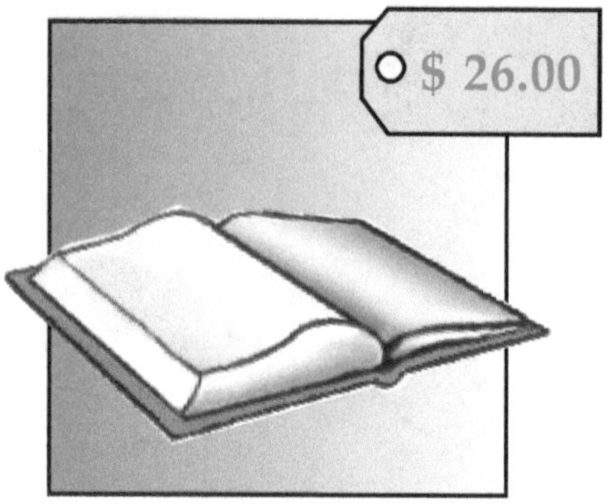

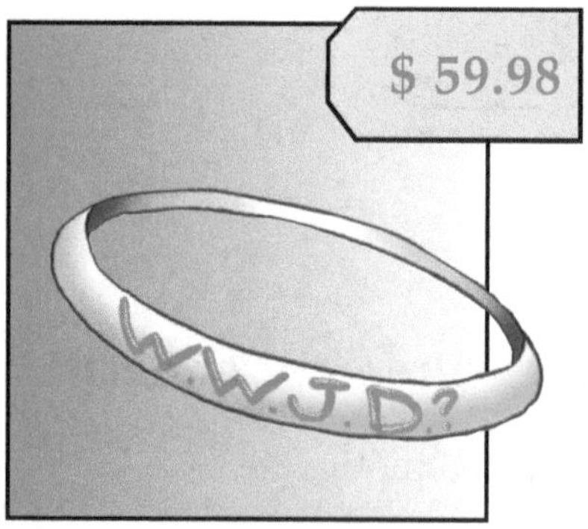

$112.95 $55.79 $22.95

$23.40 $53.98 $56.69

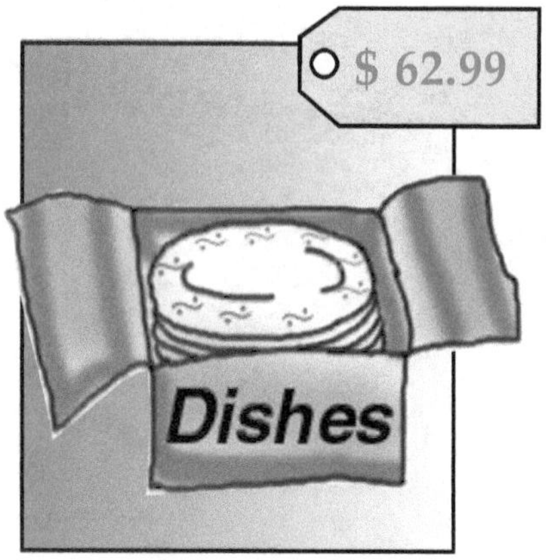

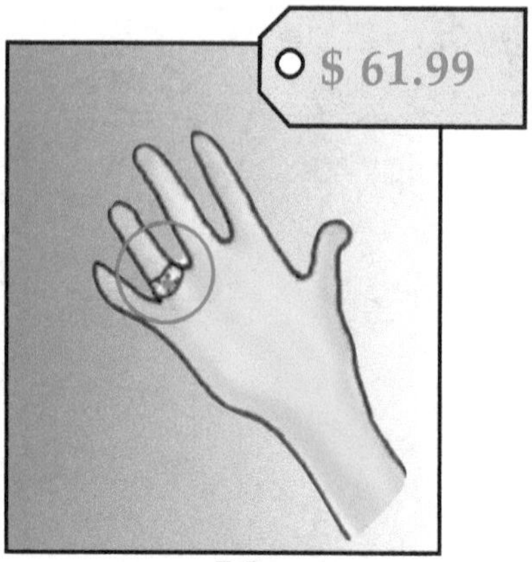

Perimeter

Sheila needs to hang a wallpaper border in a rectangular room. One wall is 35 feet long and another wall is 24 feet long. How much wallpaper border will she need?

Draw pictures to help you solve problems. Sheila knows that the room is a rectangle:

Sheila also knows that one wall is 35 ft and another wall is 24 feet:

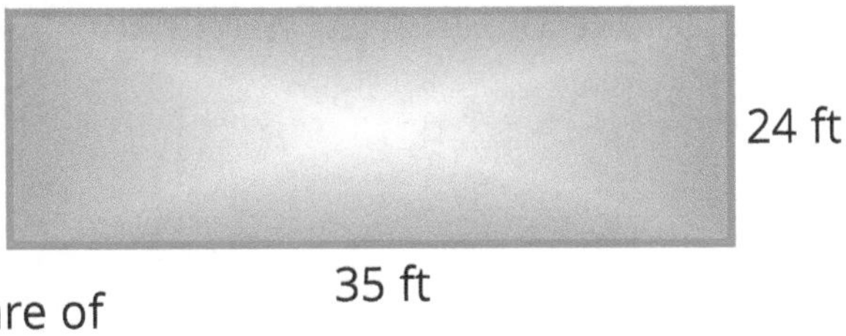

We know that a rectangle's opposing sides are of equal length, so there are two sides that are 24 ft and two sides that are 35 ft.

$24 + 24 + 35 + 35 = 118$ ft **or** $(24 \times 2) + (35 \times 2) = 118$ ft

Sheila will need at least 118 feet of border.

(1) **Draw a picture and solve.**

The Pentagon in Washington, D.C. is a building built with 5 equal sides.
If one side of the building is 560 feet long, what is the perimeter of the building?

Cindy needs to have a picture framed. The picture is a rectangle with a width of 46 inches. The length is twice as long as the width. Calculate the perimeter of the picture so Cindy will know how much picture frame molding to buy.

Kelly is purchasing a piece of land and needs to fence the entire property.
The land is a triangular shape. Side one is 350 feet long. Side two is half that long.
The third side is 15 feet longer than the second side.
What is the perimeter of the lot?

(2) Solve.

We can change Fahrenheit reading to Celsius readings by using the formula:

$$C = \frac{5}{9} \times (F - 32)$$

Use the calculator key sequence **F – 32 × 5 ÷ 9 = C**

Change the following temperatures from Fahrenheit to Celsius.
Round to the nearest whole number.

200°F	97°F	85°F	320°F	45°F	32°F

(3) Convert.

345 ml = ________ L

34 L = ________ ml

175 L = ________ ml

72 ml = ________ L

1,598 ml = ________ L

8 ml = ________ L

(4) Match the weights. Write the letters beside the answer on the lines below. If your answers are correct, it will spell a word.

1. a feather	50 Kg R
2. an egg	1 Kg C
3. a TV set	4 g Y
4. a baby kitten	1 milligram M
5. a hamster	50 milligrams E

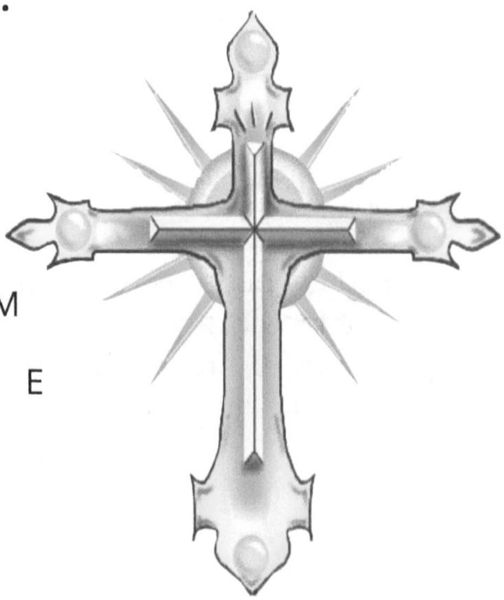

1. ____ 2. ____ 3. ____ 4. ____ 5. ____

I Peter 1:3-4

5 **Complete the Binary Place Value Chart.**

Binary Place Value Chart | **Base 10 Equivalent**

(64) 2^6	(32) 2^5	(16) 2^4	(8) 2^3	(4) 2^2	(2) 2^1	(1) 2^0	Base 10 Equivalent
							= 29
							= 10
							= 38
							= 7
							= 122
							= 42

6 **Solve for *N*.**

$5 + N = 4 + (2 \times 3)$

$(7 \times 9) + N = 8 \times 9$

$15 \times N = (100 - 40) \times 1$

$(25 \div 5) - 2 = 78 - N$

$67 + (4 \times 5) = N \times 29$

$100 + 150 = N \times 50$

7 **Find the product.**

$5{,}432 \times 56$

$8{,}429 \times 72$

$5{,}227 \times 33$

$3{,}678 \times 25$

$1{,}296 \times 15$

$2{,}807 \times 21$

Vertical Bar Graph

The Loganville Christian Academy holds an annual BBQ fundraiser.
The graph below compares the amount of money made over the past five years.
This information is shown in the **vertical bar graph** below.

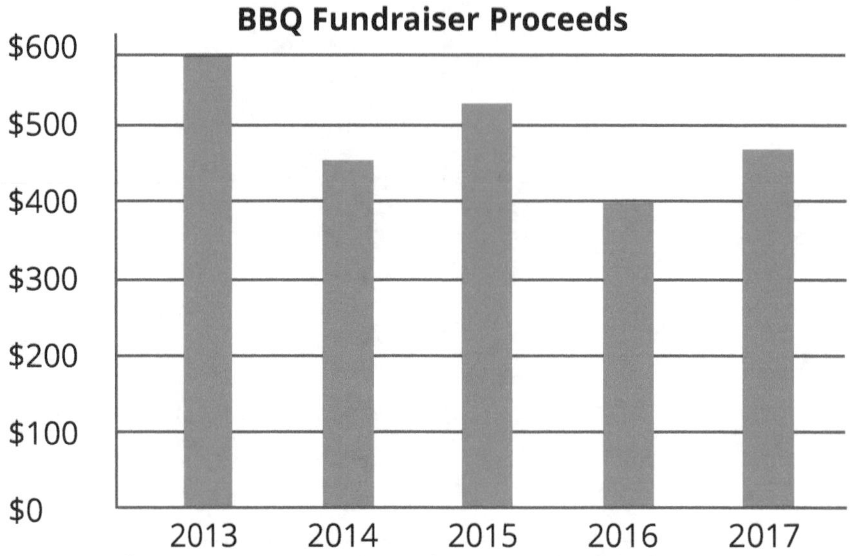

Bar graphs are used to compare related numerical information.
These graphs may be either vertical or horizontal.
This same information is presented in a **horizontal bar graph** below.

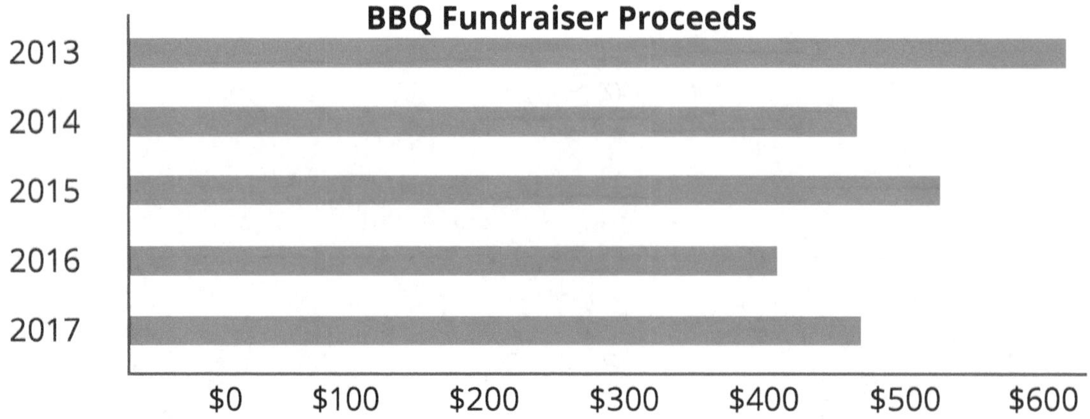

How much money was made in 2015?
Notice that the bar is $\frac{1}{4}$ of the way between the $500.00 and the $600.00 mark.

$\frac{1}{4}$ of the way between the two numbers is $525.00. The BBQ sales were $525.00 in 2015.
How much was made in 2017 through 2013 combined?

2013	$600.00
2014	$455.00
2015	$525.00
2016	$400.00
2017	+ $475.00

$2,455.00 was made off of the BBQ fundraiser over the past 5 years.

1 **Use the bar graph to answer the following questions.**

How much money did the cotton candy booth make?

How much money did the festival make on train rides?

Which booth made the most money? The least money?

How much money did all the booths make when combined?

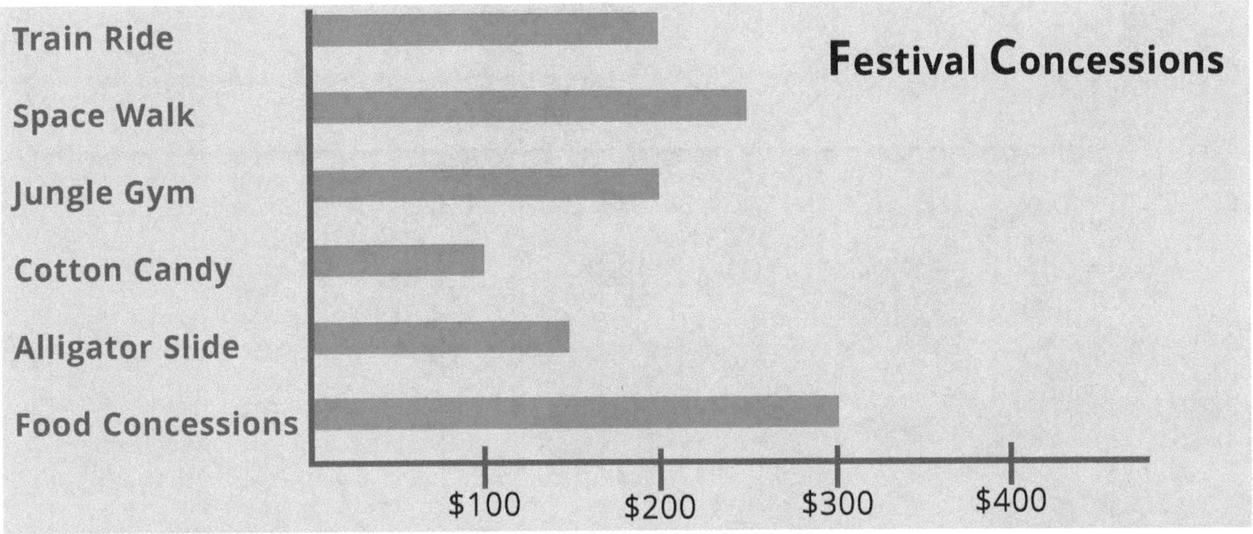

2 **Change the following temperatures from Fahrenheit to Celsius. (Round to the nearest whole number.)**

Remember to use the appropriate key sequence on the calculator.

F boiling temp.	57°F	82°F	520°F	25°F	F freezing temp.

3 **Match the measurement to the appropriate item.**

80 L

1 L

250 ml

1200 L

4 **Find the Base 2 equivalent in the puzzle. Shade the answer spaces yellow.**

10 18 12 15 20 3 9

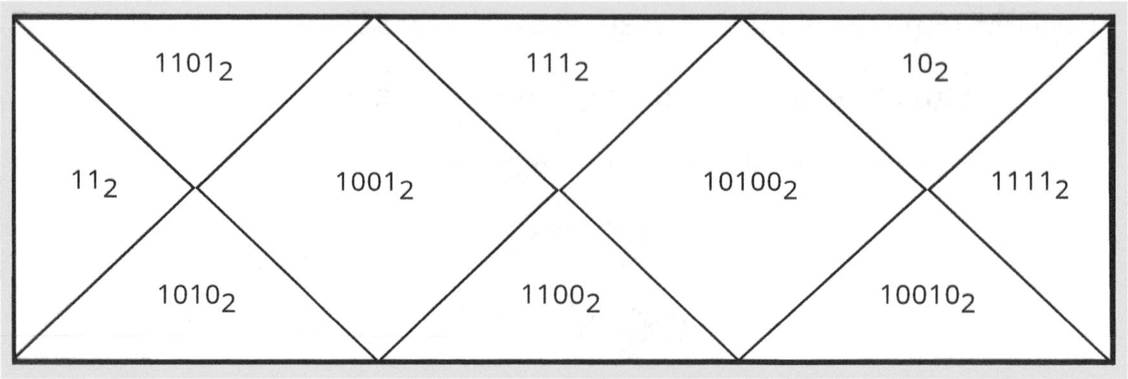

5 **Solve.**

$(10 + 2) + N = 45 \times 2$ $(100 \div 5) \times 3 = 75 - N$ $N - 850 = 600 \div 3$

$198 - N = 254 \div 2$ $(1{,}245 \div 5) \div N = 56 + 27$ $876 + (2 \times 5) = N \times 2$

6 **Circle the incorrect answers and correct them.**

4,739	6,879	9,374	9,786	5,871
x 14	x 25	x 33	x 56	x 11
66,436	171,975	390,342	548,006	64,581

7 **Solve.**

Susie began an exercise program. She exercised on Tuesday, Thursday, and Friday. She did 34 sit-ups on Tuesday, 40 on Thursday, and 50 on Friday. The following week, Susie completed 52 sit-ups on Tuesday. If she continues the pattern from the previous week, how many sit-ups will she complete on Friday?

Mr. Cown owns the local grocery store. He received a shipment of 95 watermelons on Friday. He sold $\frac{1}{5}$ of them on Friday and $\frac{3}{5}$ of them on Saturday. On Monday, he decided to discount the price of the remaining watermelons.
How many watermelons were left on Monday?

Test 10

51 points total Lessons 86-95

(1) Solve. Draw pictures if necessary. 8 pts.

$12 \div \frac{1}{2} =$ $8 \div \frac{1}{6} =$ $12 \div \frac{1}{15} =$ $25 \div \frac{1}{6} =$

$17 \div \frac{1}{9} =$ $11 \div \frac{1}{2} =$ $19 \div \frac{1}{4} =$ $9 \div \frac{1}{12} =$

(2) Divide. Rename the answers as mixed fractions in lowest terms. 8 pts.

$\frac{2}{3} \div \frac{1}{9} =$ $\frac{4}{7} \div \frac{3}{10} =$ $\frac{3}{5} \div \frac{3}{8} =$ $\frac{2}{3} \div \frac{5}{8} =$

$\frac{1}{4} \div \frac{1}{5} =$ $\frac{5}{12} \div \frac{1}{8} =$ $\frac{4}{9} \div \frac{2}{3} =$ $\frac{8}{9} \div \frac{1}{4} =$

(3) Divide. Rename the answers as mixed fractions in lowest terms. 4 pts.

$\frac{7}{12} \div 3 =$ $\frac{3}{4} \div 8 =$ $2\frac{1}{4} \div 2 =$ $4\frac{1}{7} \div 4 =$

(4) Find the estimated sum. 3 pts.

$4\frac{5}{6} + \frac{4}{9} =$ $8\frac{7}{13} + 5\frac{1}{12} + \frac{9}{10} =$ $5\frac{2}{15} + 6\frac{7}{13} =$

(5) Find the quotient. Write the answer in lowest terms. 4 pts.

$3\frac{1}{9} \div 1\frac{2}{5} =$ $3\frac{1}{7} \div 1\frac{6}{7} =$ $2\frac{3}{4} \div 1\frac{1}{4} =$ $3\frac{2}{9} \div 1\frac{1}{2} =$

(6) Measure each item to the nearest sixteenth of an inch. 2 pts.

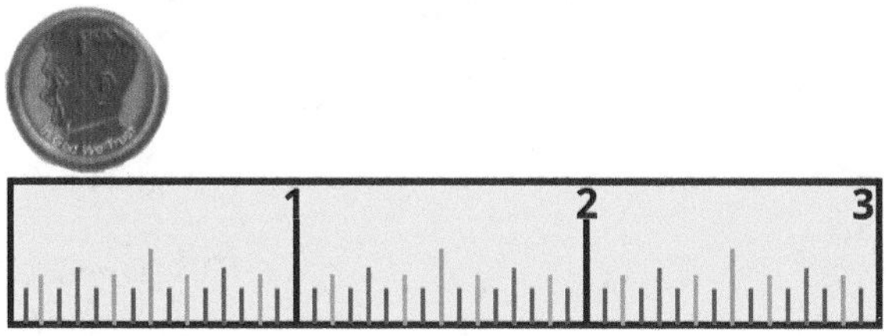

__________ inches long

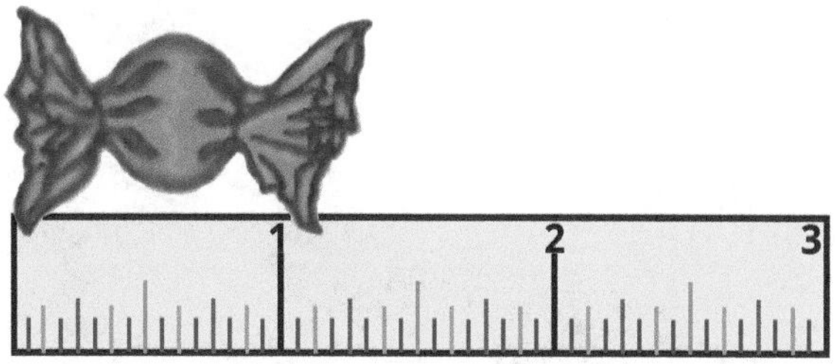

__________ inches long

(7) Match the items with their corresponding weights. 5 pts.

Small Can of Corn	14 lb
Van	1.5 oz
Hamburger	4 oz
Weight of a Cat	11 oz
Golf Ball	2 T

(8) Complete. 6 pts.

$\frac{1}{4}$ gal = ____ qt

8 c = ____ qt

1 pt = ____ qt

$4\frac{1}{2}$ qt = ____ c

160 c = ____ gal

20 pt = ____ gal

(9) Look at the picture. Circle the temperature that is the most reasonable. 4 pts.

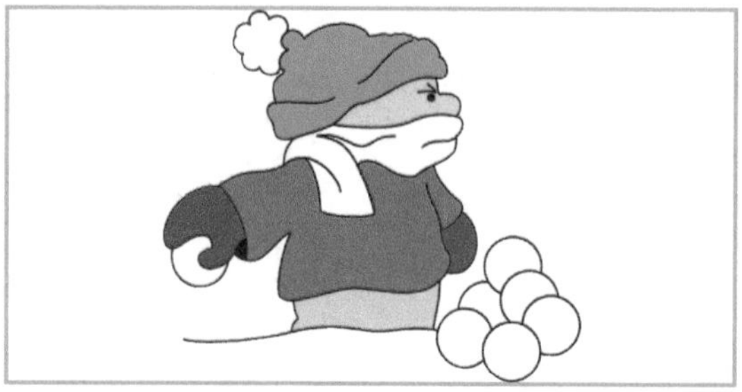

-37° F 100° F 30° F 68° F

-10° F 1° F 105° F 212° F

38° F 90° F 120° F -6° F

-12° F 10° F 45° F 113° F

(10) Complete. 7 pts.

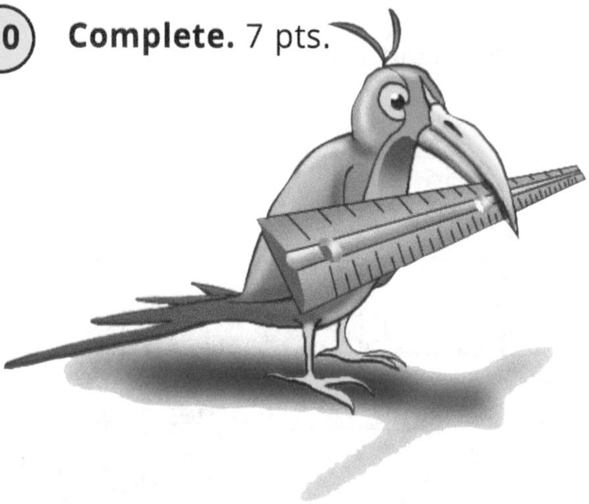

8,000 millimeter = ________ meter

4 meters = ________ millimeters

7 meter = ________ centimeters

50 millimeters = ________ centimeters

9 centimeters = ________ millimeters

2 Kilometers = ________ meters

4000 meters = ________ Kilometers

Perimeter and Area

The perimeter of a figure is the sum of the lengths of the sides of the figure.

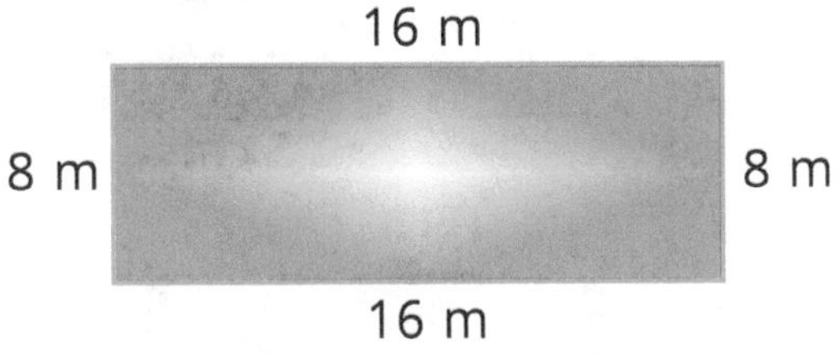

Two ways to solve the problem:

16 m + 16 m + 8 m + 8 m = 48 m The perimeter of the rectangle above is 48 m	or	perimeter = 2 • (length + width) $P = 2 \cdot (l + w)$ $= 2 \cdot (16 + 8)$ $= 2 \cdot (24)$ = 48 m

Area

The plastic to make a pencil holder is 16 cm long and 8 cm wide.

What is the area of the plastic?

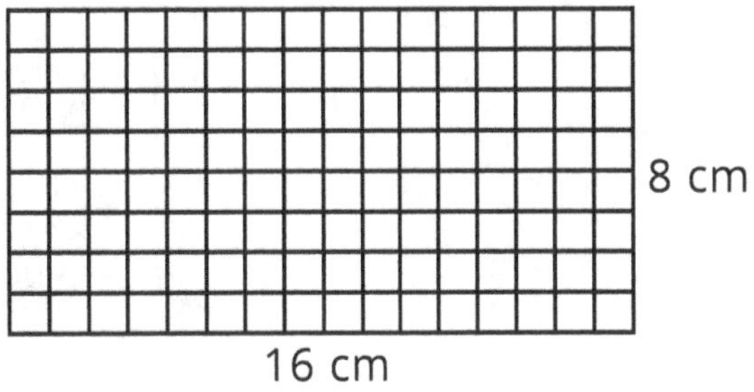

We find the area (A) of the cloth by multiplying the length of the base (b) times the height (h). (A = bh)

$$A = bh$$
$$= 16 \text{ cm} \cdot 8 \text{ cm}$$
$$= 128 \text{ cm}^2$$

The area of the plastic is 128 cm^2.

We find the area of a square by using this formula $A = s^2$

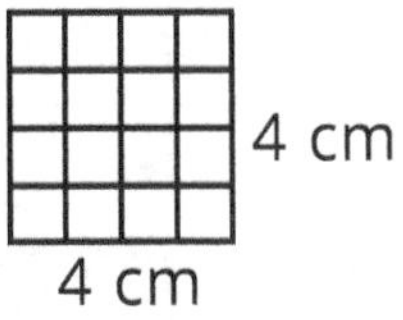

$$A = s^2$$
$$= 4 \text{ cm} \cdot 4 \text{ cm}$$
$$= 16 \text{ cm}^2$$

The area of the square is 16 cm^2.

1 **Find the perimeter and write the answer below.**

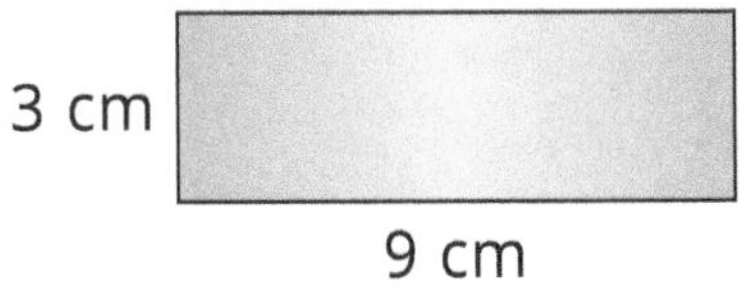

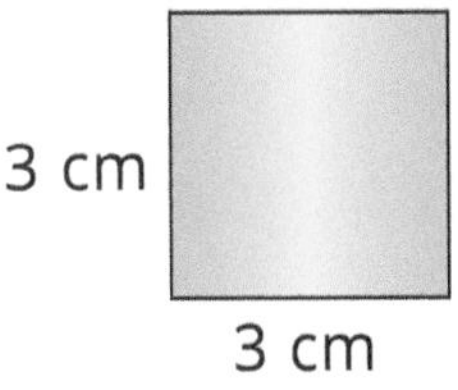

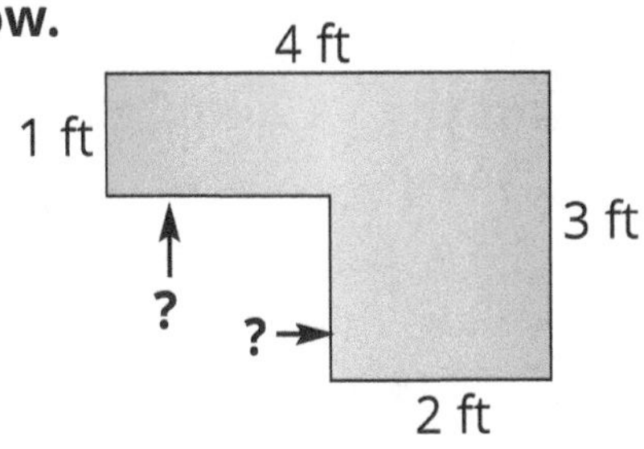

__________ __________ __________

Find the area and write the answer on the line below.

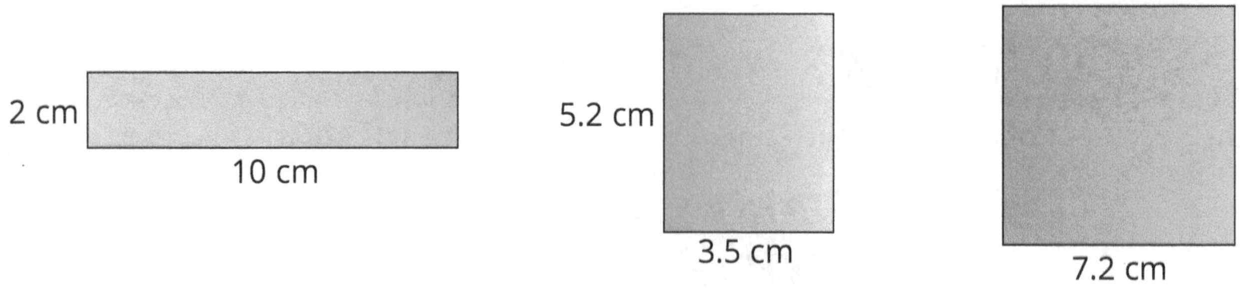

______ ______ ______

② Read each Fahrenheit thermometer. Write the temperature on the lines below.

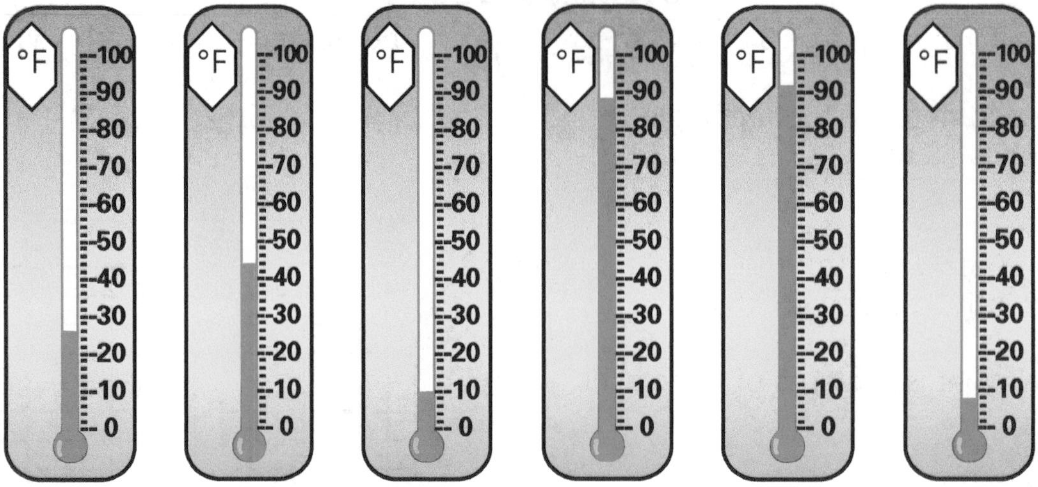

______ ______ ______ ______ ______ ______

③ Read each Celsius thermometer. Write the temperature on the lines below.

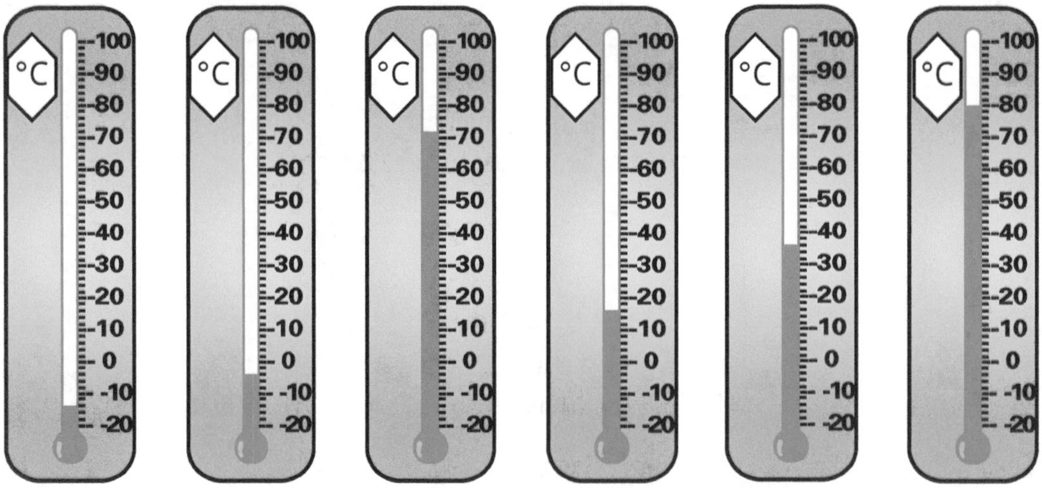

______ ______ ______ ______ ______ ______

④ Find the value of each expression.

20 ÷ 2 + 7	9 x 7 + 16	73 + 7 – 5 • 2	(7 + 13) • 4
(13 + 9) • 2 + 44	51 + 67 – 21 ÷ 3	4 • (68 + 40) – 107	78 – 16 + (11 • 9)

5 **Write each product with the decimal point in the correct place. Place your answer in the crossword puzzle.** The decimal point will occupy one space.

1.		2.					4.		
1.				3.					
									5.
2.				3.					
	5.								

Down

1. 9.6 x 2
2. 8.2 x 4
3. 73.35 x 4
4. 3.22 x 4
5. 0.14 x 7

Across

1. 4.646 x 2
2. 0.7 x 4
3. 9.2 x 4
4. 6 x0.3
5. 9.07 x 6

6 **Multiply.** Reduce the answers to the lowest terms. Find the answers in the table below and shade them. The remaining letters spell the name of a man who said "Yes" to God when he was asked to go to the house of Judas and find Saul.

$\frac{1}{2} \times \frac{2}{7} =$ $\frac{2}{3} \times \frac{3}{8} =$ $\frac{5}{9} \times \frac{2}{5} =$ $\frac{1}{3} \times \frac{9}{9} =$

$\frac{2}{9} \times 2 =$ $4 \times \frac{1}{2} =$ $\frac{2}{3} \times \frac{3}{2} =$ $\frac{3}{2} \times \frac{1}{8} =$

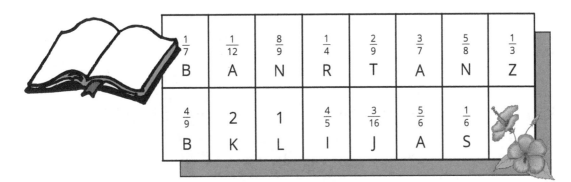

$\frac{1}{7}$ B	$\frac{1}{12}$ A	$\frac{8}{9}$ N	$\frac{1}{4}$ R	$\frac{2}{9}$ T	$\frac{3}{7}$ A	$\frac{5}{8}$ N	$\frac{1}{3}$ Z
$\frac{4}{9}$ B	2 K	1 L	$\frac{4}{5}$ I	$\frac{3}{16}$ J	$\frac{5}{6}$ A	$\frac{1}{6}$ S	

Write the man's name here.________________

Area of a Parallelogram

A parallelogram can be cut apart to make a rectangle.

The area of a rectangle and a parallelogram are the same.

To find the area (A) of a parallelogram, we find the product of its base (b) and height (h).

$A = bh$

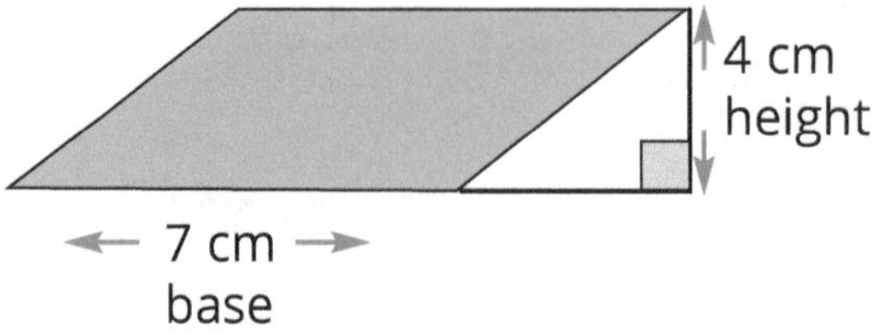

$$\begin{aligned} A &= b \cdot h \\ &= 7\text{ cm} \cdot 4\text{ cm} \\ &= 28\text{ cm}^2 \end{aligned}$$

(The height is the perpendicular distance between the base and its opposite side.)

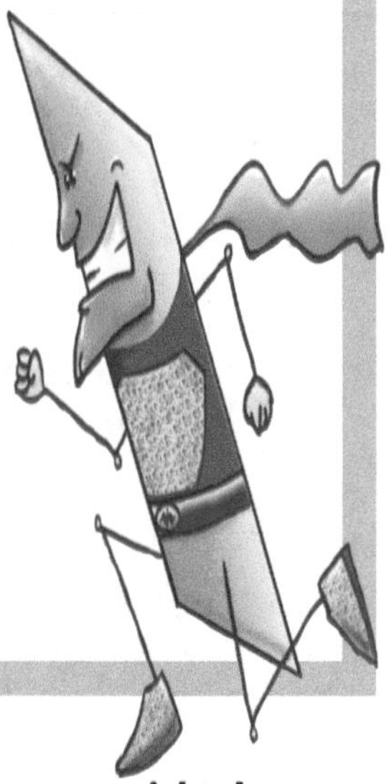

1 **Find the area of each parallelogram and write it on the line provided.**

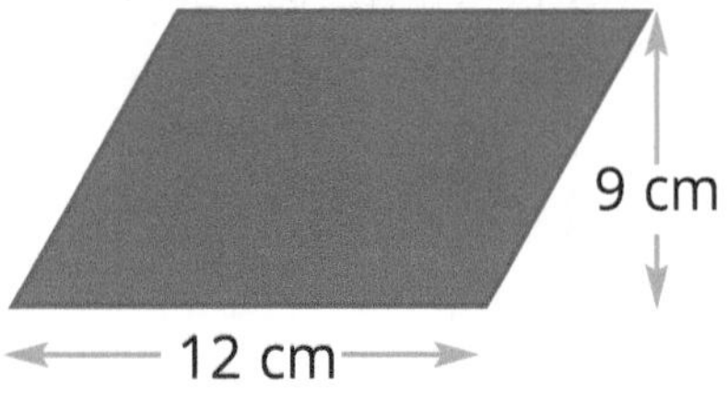

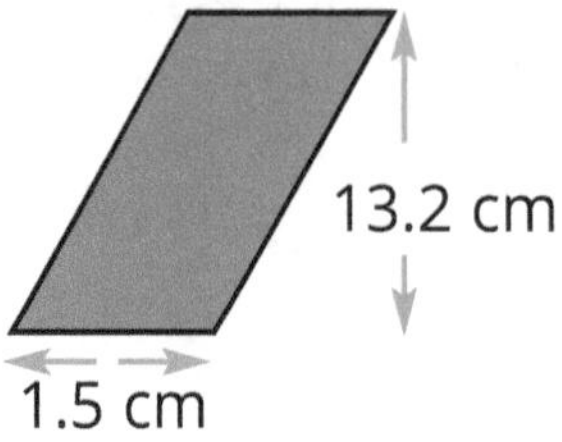

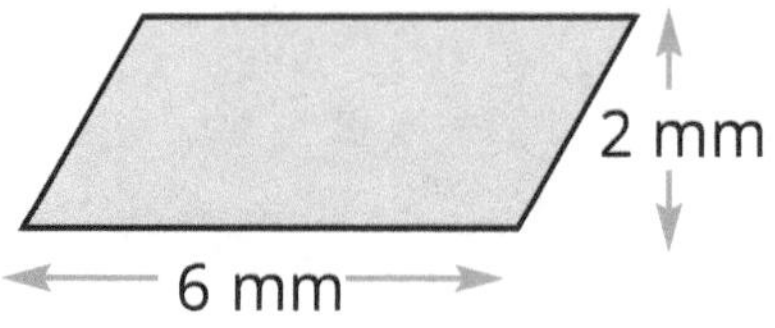

__________ __________ __________

Given the following data, find the area of each parallelogram.

base = 47 cm
height = 18 cm

Area = __________ cm^2

base = 50 mm
height = 79 mm

Area = __________ mm^2

base = 2.07 m
height = 0.7 m

Area = __________ m^2

2 **Use the formula P = 2 (l + w) to find the perimeter of each figure.**

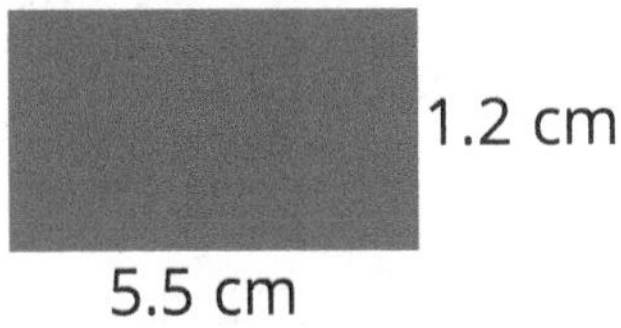

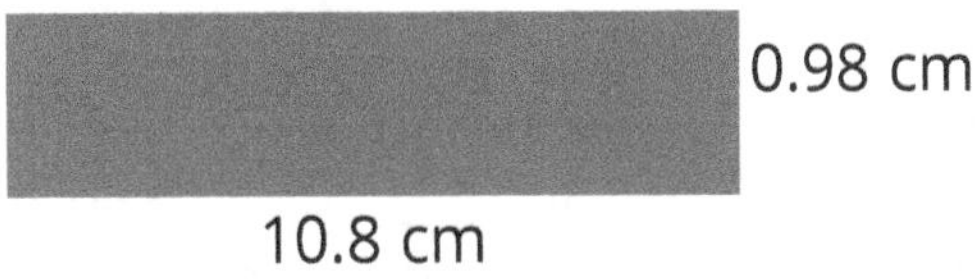

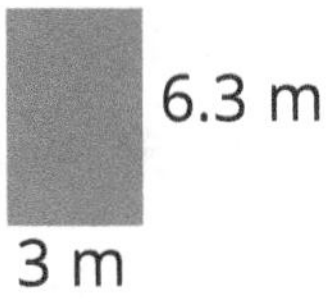

__________ __________ __________

Find the perimeter of each figure.

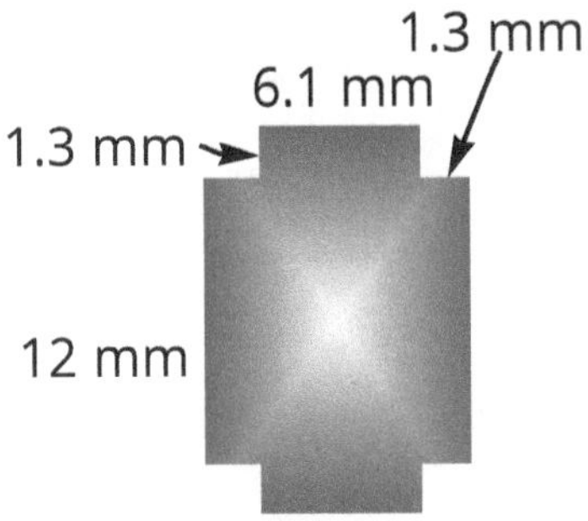

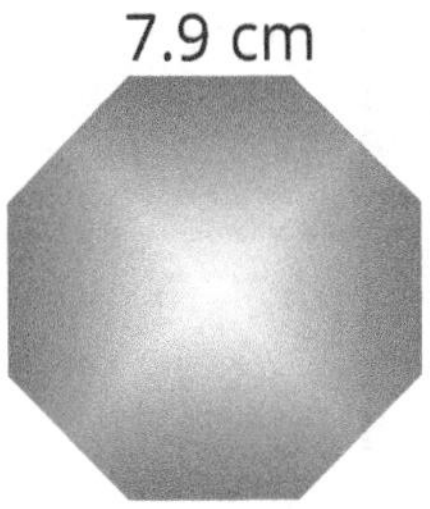

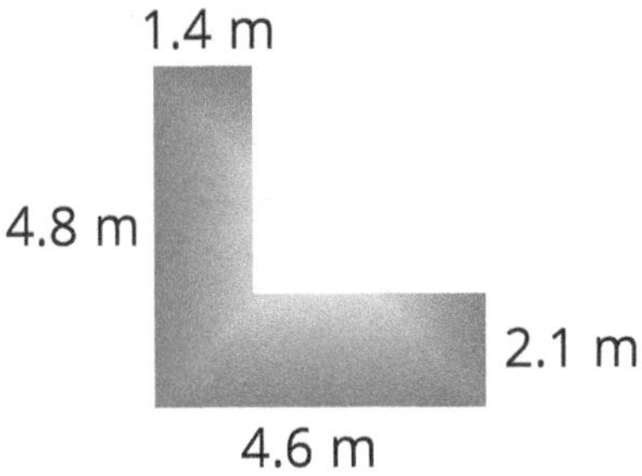

__________ __________ __________

3 **Draw a line on each thermometer at the temperature indicated.**

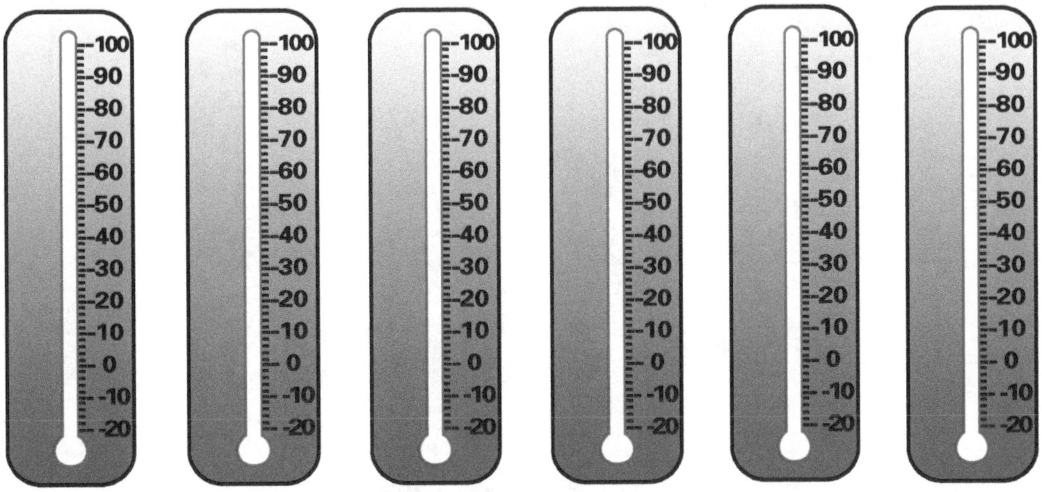

-8°C 19°C -12°C 79°C 99°C -1°C

4 **Add.**

12.8 + 109.3 + 41 + 88.27 =

172.9 + 0.3 + 9.86 + 12 =

9.03 + 12.33 + 19 + 0.21 =

44.3 + 142 + 0.356 + 10 =

5 **Multiply. Reduce answers to the lowest terms. If the answer is less than $\frac{1}{2}$ shade the box. The shaded boxes will complete this verse from Corinthians 13:13: And now these three remain:**

F $\frac{1}{9} \times \frac{3}{9}$	L $\frac{8}{9} \times \frac{5}{7}$	A $\frac{1}{2} \times \frac{3}{4}$	I $\frac{2}{7} \times \frac{2}{5}$	R $\frac{4}{5} \times \frac{2}{3}$	T $\frac{6}{8} \times \frac{2}{5}$	H $\frac{1}{11} \times \frac{3}{7}$
K $\frac{7}{8} \times \frac{4}{5}$	H $\frac{1}{2} \times \frac{3}{4}$	B $\frac{6}{8} \times \frac{7}{9}$	O $\frac{1}{12} \times \frac{2}{9}$	J $\frac{2}{3} \times \frac{5}{6}$	P $\frac{1}{7} \times \frac{3}{4}$	E $\frac{3}{10} \times \frac{2}{5}$
L $\frac{1}{4} \times \frac{3}{4}$	F $\frac{4}{5} \times \frac{6}{7}$	Y $\frac{5}{6} \times \frac{5}{6}$	O $\frac{1}{2} \times \frac{6}{9}$	F $\frac{3}{4} \times \frac{2}{3}$	V $\frac{1}{8} \times \frac{3}{4}$	E $\frac{1}{8} \times \frac{3}{7}$

And these three remain: ______________________________

6 **Find the missing number and write it in the box provided.**

$$\begin{array}{r} 1.99 \\ \times \quad \square \\ \hline 9.95 \end{array} \qquad \begin{array}{r} 4.07 \\ \times \quad \square \\ \hline 32.56 \end{array} \qquad \begin{array}{r} 0.89 \\ \times \quad \square \\ \hline 2.67 \end{array}$$

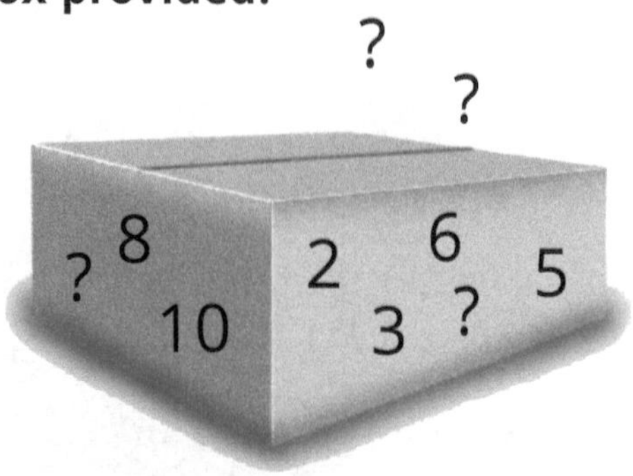

Area of a Triangle

The area of a triangle is one-half of the area of a parallelogram.
Look at the example below. If we cut the parallelogram along the diagonal, we have two identical triangles.

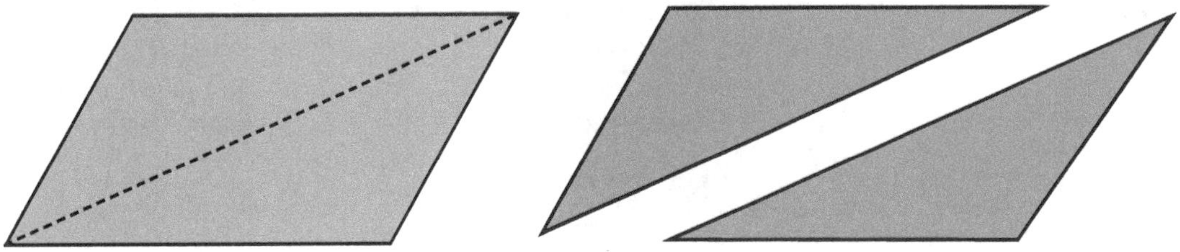

$$\text{Area} = \frac{\text{base x height}}{2}$$

or

$$A = \frac{bh}{2}$$

The height is the perpendicular distance 3 cm (height) between the base and the vertex opposite the base.

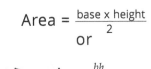

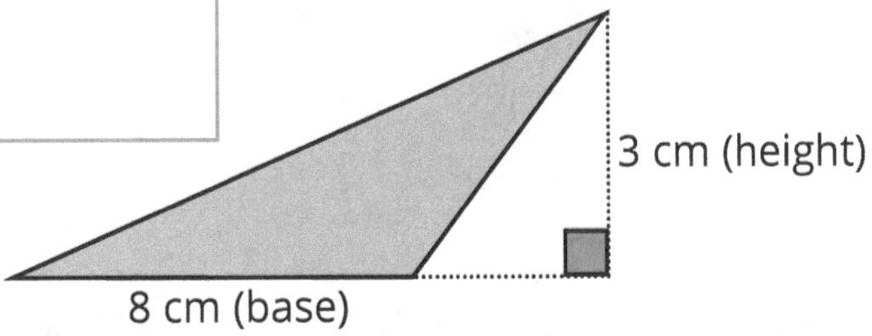

$$A = \frac{8 \times 3}{2}$$

$$A = \frac{24}{2}$$

$$A = 12 \text{ cm}^2$$

1 **Find the area of each triangle.** Write the answer on the line provided.

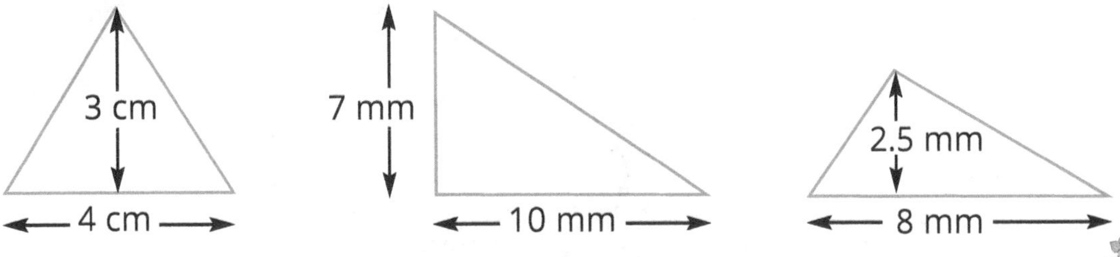

_______________ _______________ _______________

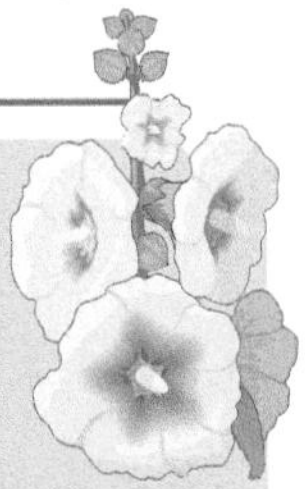

Given the following data, find the area of each triangle.

base = 40 cm height = 18 cm	base = 5 mm height = 16 mm	base = 15.5 cm height = 4 cm
Area =__________ cm^2	Area =__________ mm^2	Area =__________ cm^2
base = 18 m height = 18 m	base = 27 mm height = 20 mm	base = 8.5 m height = 8 m
Area =__________ m^2	Area =__________ mm^2	Area =__________ m^2

(2) **Place the proper letters or numbers in the blanks below.** Then, solve the problems.

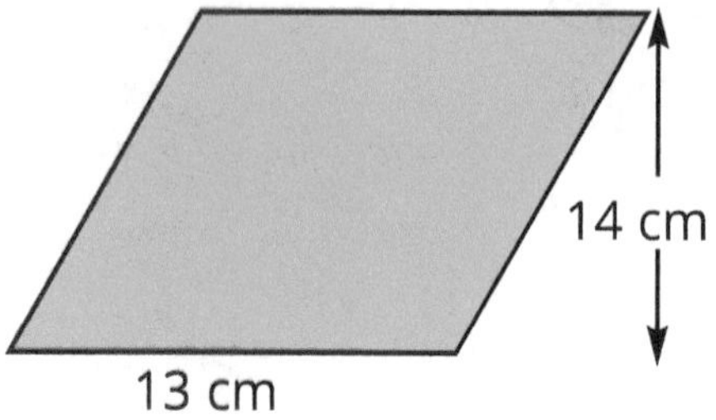

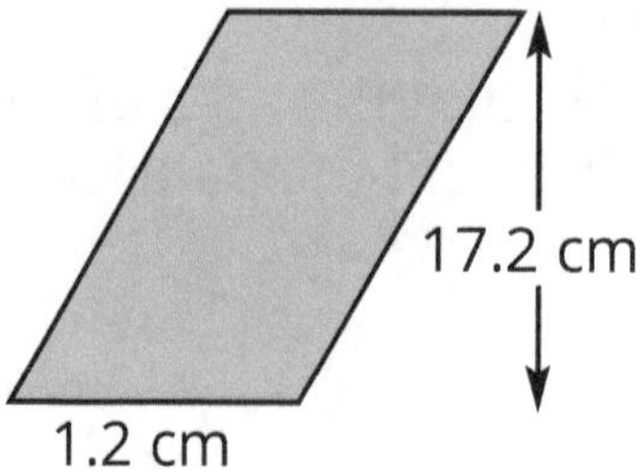

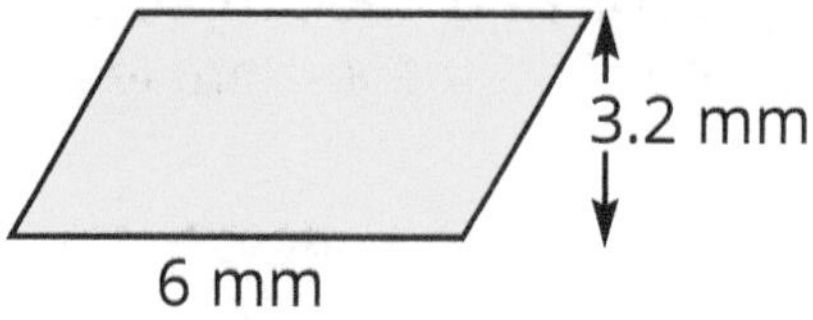

Area = base x height	Area = base x height	Area = base x height
A = ____ x ____	A = ____ x ____	A = ____ x ____
A __________ cm^2	A __________ cm^2	A __________ mm^2

Given the following data, find the area of each parallelogram.

base = 47 cm height = 18 cm	base = 50 mm height = 7.9 mm	base = 2.07 m height = 0.7 m
Area =__________ cm^2	Area =__________ mm^2	Area =__________ m^2

(3) **Given the perimeter, find the length of the missing side/sides.**

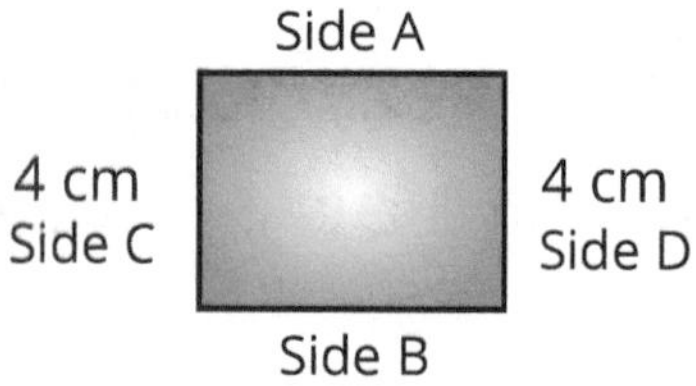

Side A = ________
Side B = ________
Side C = 4 cm
Side D = 4 cm

Perimeter = 18 cm

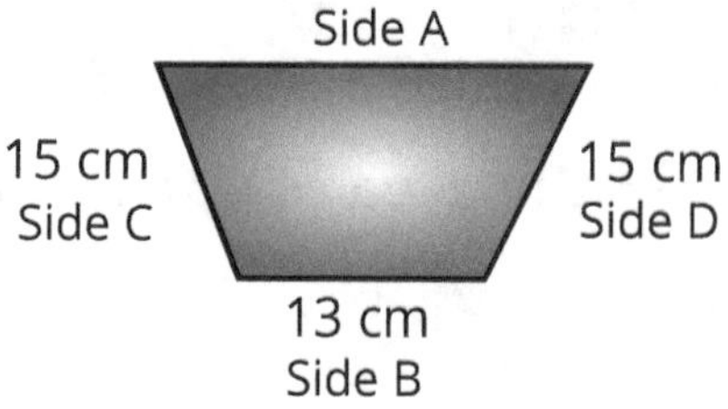

Side A = ________
Side B = 13 cm
Side C = 15 cm
Side D = 15 cm

Perimeter = 63 cm

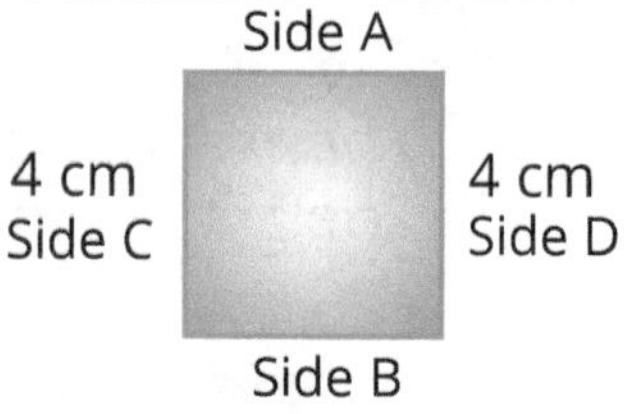

Side A = ________
Side B = ________
Side C = 4 cm
Side D = 4 cm

Perimeter = 16 cm

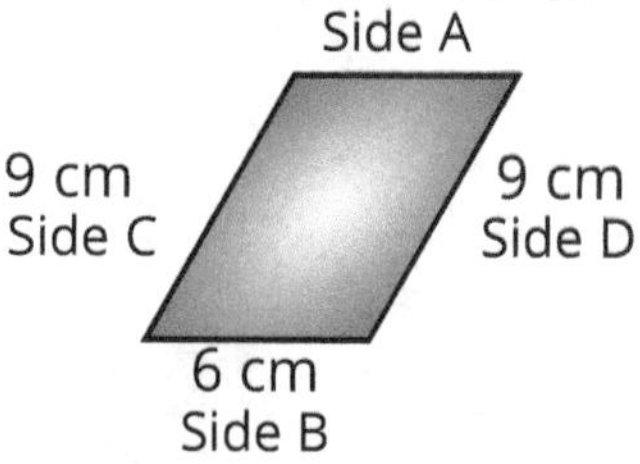

Side A = ________
Side B = 6 cm
Side C = 9 cm
Side D = 9 cm

Perimeter = 30 cm

4 **Find the area of the following figures.** Write the answers on the lines provided.

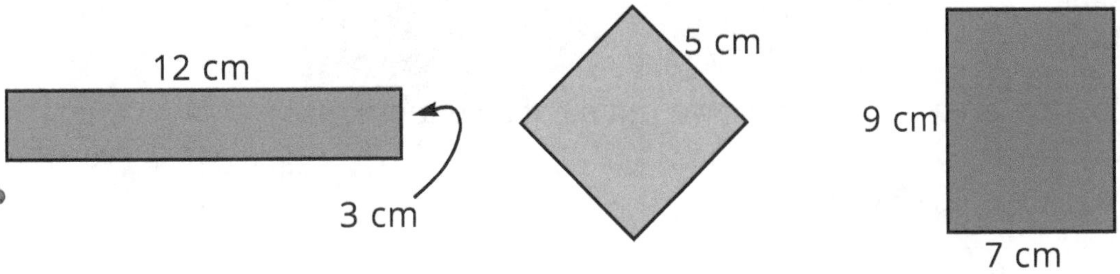

____________ ____________ ____________

5 **Multiply.** Place the answers in order from largest to smallest. The letters next to the answers when placed in the correct order spell a very important word.

$$\begin{array}{r} 93{,}102 \\ \times\ 3{,}012 \\ \hline \end{array}$$ R

$$\begin{array}{r} 60{,}102 \\ \times\ 2{,}181 \\ \hline \end{array}$$ C

$$\begin{array}{r} 8{,}111 \\ \times 2{,}124 \\ \hline \end{array}$$ E

$$\begin{array}{r} 72{,}091 \\ \times 31{,}122 \\ \hline \end{array}$$ G

$$\begin{array}{r} 14{,}712 \\ \times 10{,}323 \\ \hline \end{array}$$ A

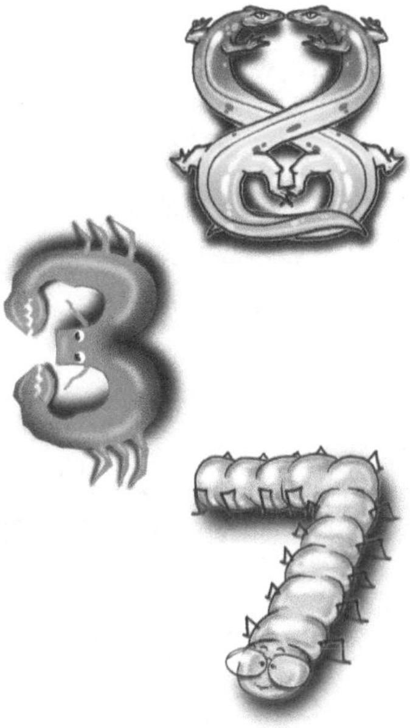

1. ________________ ____
2. ________________ ____
3. ________________ ____
4. ________________ ____
5. ________________ ____

6 **Multiply the fractions.**

$\frac{2}{5} \times 2 =$ $10 \times \frac{1}{2} =$ $\frac{11}{33} \times \frac{1}{3} =$ $\frac{3}{5} \times \frac{5}{8} =$

7 **Multiply.**

$$\begin{array}{r} 132.9 \\ \times\ \ 8.2 \\ \hline \end{array}$$

$$\begin{array}{r} 44.9 \\ \times\ 9.1 \\ \hline \end{array}$$

$$\begin{array}{r} 7.98 \\ \times\ 1.40 \\ \hline \end{array}$$

$$\begin{array}{r} 65.7 \\ \times\ 0.5 \\ \hline \end{array}$$

Area of Circle

Let's find the area of a circle with a radius of 2 centimeters.

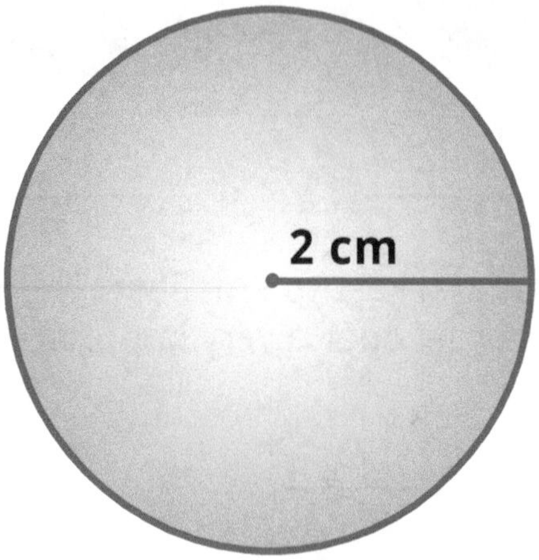

$A = \pi \cdot r \cdot r$ or πr^2 is the formula used to find the area of a circle.
The number for π is approximately 3.14.

$A = \pi r^2$
$= 3.14\ (2\ cm \times 2\ cm)$
$= 3.14\ (4\ cm^2)$
$= 12.56\ cm^2$

The area of the circle is about 12.56 square centimeters.

1 **Fill in the blanks under each circle. Round the answer to the nearest tenth.**

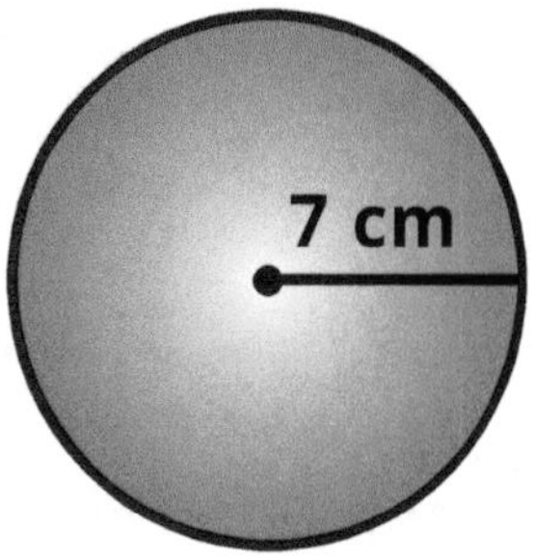

$A = \pi r^2$
= 3.14 (_____ cm x _____ cm)
= 3.14 (_____ cm^2)
= __________ cm^2

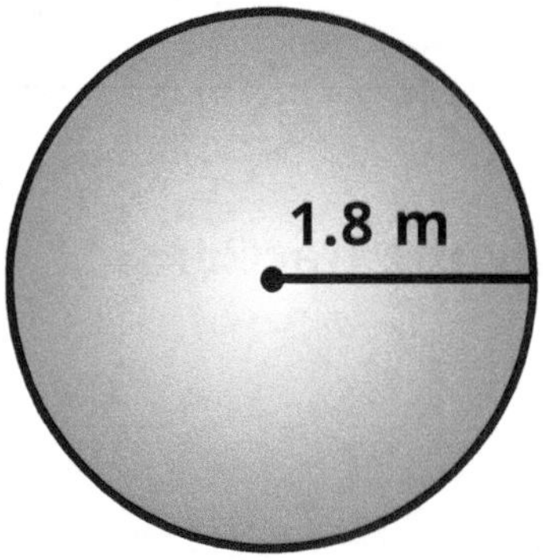

$A = \pi r^2$
= 3.14 (_____ m x _____ m)
= 3.14 (_____ m^2)
= __________ m^2

2 **Find the area of the circles given the diameter.**
Round the answer to the nearest tenth. (Remember the radius is $\frac{1}{2}$ the diameter.)

Diameter = 10 cm

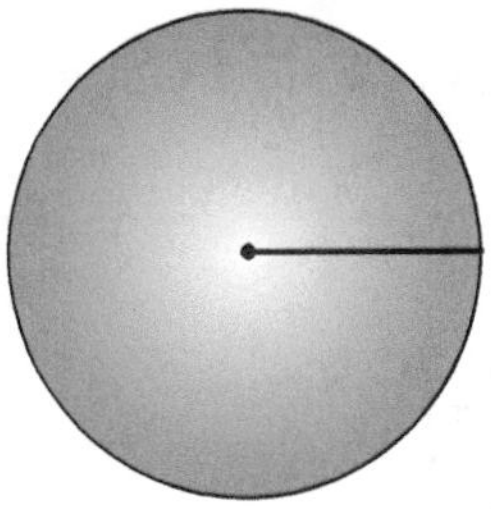

______ cm^2

Diameter = 6 m

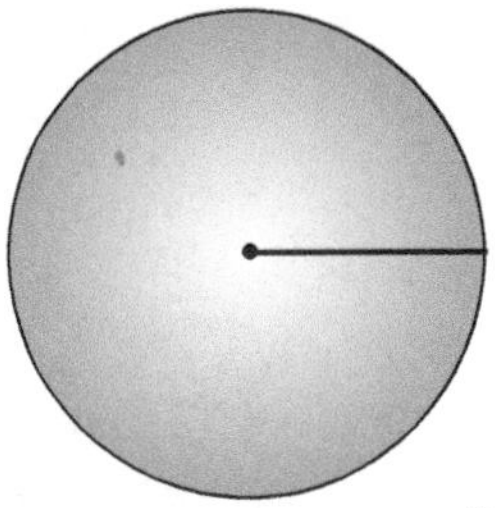

______ m^2

Diameter = 1.8 cm

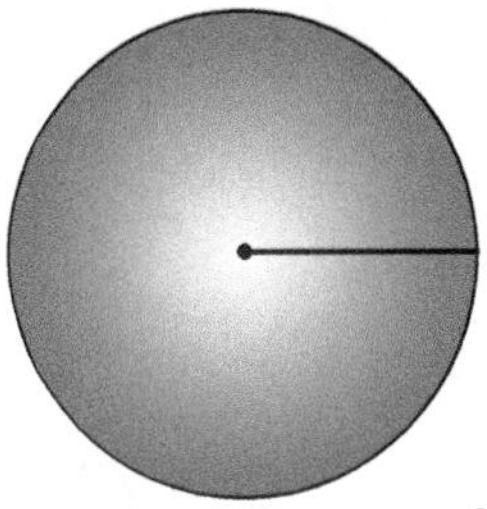

______ cm^2

3 **Find the area of the triangles and parallelograms.**
Round the answers to the nearest tenth.

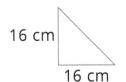

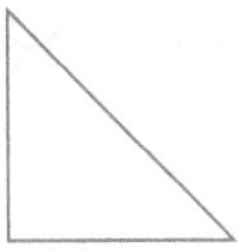

Area = ______

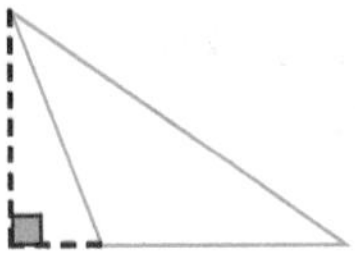

Area = ______

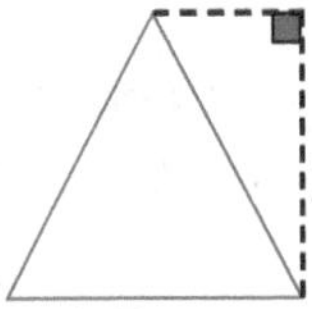

Area = ______

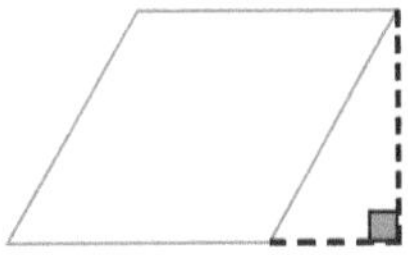

Area = ______

Area = ______

Area = ______

4 **Find the area of these figures.**

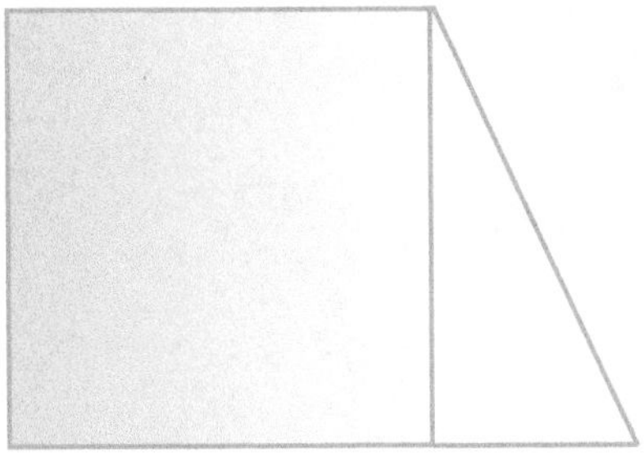

Area = ______

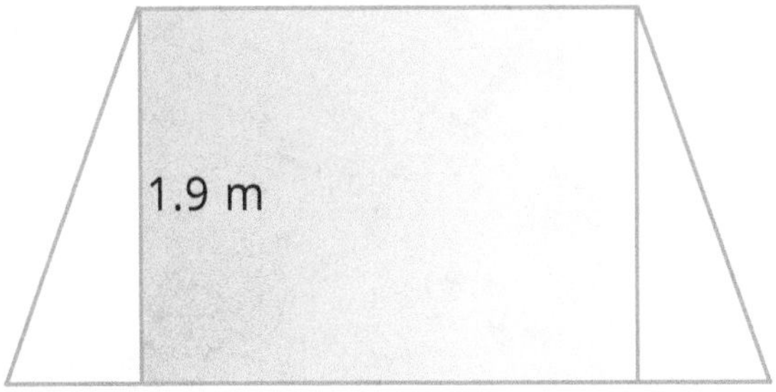

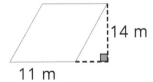

Area = ______

5 **Simplify and multiply.**

$\frac{9}{11} \cdot \frac{2}{3}$ $\frac{14}{16} \cdot \frac{2}{21}$ $\frac{10}{9} \cdot \frac{6}{15}$

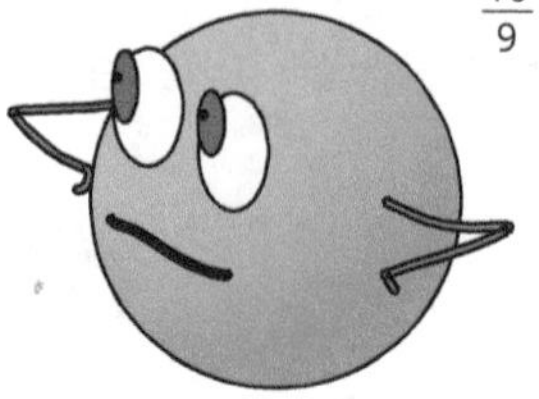

$\frac{6}{11} \cdot \frac{2}{12}$ $\frac{7}{14} \cdot \frac{2}{1}$ $\frac{20}{21} \cdot \frac{3}{15}$

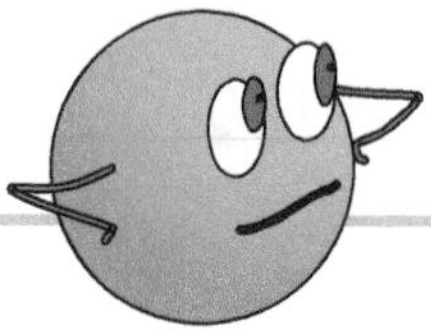

6 **Are you ready for a mind bender? The circles contain factors and the squares contain products. Pair sets of factors with the correct product.**

9.4 3.1 0.5 2.6 2.2 5.2

1.3 16.12 20.68

Volume

The volume of a cube is the number of cubic units it takes to fill it.
We use the formula V = Bh. Volume = (area of the base) x (height)

Let's start by finding the area of the base.

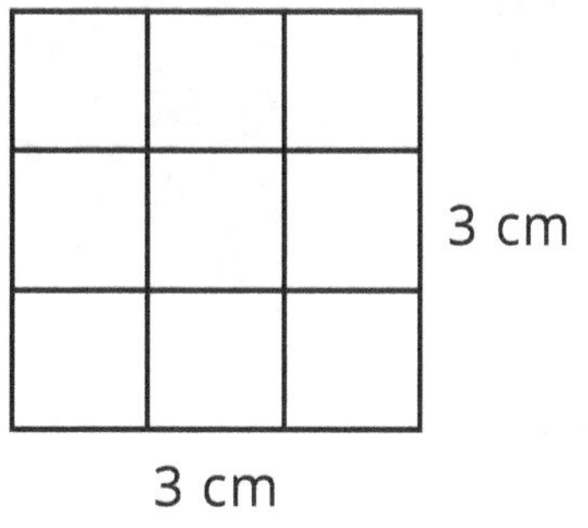

Area = base x height
A = bh
A = 3 cm x 3 cm
A = 9 cm^2

Now that we have the area of the base, multiply the answer by the height.

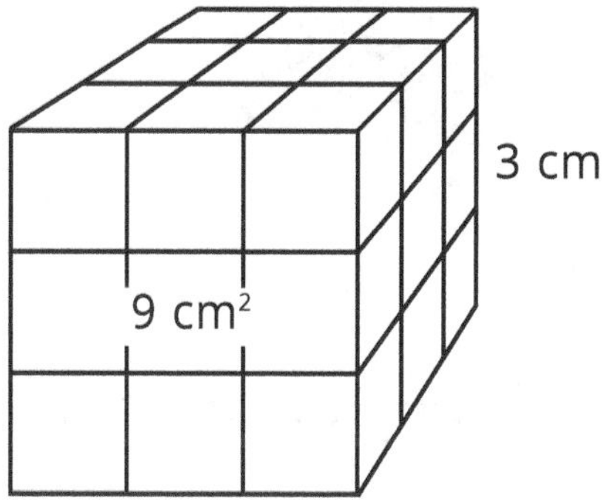

Volume = Base x height
V = Bh
V = 9 cm^2 x 3 cm
V = 27 cm^3

1 **Find the volume of each figure.**

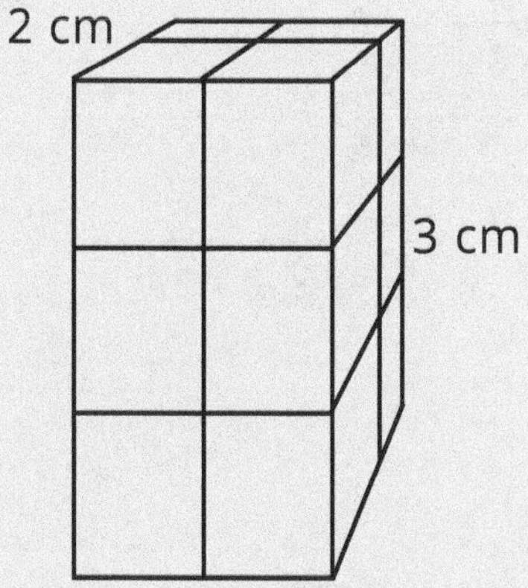

Volume = ________ cm^3

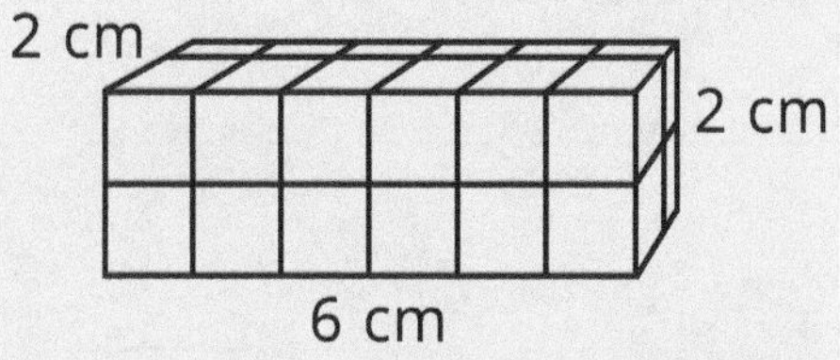

Volume = ________ cm^3

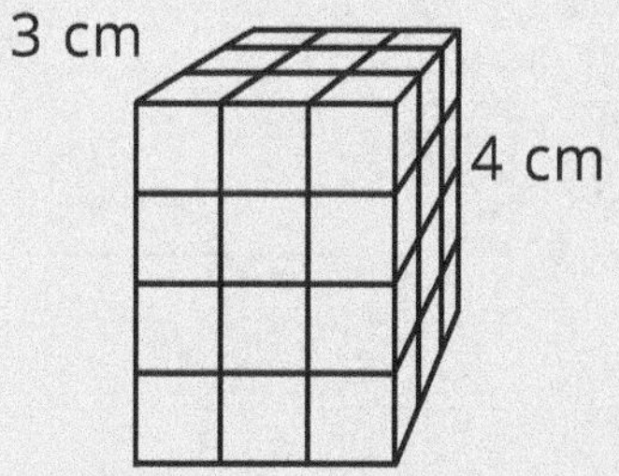

Volume = ________ cm^3

(2) Given the radius or the diameter, find the area of each circle.
Round the answer to the nearest tenth.

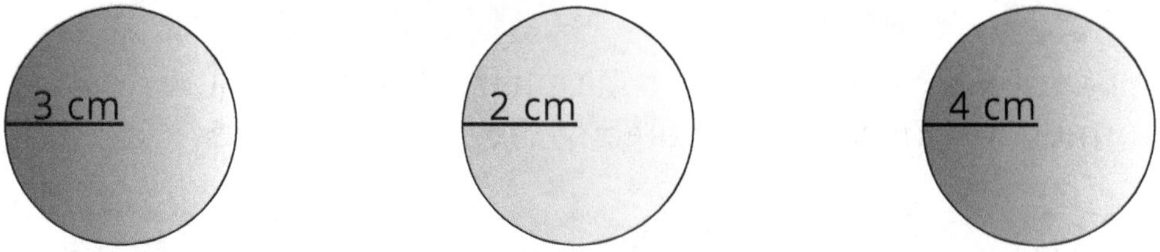

Area = ____________ Area = ____________ Area = ____________

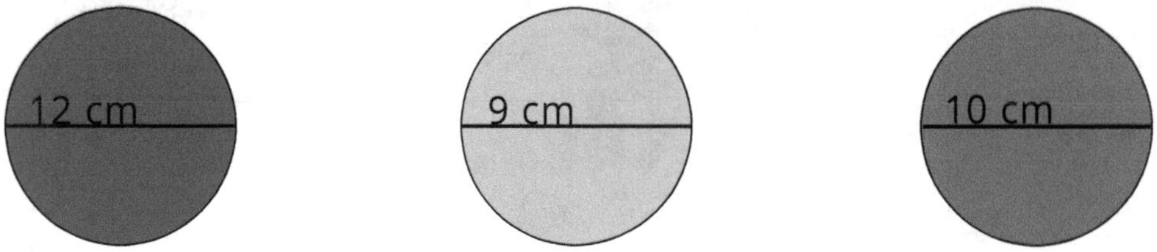

Area = ____________ Area = ____________ Area = ____________

(3) Find the area of the triangle and parallelogram.

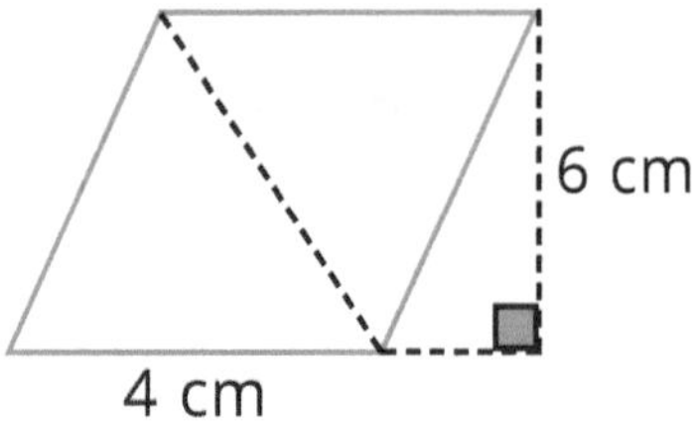

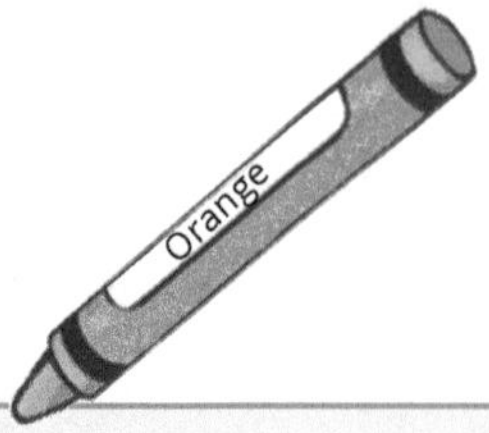

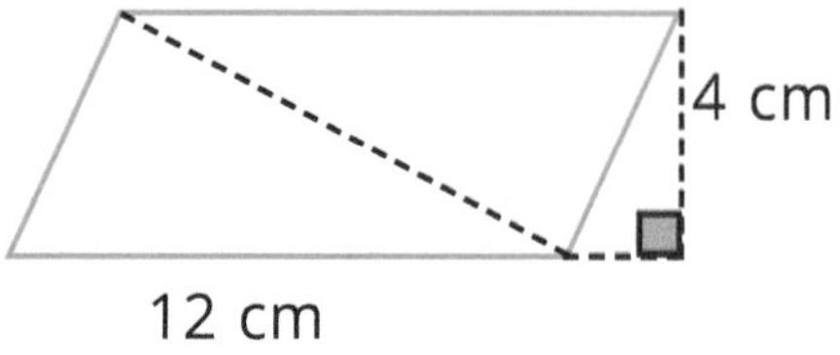

Parallelogram: A = bh

A = ____________

Triangle: A = $\frac{1}{2}bh$

A = ____________

Parallelogram: A = bh

A = ____________

Triangle: A = $\frac{1}{2}bh$

A = ____________

(4) Divide.

$342\overline{)33{,}174}$ $254\overline{)16{,}764}$ $602\overline{)25{,}886}$

$149\overline{)8{,}642}$ $119\overline{)65{,}688}$ $421\overline{)30{,}733}$

5 **Divide. Circle the right answer.**

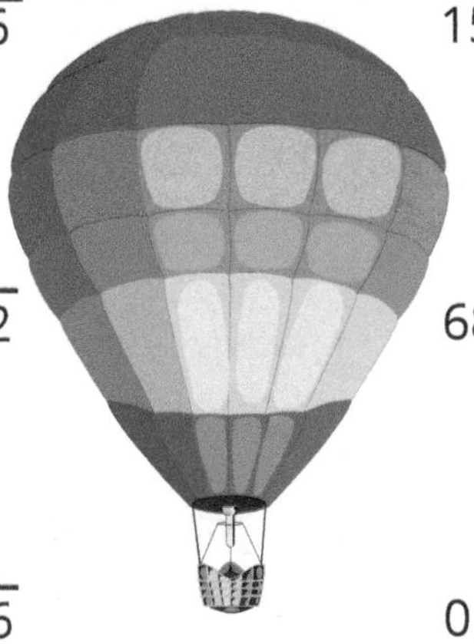

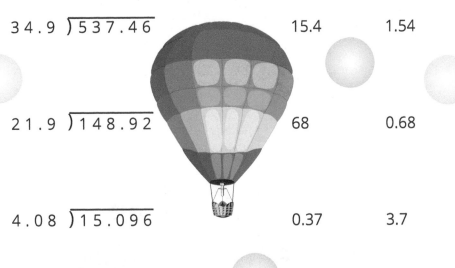

$34.9\overline{)537.46}$	15.4	1.54	154
$21.9\overline{)148.92}$	68	0.68	6.8
$4.08\overline{)15.096}$	0.37	3.7	37
$5.61\overline{)72.93}$	1.3	130	13

6 **Rename each fraction. If the fraction is $\frac{1}{2}$ or less, shade the box and find your way through the maze.**

Start (at top of the third column)

$\frac{35}{40}$	$\frac{20}{25}$	$\frac{16}{32}$	$\frac{14}{28}$
$\frac{32}{40}$	$\frac{8}{20}$	$\frac{10}{12}$	$\frac{5}{25}$
$\frac{18}{32}$	$\frac{6}{9}$	$\frac{15}{25}$	$\frac{4}{12}$
$\frac{9}{12}$	$\frac{10}{50}$	$\frac{3}{12}$	$\frac{18}{81}$
$\frac{8}{10}$	$\frac{16}{64}$	$\frac{6}{8}$	$\frac{8}{12}$

End (at bottom of the second column)

Volume of a Cylinder

We find the volume for a cylinder by multiplying the area of the base times the height.

Volume = Bh

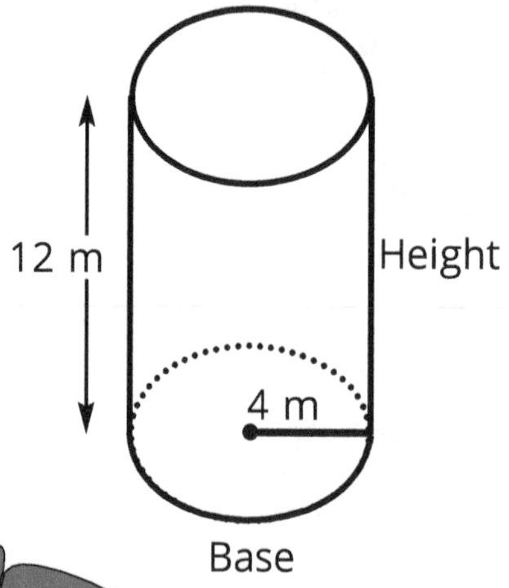

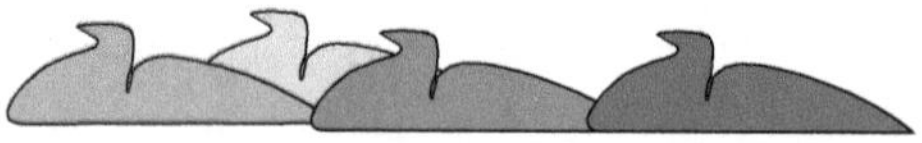

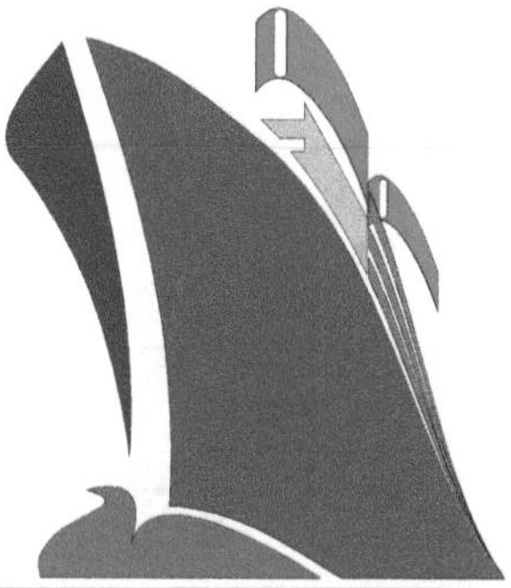

Step 1. Find the area of the base.

$A = \pi r^2$

$= 3.14 \times (4\ m)^2$

$= 50.24\ m^2$

Step 2. Multiply the area of the base times the height.

V = (area of the base) x (height)

$= 50.24\ m^2 \times 12\ m$

$= 602.88\ m^3$

The volume of the cylinder rounded to the nearest tenth about 602.9 m^3.

1 **Find the volume of each cylinder.** Round the answer to the tenths.

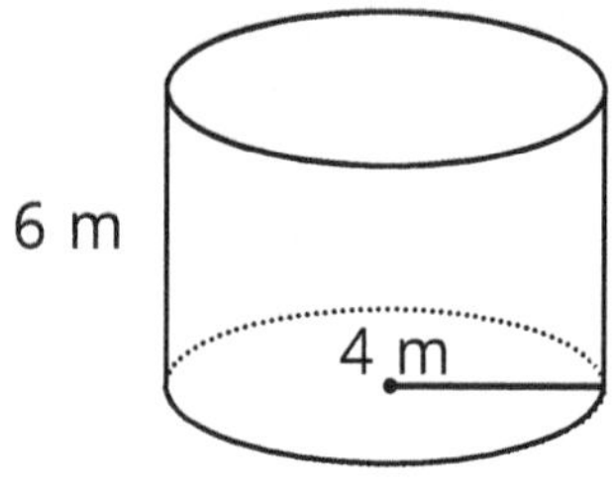

Volume = ______________ m^3

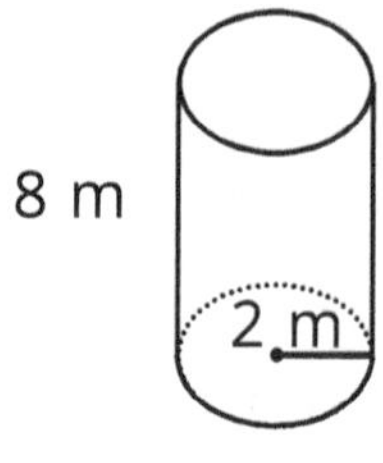

Volume = ______________ m^3

radius: 9 m
height: 2 m

Volume = ______________ m^3

radius: 3.5 m
height: 5 m

Volume = ______________ m^3

radius: 8 m
height: 10 m

Volume = ______________ m^3

radius: 2.8 m
height: 7 m

Volume = ______________ m^3

2 **Find the volume of each figure.**

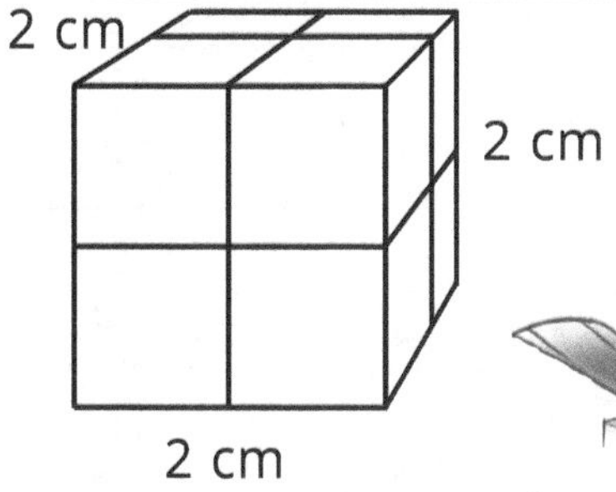

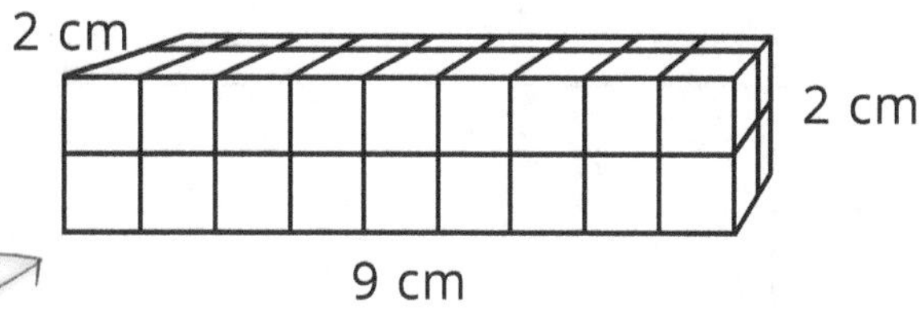

Volume = ___________ cm^3

Volume = ___________ cm^3

3 **Given the radius or the diameter, find the area of each circle.**
Round the answer to the nearest tenth.

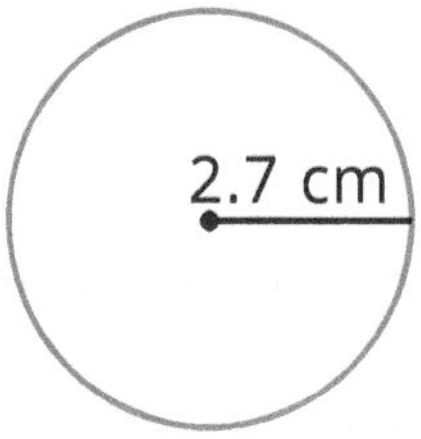

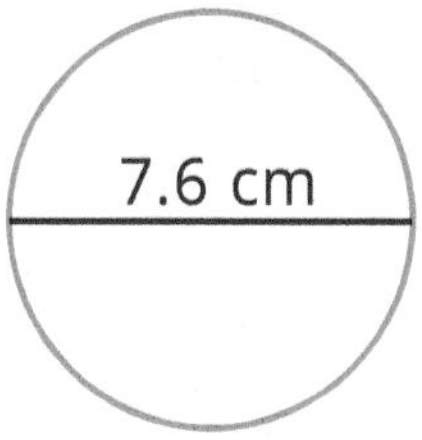

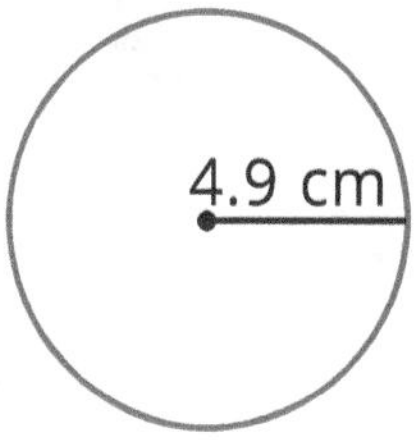

Area = ___________ Area = ___________ Area = ___________

The diameter of the round kitchen table is 2.5 meters.
What is the area of the tabletop?

The round piece of glass in the picture frame has a diameter of 20 cm.
What is the area of the glass?

4 **Find the area of each triangle.** Round the answer to the nearest tenth.

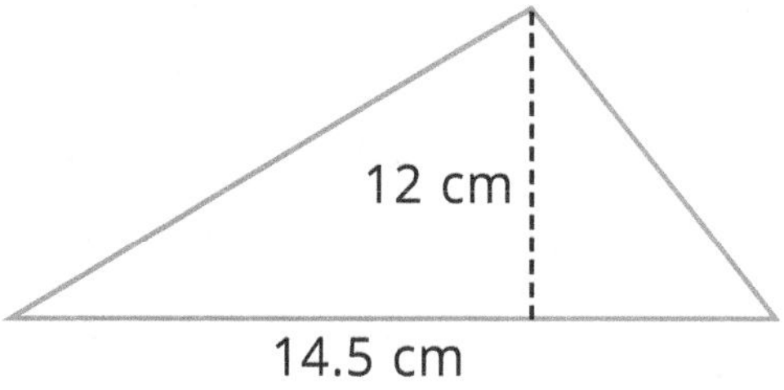

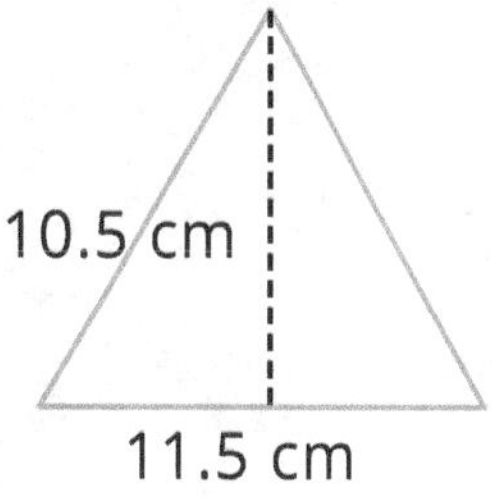

A = ___________ A = ___________

5 **Read the number clues and write the mystery number on the line provided.**
Who Am I?

I have three digits and I am an even number.

The sum of my digits is 12.

The product of my digits is 28.

The number in the tens place is 1.

I am ___________.

(6) **Divide.** Circle the correct answer. The letters beside the correct answers spell the solution to the riddle. What musical instrument doesn't tell the truth?

5.78 ÷ 34	1.7 R	0.17 A	17 P
7.74 ÷ 86	0.9 O	0.09 L	0.009 N
84.24 ÷ 39	2.16 Y	216 T	21.6 K
554.4 ÷ 77	7.02 S	7.2 R	7.002 M
35.34 ÷ 57	0.062 B	0.62 E	6.20 D

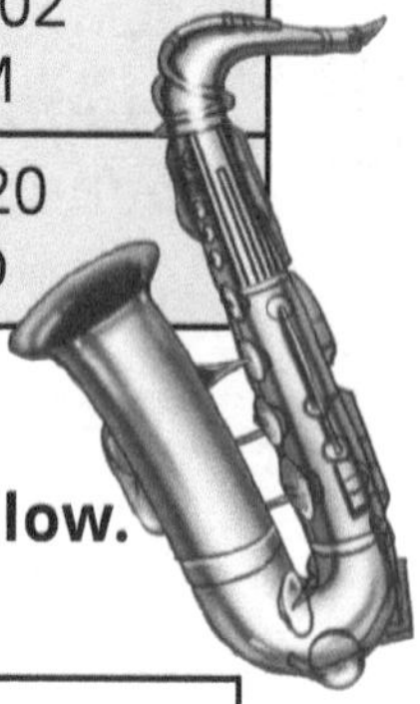

_____ _____ _____ _____ _____

(7) **Use the information on the graph to answer the questions below.**

State Populations

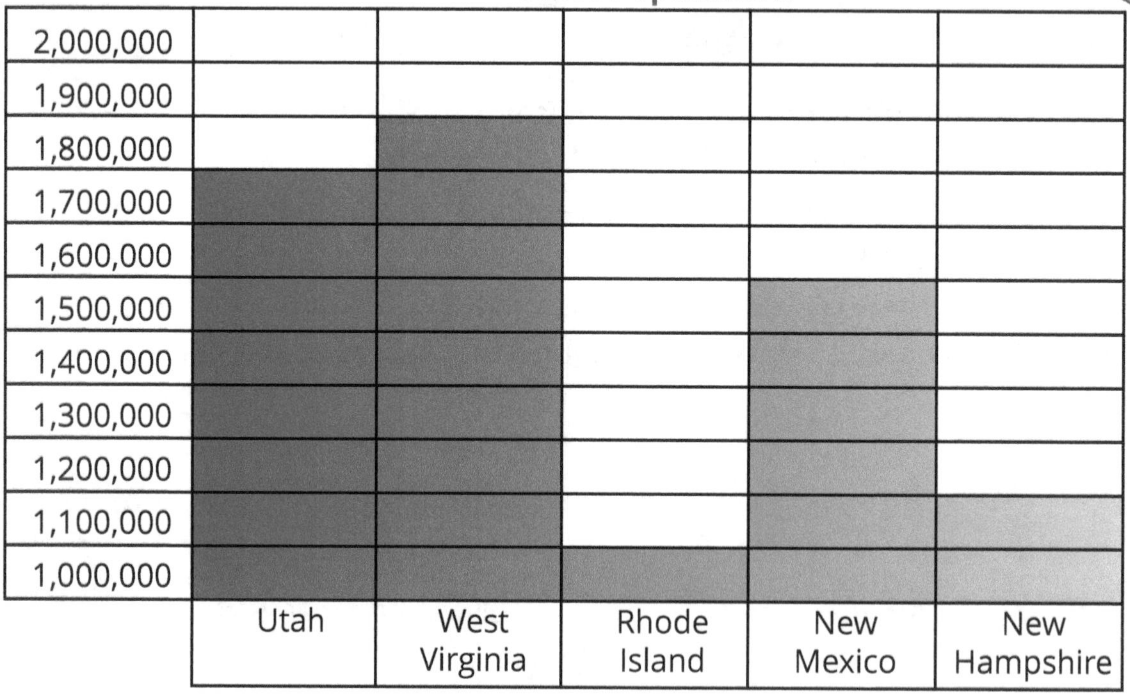

1. South Carolina's population is over 3 million.
   Does Utah or South Carolina have the largest population?
2. Maine's population is about one million two hundred thousand.
   Which states on the bar graph have a lower population than Maine?
3. Which state on the bar graph has the largest population? Smallest?
4. Tennessee's population is 5 million.
   What is the difference between the population of Tennessee and Utah?
5. Alaska's population is 500,000.
   How much greater is the population of Rhode Island than Alaska?

Surface Area

The surface area of a 3-dimensional figure is the combined area of all the faces.

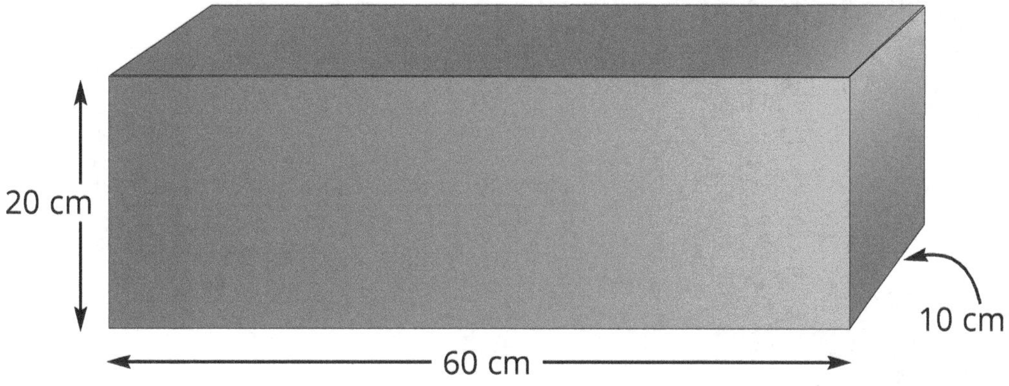

FRONT	TOP	SIDE
20 cm x 60 cm = 1200 cm^2	60 cm x 10 cm = 600 cm^2	20 cm x 10 cm = 200 cm^2

Each face has a congruent face opposite it, so we will multiply each part of the figure by 2.

Front	1,200 cm^2 x 2 =	2,400 cm^2
Top	600 cm^2 x 2 =	1,200 cm^2
Side	200 cm^2 x 2 =	+ 400 cm^2
	Add to find total	**4,000 cm^2**

The surface area of the box is 4,000 cm^2.

(1) **Find the surface area of the two boxes.**

Front 30 cm x 10 cm = ______ x 2 = ______
Top 10 cm x 5 cm = ______ x 2 = ______
Side 30 cm x 5 cm = ______ x 2 = ______
Total ______

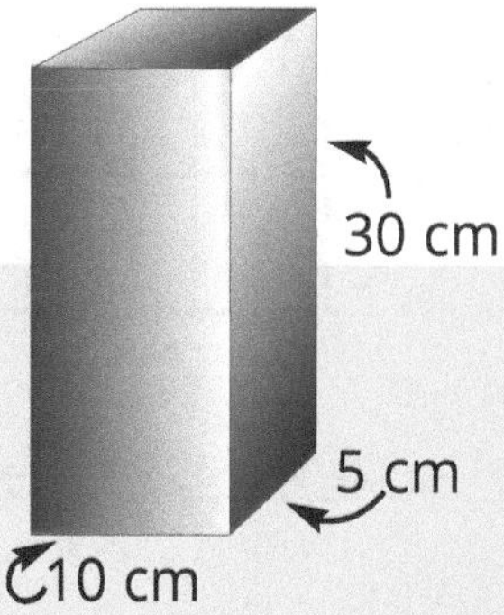

Front 15 cm x 25 cm = ______ x 2 = ______
Top 15 cm x 15 cm = ______ x 2 = ______
Side 15 cm x 25 cm = ______ x 2 = ______
Total ______

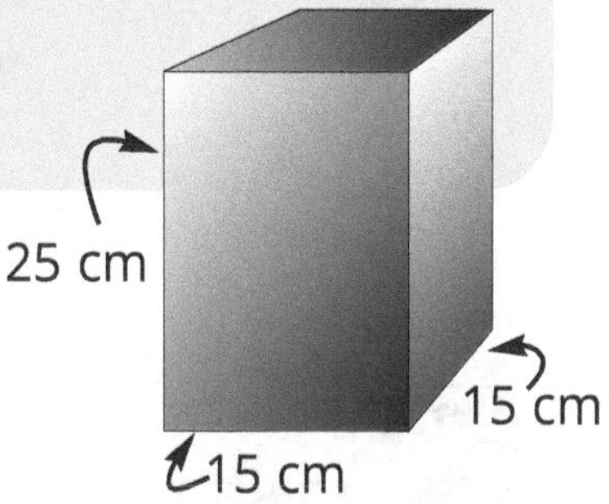

(2) **Find the volume of each figure in cubic centimeters.**

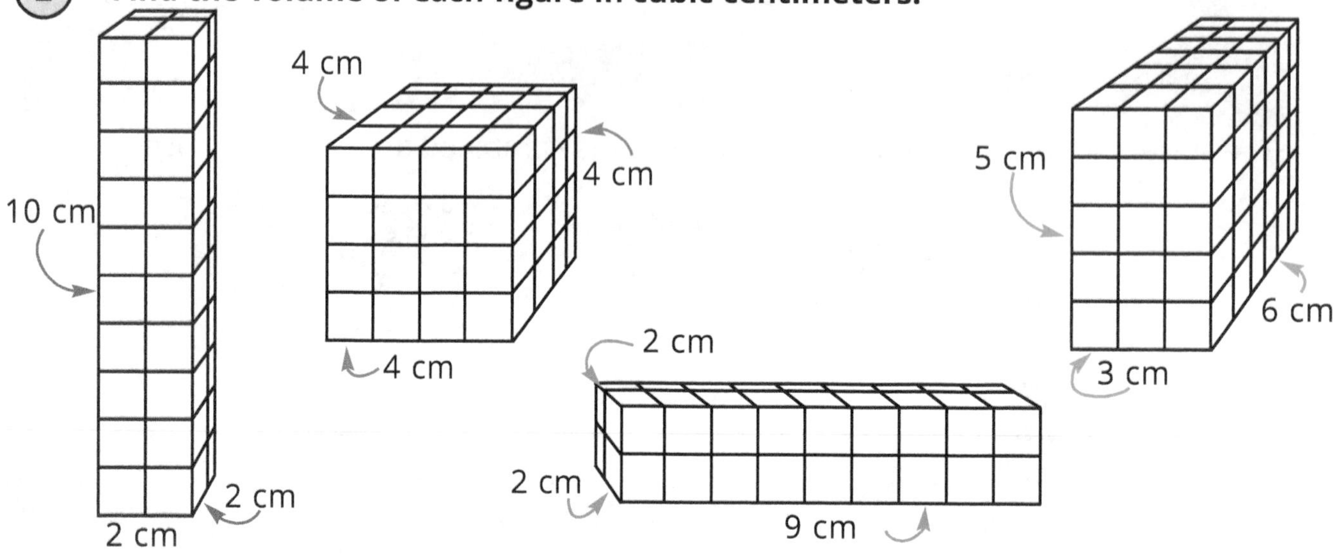

1. __________ 2. __________ 3. __________ 4. __________

(3) **Use the grid paper to draw and shade in the figures described.**

Draw a rectangle whose height is 4 cm and whose area is 36 cm^2.

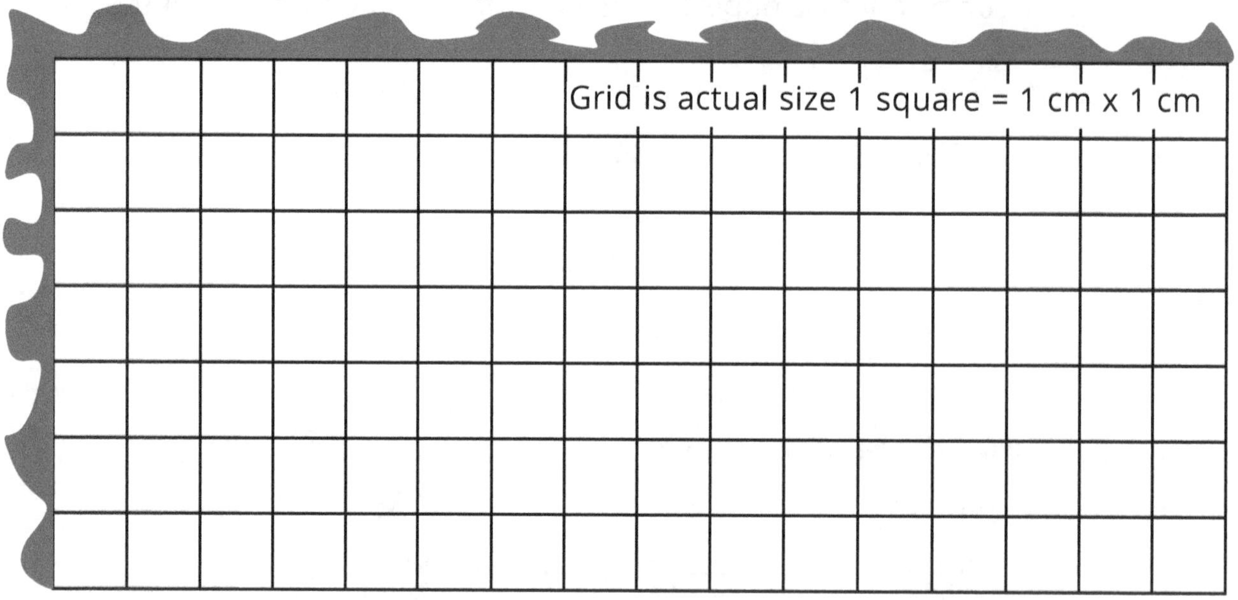

Draw a figure whose area is 10 cm^2, and whose height is 2 cm.

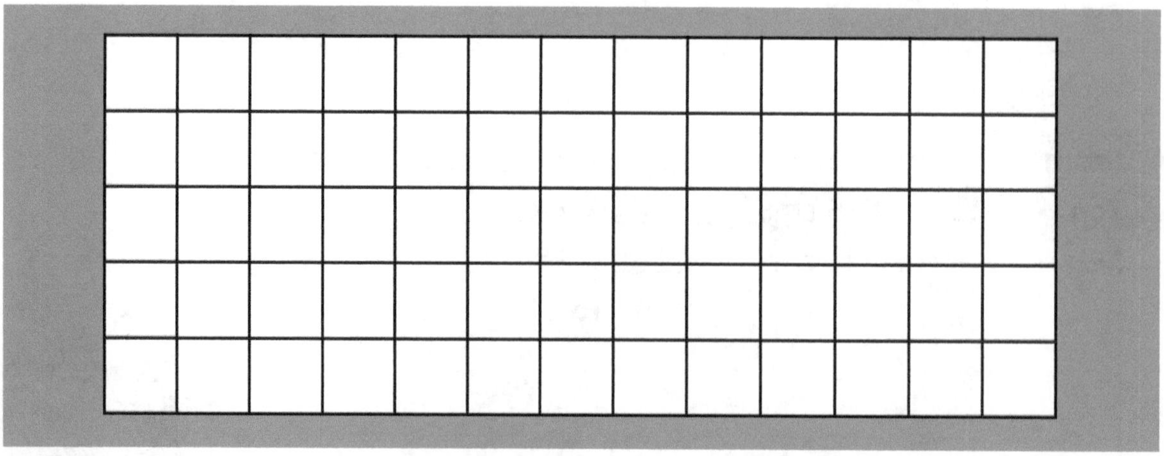

4 **Draw these circles. You will need a compass and centimeter ruler.** Then, give the area of each circle. Round the answer to the nearest tenth.

1. Draw a circle with a radius of 3 cm.	2. Draw a circle with the diameter of 4 cm.
Area = ________ cm^2	Area = ________ cm^2

5 **Do the division problems.** Beside each answer is a letter. Look at the box. When you find the answer to a problem, place the letter above it.
The letters spell the solution to this riddle:

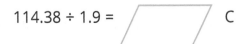

What kind of fish can you find in a birdcage?

114.38 ÷ 1.9 = ☐ C

7.384 ÷ 1.3 = ☐ P

18.368 ÷ 6.4 = ☐ H

16.377 ÷ 5.3 = ☐ E

227.92 ÷ 4.4 = ☐ R

___	___	___	___	___
5.68	3.09	51.8	60.2	2.87

6 **Rename.**

$\frac{5}{10}$ = ________ $\frac{9}{30}$ = ________ $\frac{6}{18}$ = ________ $\frac{33}{77}$ = ________

$\frac{35}{80}$ = ________ $\frac{12}{40}$ = ________ $\frac{81}{99}$ = ________ $\frac{21}{30}$ = ________

$\frac{14}{49}$ = ________ $\frac{45}{55}$ = ________ $\frac{27}{36}$ = ________ $\frac{8}{10}$ = ________

Problem Solving

We will use the formulas we have learned and apply them to word problems. First, let's review the formulas.

Perimeter of a rectangle $P = 2(l + w)$

Area of a triangle $A = \frac{bh}{2}$

Area of a parallelogram $A = bh$

Area of a rectangle $A = bh$

Area of a circle $A = \pi r^2$

Volume of a box $V = Bh$

Volume of a cylinder $V = Bh$

Which formulas apply to more than one type of problem? $A = bh$ is the formula for finding both the area of a parallelogram and the area of a rectangle. $V = Bh$ is the formula for finding the volume of a cylinder and the volume of a cube. Even though the formulas are the same, they are applied in very different ways.
Look at the example below.

Which container has the greater volume?

Container A

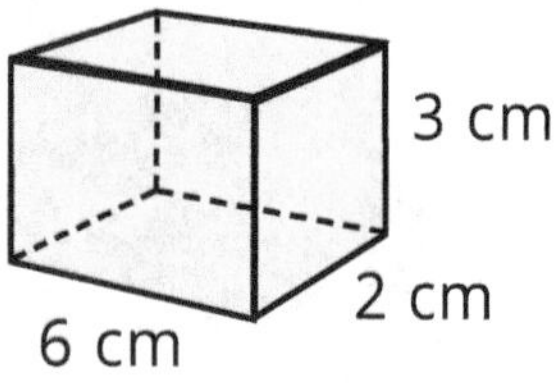

Container B

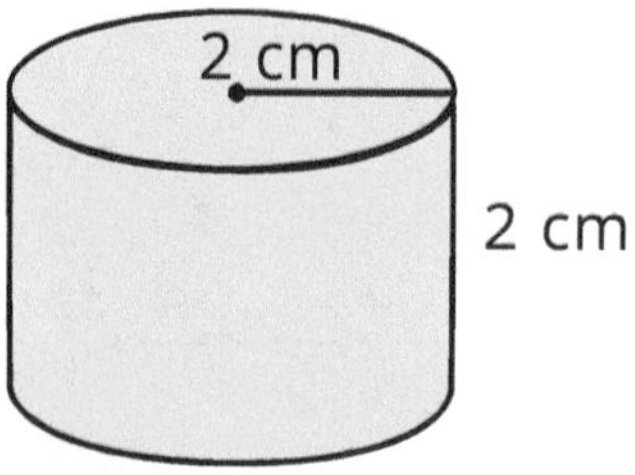

Container A
Volume = Base • height
$V = Bh$
$V = (6\text{ cm} \times 2\text{ cm}) \times 3\text{ cm}$
$V = 12\text{ cm}^2 \times 3\text{ cm}$
$V = 36\text{ cm}^3$

Container B
Volume = Base • height
$V = Bh$
$V = \pi r^2 \times 2\text{ cm}$
$V = 3.14 \times (2\text{ cm})^2 \times 2\text{ cm}$
$V = 12.56\text{ cm}^2 \times 2\text{ cm}$
$V = 25.12\text{ cm}^3$

Container A has the greater volume.

You can see that although we use the same formula to find the volume of each container, the procedure for finding the base of the container is different.

1 Problem solving.

1. Gary's window was broken by a baseball. The window frame measures 100 cm wide by 200 cm high. What is the area of the glass Gary needs to buy to fix the window?

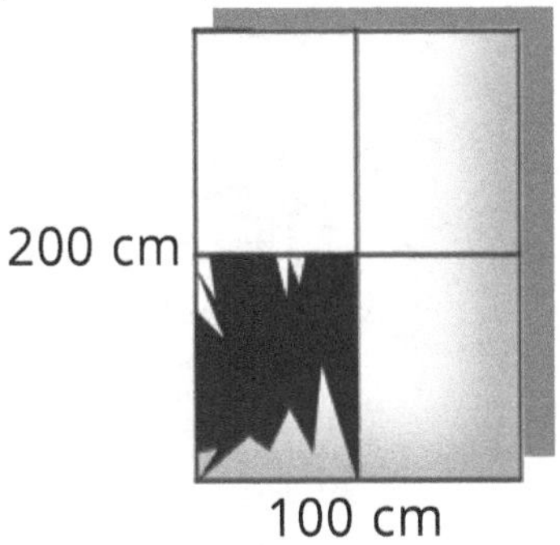

2. What is the volume of container A?

3. What is the volume of the cylinder?

4. What is the perimeter of the tablecloth?

Container A

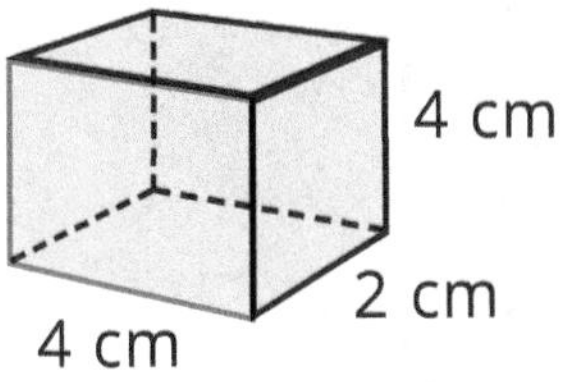

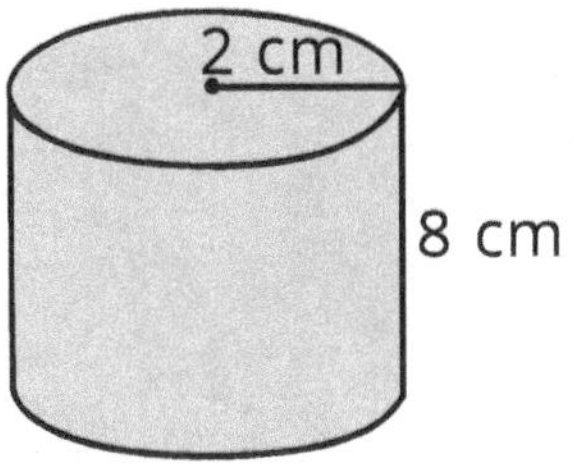

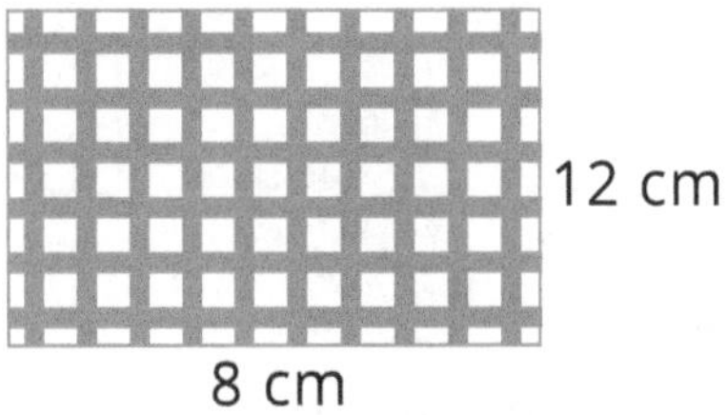

2 Find the surface area of the figure below.

Front	6 cm x 12 cm = ________	x 2 = ________	
Top	6 cm x 2 cm = ________	x 2 = ________	
Side	12 cm x 2 cm = ________	x 2 = ________	
		Total ________	

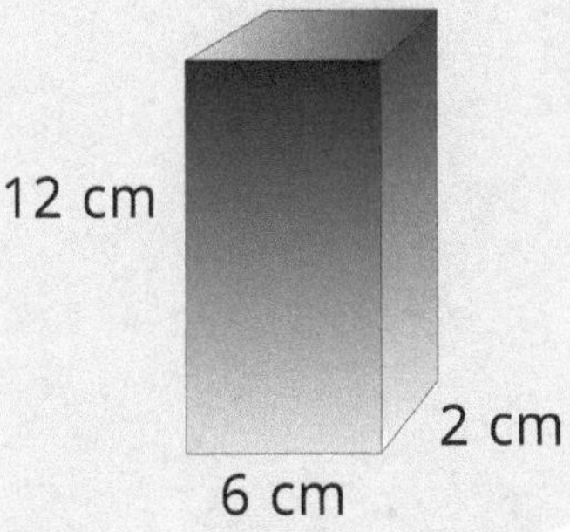

3 Find the volume of each cylinder. Round the answers to the nearest tenth.

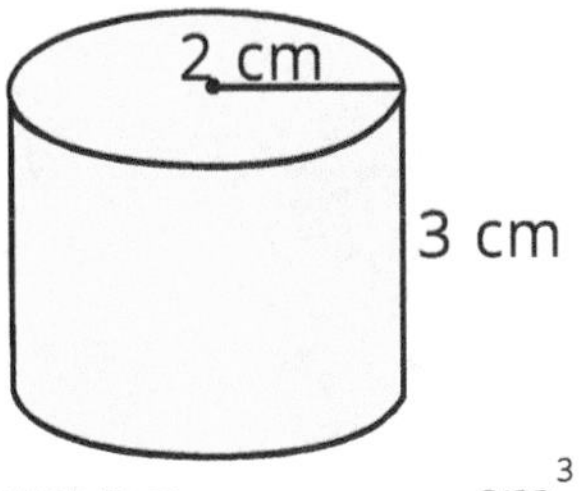

Volume = cm^3

Volume = cm^3

4 Complete the table.

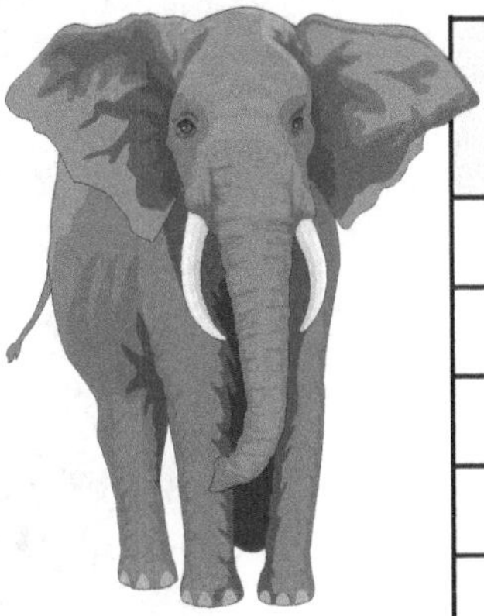

Volume of a Prism

Length of Base	Width of Base	Area of Base	Height	Volume
6 cm	9 cm		2 cm	
	4 m	36 m^2		360 m^3
7 mm		14 mm^2		350 mm^3
4 cm		24 cm^2	17 cm	
18 m	8 m		6 m	

5 **Arrange the numbers in the boxes to get the product.**

1 4 7 9

$$\begin{array}{r} \square\square\square \\ \times \quad \square \\ \hline 788 \end{array}$$

0 5 8 9

$$\begin{array}{r} \square\square\square \\ \times \quad \square \\ \hline 4,572 \end{array}$$

2 3 5 6

$$\begin{array}{r} \square\square\square \\ \times \quad \square \\ \hline 1,810 \end{array}$$

6 **Divide.**

$\frac{1}{8} \div \frac{2}{3} =$ $\frac{4}{5} \div \frac{3}{4} =$ $\frac{5}{12} \div \frac{1}{2} =$ $\frac{8}{11} \div \frac{4}{5} =$

$\frac{3}{7} \div \frac{1}{5} =$ $\frac{5}{9} \div \frac{6}{7} =$ $\frac{4}{13} \div \frac{5}{8} =$ $\frac{3}{10} \div \frac{3}{9} =$

Time Zones

There are 24 time zones in the world. Twelve zones are east of the International Date Line and twelve zones are west of it. When you cross the International Date Line going west, the date moves forward one day. When you cross the International Date Line going east, the date moves back. Look at the map below.
If a traveler goes from Southampton, Australia east to Los Angeles, California, the date goes back one day.

When you cross one individual time zone going west, the clocks are one hour earlier. When you cross one time zone going east, the clocks are one hour later.

From April to October many regions use Daylight Saving Time. The clocks are set one hour ahead of the standard time for that zone.

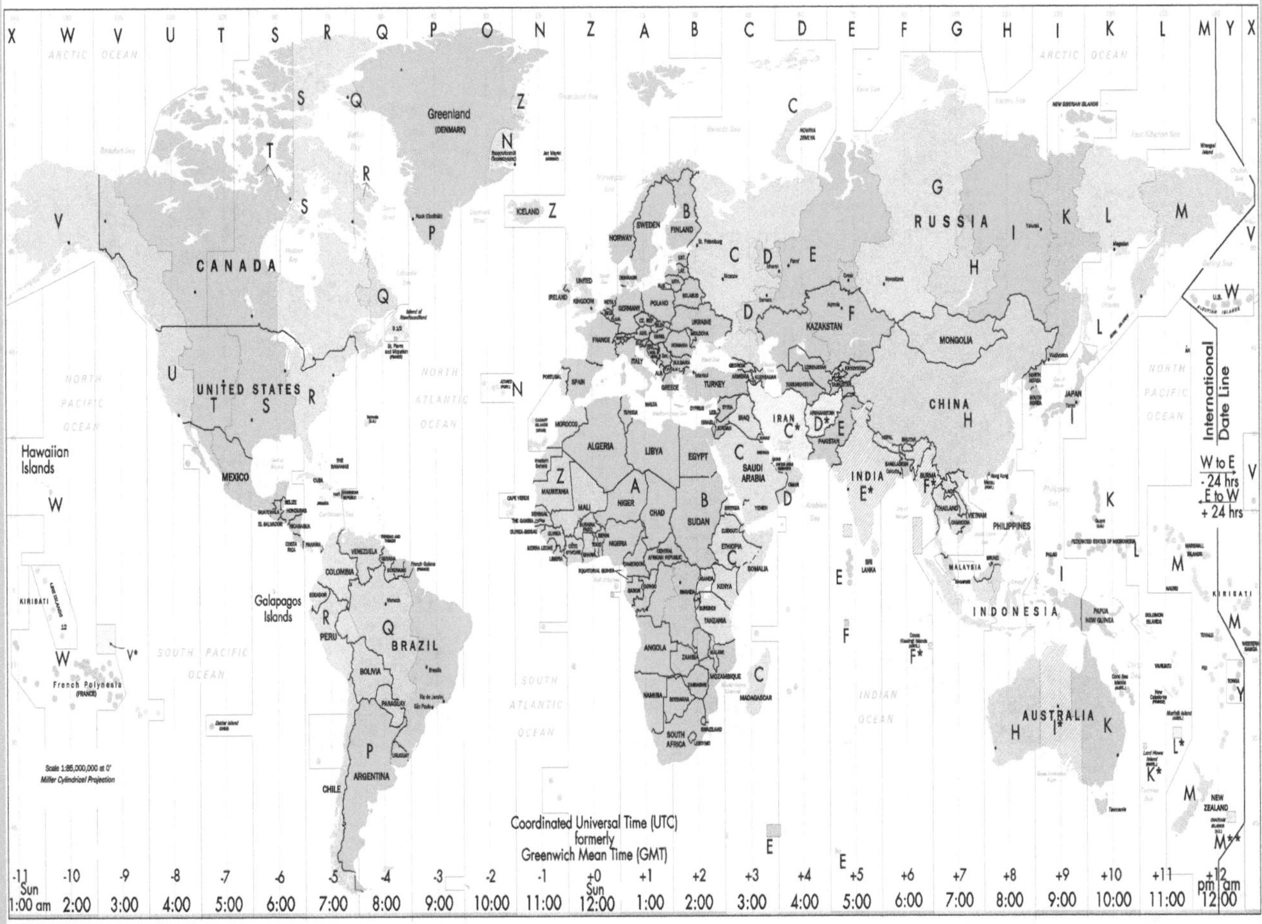

Find the following locations on the map or world atlas:

Paris, France; Kabul, Afghanistan; Tokyo, Japan; Rockhampton, Australia; Anchorage, Alaska; Los Angeles, California; Shreveport, Louisiana; Atlanta, Georgia; Columbus, Ohio; Baltimore, Maryland; New York, New York; and Georgetown, Guyana.

(1) **Use the world time zone map to complete the table.** If it is 12:00 midnight at the International Date Line, what are the times in the cities listed in the table?

City	Paris, France	Kabul, Afghanistan	Tokyo, Japan	Rockhampton, Australia
Time				
City	Georgetown, Guyana	Columbus, Ohio	Salt Lake City, Utah	Topeka, Kansas
Time				
City	Anchorage, Alaska	Atlanta, Georgia	Los Angeles, California	Shreveport, Louisiana
Time				

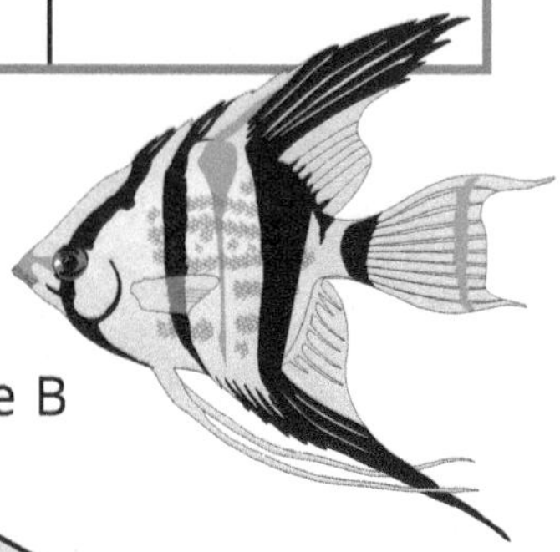

(2) **Solve.**

Circle the triangle that has the greater area.

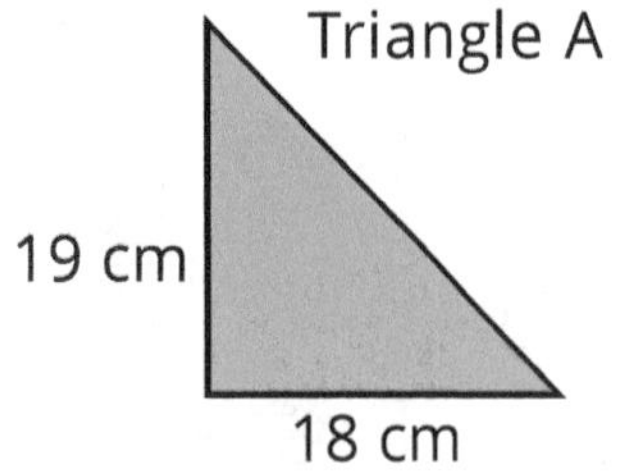

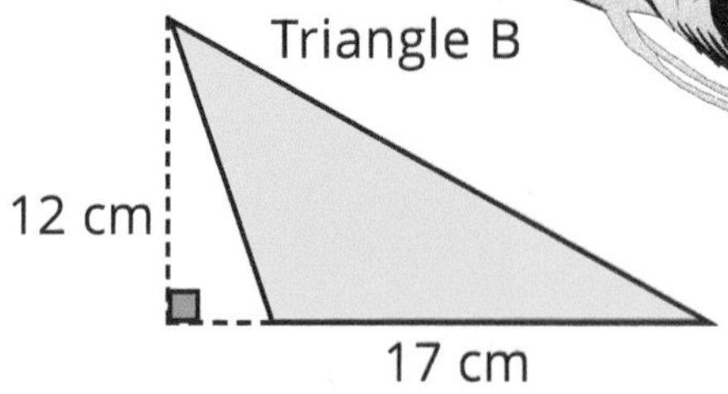

Circle the rectangle that has the greater area.

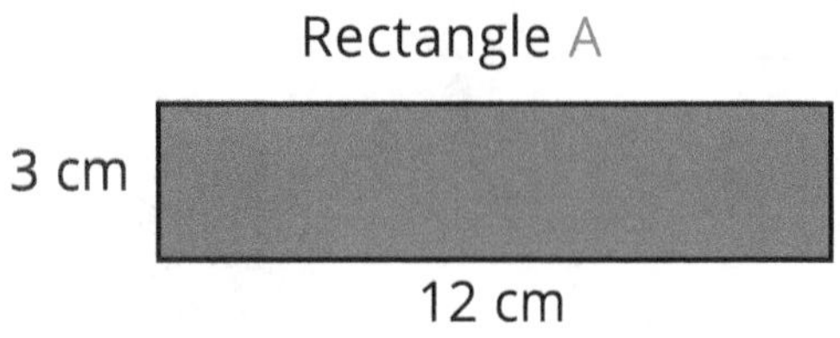

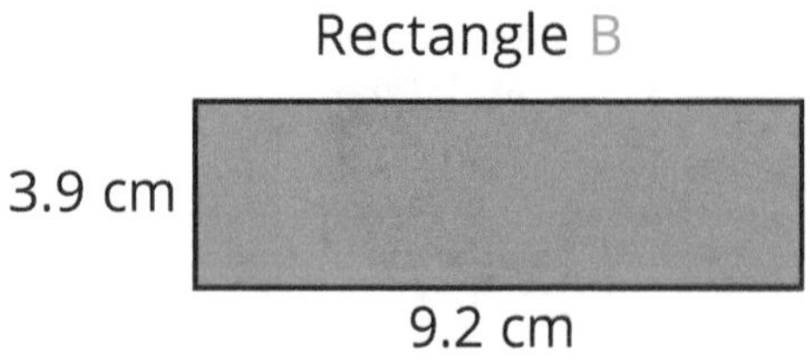

(3) **Find the surface area of the box.**

Front 7.9 cm x 4.5 cm = ______ x 2 = ______

Top 7.9 cm x 4.5 cm = ______ x 2 = ______

Side 4.5 cm x 4.5 cm = ______ x 2 = ______

Total ______

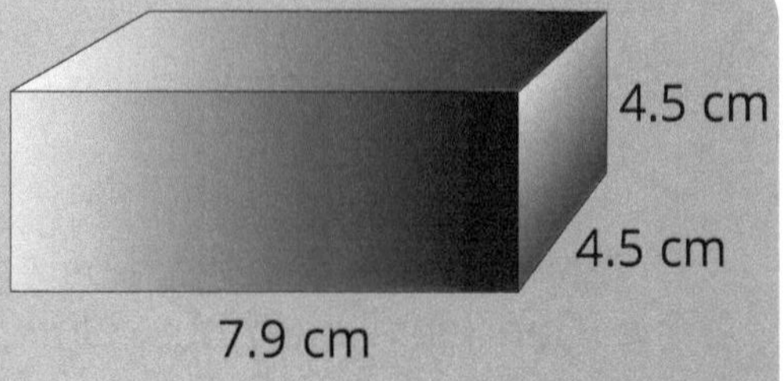

④ **Complete the table.** Round the answers to the nearest tenth.

Volume of Cylinders

Radius	Height of the Cylinder	Volume of the Cylinder
10 cm	5 cm	
8 m	12 m	
11 cm	7 cm	

⑤ **Multiply.** Find your answers in the puzzle below.
If all of your answers are correct you will have a path from start to finish.

5.9 × 2	4.3 × 5	9.29 × 10	17.7 × 13	0.132 × 8
32.9 × 6	70.3 × 6	0.99 × 15	33.01 × 25	5.077 × 4

Start

11.8	444	90.8	88.86	100.2	115.7	65.8
70.8	21.5	230.1	15.9	34.9	14.85	825.25
66	92.9	50.4	1.056	197.4	421.8	20.308

Finish

⑥ **Divide each of these fractions.**
Add zeros in the dividend until the quotient is zero.

$\frac{1}{2}$ = ______ $\frac{1}{4}$ = ______ $\frac{8}{10}$ = ______

$\frac{4}{5}$ = ______ $\frac{5}{8}$ = ______ $\frac{7}{8}$ = ______

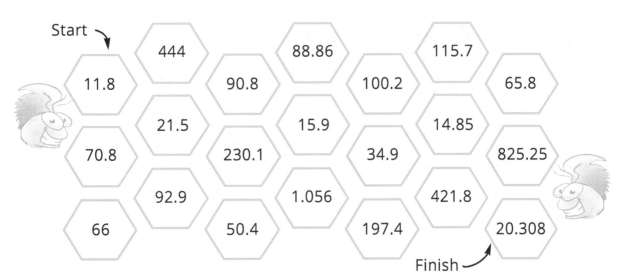

$\frac{1}{10}$ = ______ $\frac{9}{12}$ = ______ $\frac{5}{8}$ = ______

Problem Solving - Two Step Problems

Some word problems require more than one mathematical operation. Read the problem below and identify the two operations necessary to solve the problem.

John, Arthur and Phillip had a garage sale. They agreed to share the profits evenly. On Monday, they made $43.25. Tuesday their profit was $26.25. Wednesday they made $50.50. How much profit did each boy make at the garage sale?

To find the total amount the boys earned the three amounts earned each day should be added.

($43.25 + $ 26. 25 + $50.50 = $120.00)

To find the profit for each boy, divide $120.00 by 3.
($120.00 ÷ 3 = $40.00)
This is called finding the average.

Each boy earned $40.00.

(1) Read each word problem and identify the two operations required to solve the problem. You do not need to find the answer.

1. Paul's three test grades are: 91%, 88%, and 95%.
   What is Paul's average grade for tests?

2. Evelyn gets five dollars allowance every week. She wants to buy a new pair of pants and a matching shirt. The price for the pants is $25.00 and the cost of the shirt is $19.00. How long will it take Evelyn to save to make both purchases at once?

3. There are 12 people on the soccer team. If each person needs kneepads that cost $6.00 and a shirt that costs $15.00, how much will it cost for the whole team to have kneepads and shirts?

4. Theodore had $15.00 when he left home. He bought a super saver lunch for $2.99 for himself and three friends. How much money did Theodore have left after lunch?

2 **Write the answers on the spaces provided.**

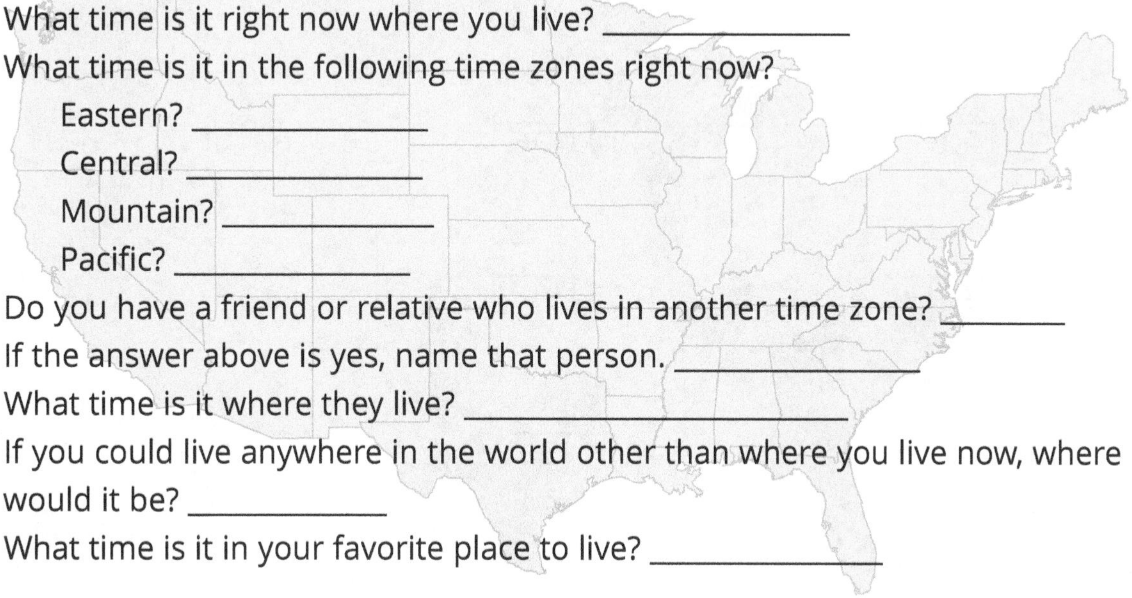

1. In what time zone do you live? ______________________
2. What time is it right now where you live? ________________
3. What time is it in the following time zones right now?
   - Eastern? _______________
   - Central? _______________
   - Mountain? ______________
   - Pacific? _______________
4. Do you have a friend or relative who lives in another time zone? ________
5. If the answer above is yes, name that person. ________________
6. What time is it where they live? _________________________
7. If you could live anywhere in the world other than where you live now, where would it be? _____________
8. What time is it in your favorite place to live? _______________

3 **Find the surface area of the figure below.**

Front 15.3 cm x 5.2 cm = ______ x 2 = _______

Top 15.3 cm x 2 cm = _______ x 2 = _______

Side 5.2 cm x 2 cm = ________ x 2 = _______

Total _______

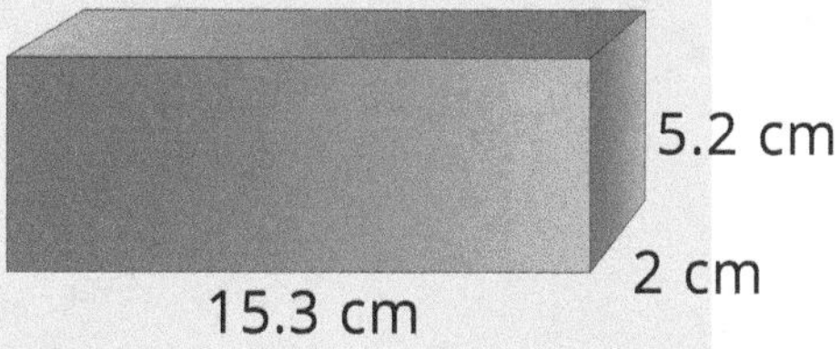

4 **Combine three fractions in adjacent cells to equal five. Use each cell only once. You may not use cells like this: You may use cells like this:**

$\frac{5}{8}$	$\frac{1}{2}$	$\frac{11}{4}$
$\frac{2}{8}$	$\frac{14}{8}$	$\frac{6}{6}$
$\frac{1}{8}$	$\frac{2}{3}$	$\frac{1}{6}$

$\frac{9}{8}$	$\frac{8}{4}$	$\frac{7}{10}$
$\frac{2}{4}$	$\frac{1}{7}$	$\frac{7}{5}$
$\frac{15}{3}$	$\frac{42}{20}$	$\frac{15}{10}$

5 **Circle the equivalent division problem.**

$1.9\overline{)0.152}$	=	$19\overline{)1.52}$	$.19\overline{)152}$	$19\overline{)0.152}$
$5.3\overline{)10.6}$	=	$5.3\overline{)1.06}$	$53\overline{)106}$	$53.1\overline{)10.6}$
$1.23\overline{)861}$	=	$1.23\overline{)8.61}$	$1.23\overline{)86.1}$	$123\overline{)86100}$
$2.9\overline{)11.52}$	=	$29\overline{)115.2}$	$2.9\overline{)1.152}$	$29\overline{)1152}$

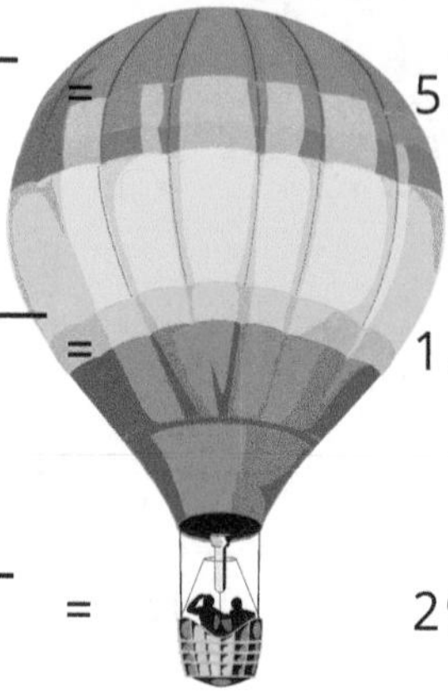

6 **Divide.**

$6\frac{1}{2} \div 4\frac{1}{3} =$ __________ $2\frac{2}{5} \div 1\frac{1}{2} =$ __________

$7\frac{1}{2} \div 2\frac{1}{4} =$ __________ $1\frac{2}{7} \div 3\frac{1}{2} =$ __________

7 **Write each fraction in simplest form.**

$\frac{50}{60}$	$\frac{27}{30}$	$\frac{20}{45}$	$\frac{4}{40}$	$\frac{36}{54}$	$\frac{14}{35}$
$\frac{13}{104}$	$\frac{12}{178}$	$\frac{72}{81}$	$\frac{18}{78}$	$\frac{75}{100}$	$\frac{27}{108}$
$\frac{12}{32}$	$\frac{12}{144}$	$\frac{95}{100}$	$\frac{15}{60}$	$\frac{27}{36}$	$\frac{49}{84}$

(1) **Circle the most accurate estimate of weight.** 4 pts.

Fly
1 gram 1 kilogram

Turtle
1 gram 1 kilogram

Rabbit
1 gram 1 kilogram

Paper Clip
1 gram 1 kilogram

(2) **Complete the answers.** 6 pts.

1 kg = _________ g   5.9 kg = _________ g   0.33 kg = _________ g

1 g = _________ kg   4700 g = _________ kg   109 g = _________ kg

(3) **Complete.** 5 pts.

0.703 L = _________ ml   3,000 ml = _________ L   9.8 L = _________ ml

15 L = _________ ml   600 ml = _________ L

(4) **Look at the picture. Circle the temperature that is most reasonable.** 4 pts.

-17° C   110° C   10° C   68°C

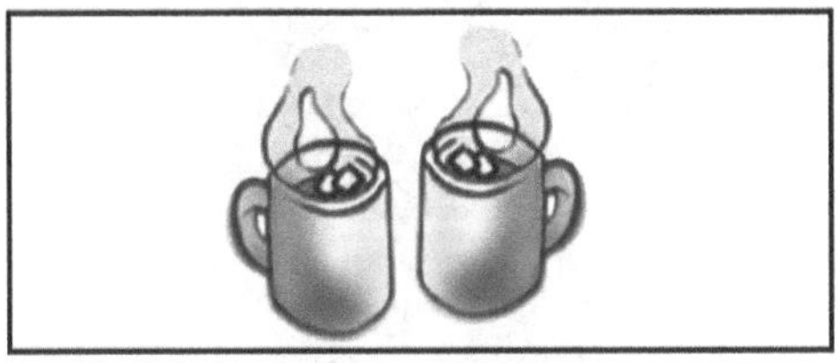

-47° C   1° C   85° C   140° C

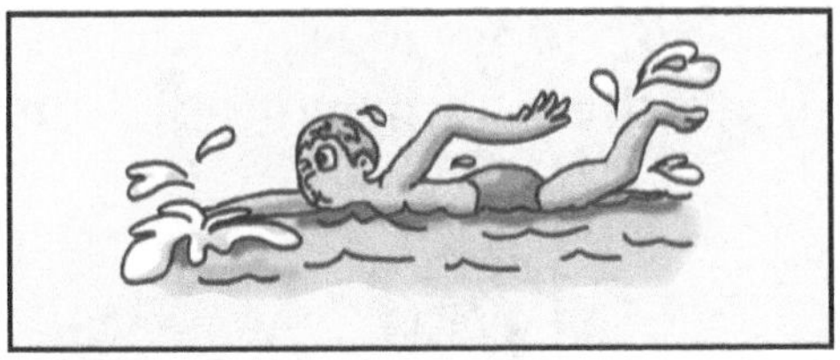

35° C   80° C   -20° C   6° C

37° C   15° C   -18° C   100° C

(5) **Find the perimeter of the lot.** 1 pt.

15 feet
8 feet
4 feet
7 feet

The perimeter is _________ feet.

(6) **Each month the youth group held a car wash. Their profits are recorded on the bar graph below.** Look at the information and answer the questions. 5 pts.

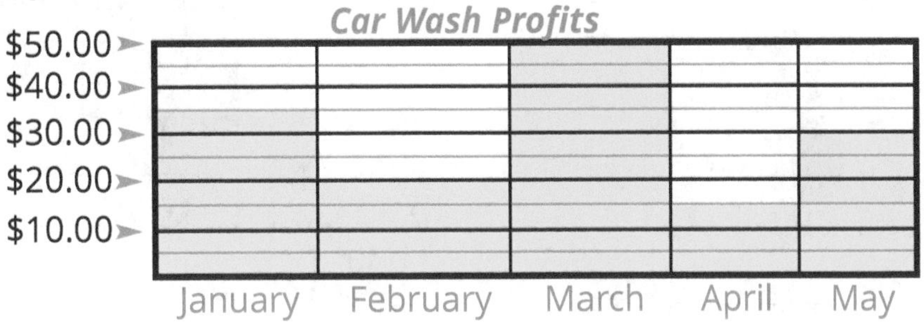

__________ 1. How much money did the youth group make in March?
__________ 2. How much money did the youth group make in total from all 5 car washes?
__________ 3. What month did they make the least amount of profit?
__________ 4. If each car paid $2.50 to have their car washed, how many cars were washed in May?
__________ 5. Which month did the youth group wash 14 cars?

(7) Find the perimeter and area and write the answer on the lines below. 6 pts.

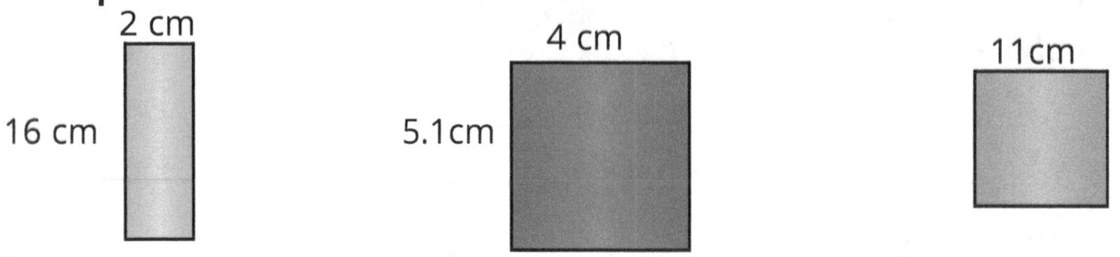

Perimeter = __________
Area = __________

Perimeter = __________
Area = __________

Perimeter = __________
Area = __________

(8) Find the area of each parallelogram and write it on the line provided. 6 pts.

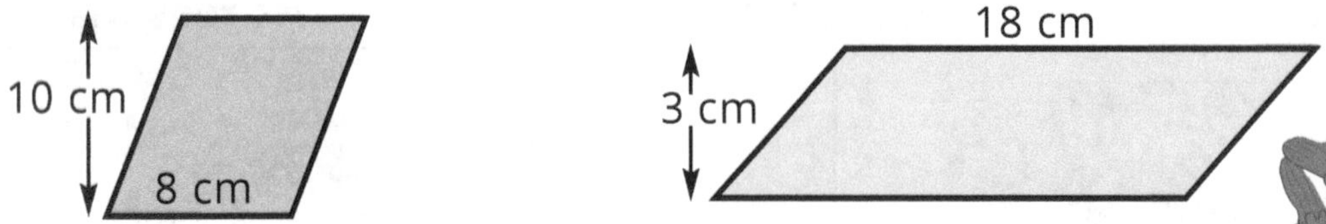

Area = base × height
A = __________ × __________
A = __________ cm^2

Area = base × height
A = __________ × __________
A = __________ cm^2

(9) Find the area of each triangle and write it on the line provided. 2 pts.

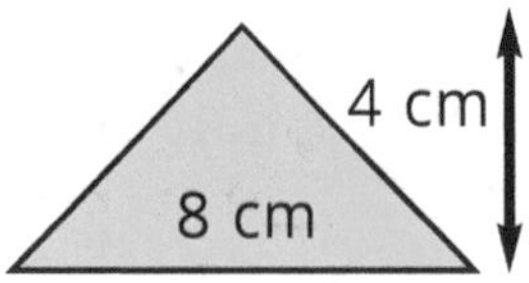

$A = \frac{bh}{2}$

A = __________ cm^2

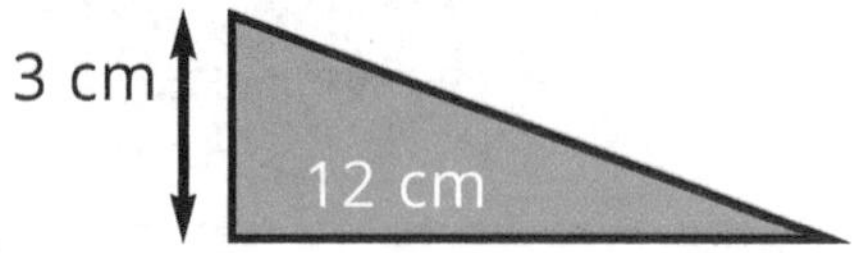

$A = \frac{bh}{2}$

A = __________ cm^2

(10) Fill in the blanks next to each circle. Round to the nearest tenth. 8 pts.

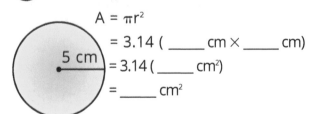

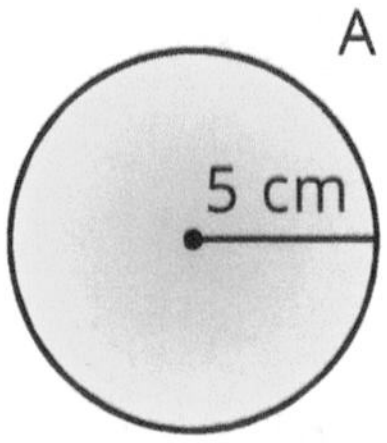

$A = \pi r^2$
= 3.14 (_____ cm × _____ cm)
= 3.14 (_____ cm^2)
= _____ cm^2

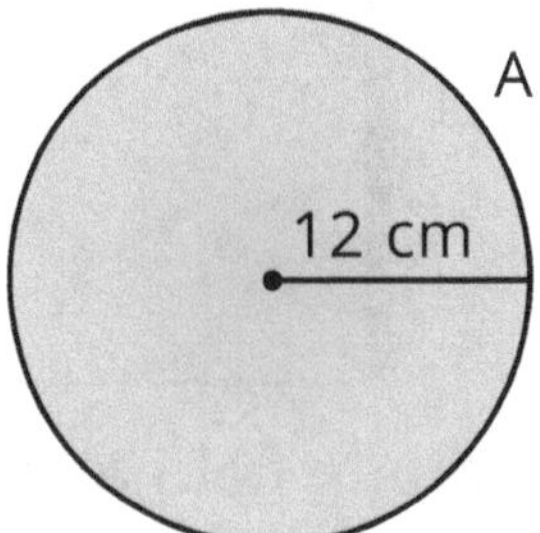

$A = \pi r^2$
= 3.14 (_____ cm × _____ cm)
= 3.14 (_____ cm^2)
= _____ cm^2

(11) Find the volume of each figure. 2 pts.

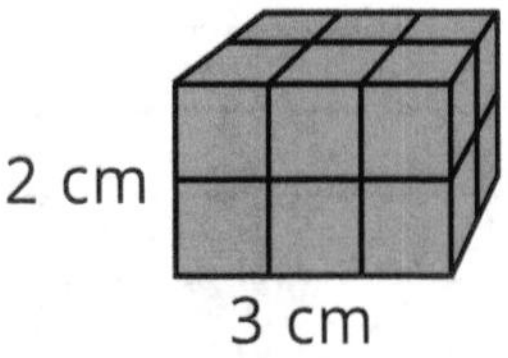

Volume = __________ cm^3

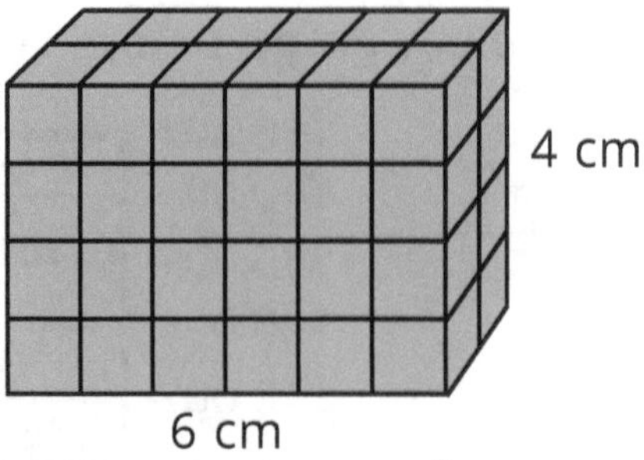

Volume = __________ cm^3

Protractors

A protractor is an instrument used to measure angles.
The angles are measured in degrees.
The protractor below is marked with 180 degree (180) units. What is the measure of ∠XYZ?

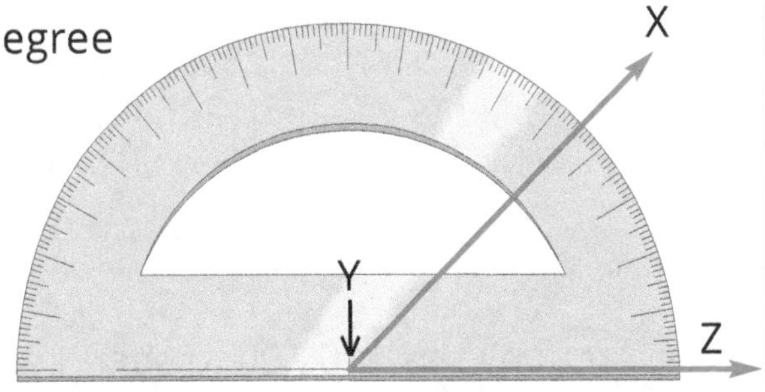

Follow these simple steps to measure an angle with a protractor.

1. Place the arrow on the protractor on the vertex of the angle.
2. Place the zero edge on one side of the angle.
3. Read the measure of the angle.

∠XYZ measures 45°.

1 **Give the measure of each angle.**
You may need to extend the sides of the angle for easier reading.

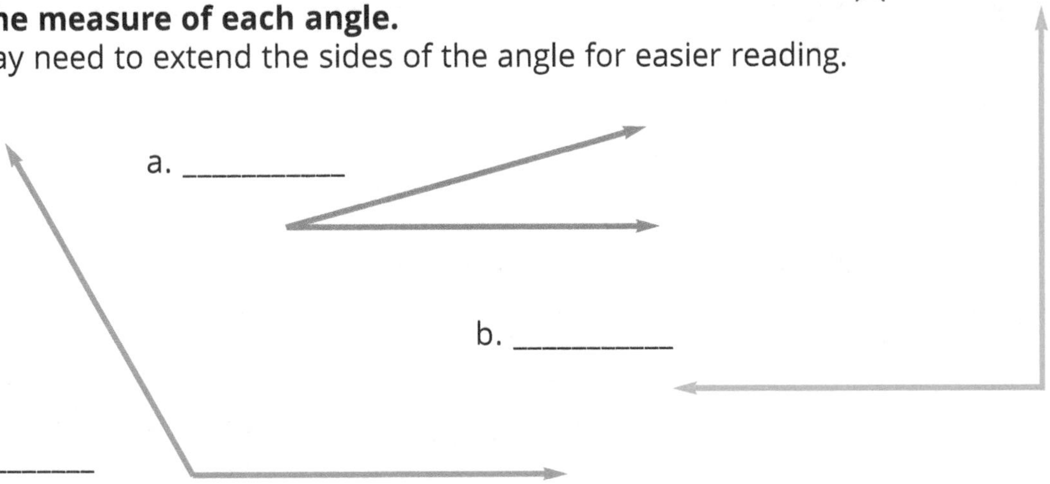

a. ___________

b. ___________

c. ___________

2 **Find the area of each triangle.**

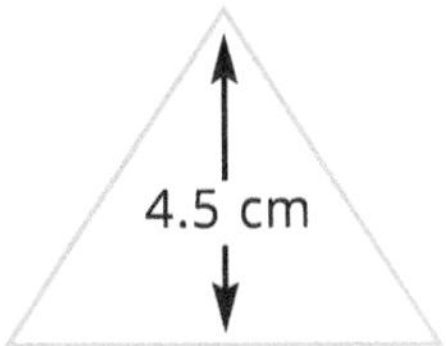

b = ______________
h = ______________
area = ___________

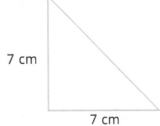

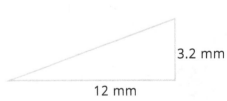

b = ______________
h = ______________
area = ___________

b = ______________
h = ______________
area = ___________

③ Solve these multiple step problems.

Adam and Paul shoveled snow in the neighborhood. They shoveled 15 driveways and charged twelve dollars a driveway. If the boys split the profit evenly, how much did each boy earn?

The youth group makes 25 loaves of bread every month for the homeless shelter. If the ingredients cost $3.12 per loaf of bread, how much does it cost them to make 25 loaves? If they have $150.00, do they have enough money to make bread for two months?

Mrs. Anthony has $100.00 to spend on mystery books for the school library. Each book costs $9.95 in hard cover and $4.95 in paperback. If she buys all hard cover books, how many can she buy? If she buys all paperback books, how many can she buy? How many more paperback books than hard cover books can she buy using $100.00?

Stephanie wants to earn $115.00 in the month of September to buy a pair of hockey-style roller blades. If she earns 15 dollars a day, how many days will she have to work in the month of September to make her goal?

④ If it is 10:00 A.M. in Atlanta, Georgia, what time is it in:

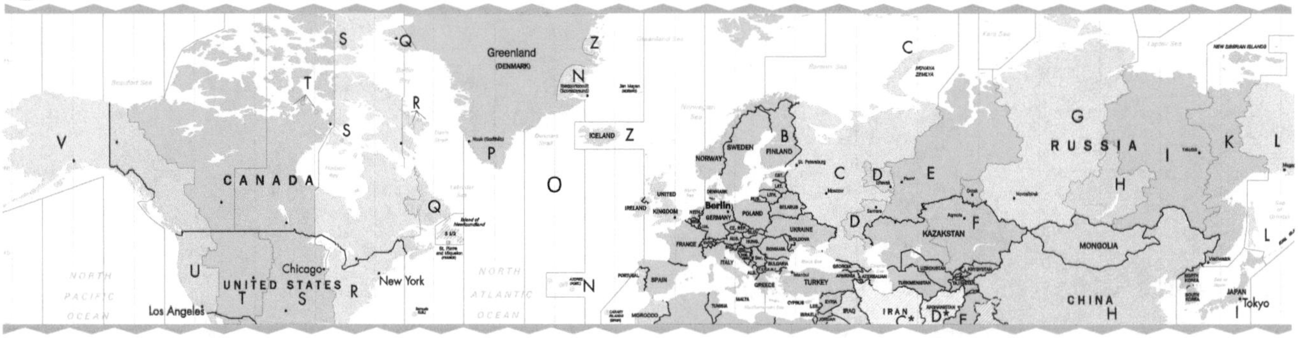

a. San Jose, California? ____________ b. Juneau, Alaska? ____________

c. Dublin, Ireland? ____________ d. Tokyo, Japan? ____________
in time zone Z

⑤ Find the least common multiple for each set of numbers.

2, 3 ____________ 2, 4 ____________ 2, 7 ____________

5, 8 ____________ 4, 6 ____________ 3, 9 ____________

8, 10 ____________ 7, 11 ____________ 5, 13 ____________

6 **Divide each of these fractions. Write the answers as repeating decimals.**

$\frac{5}{11}$ = ____________ $\frac{9}{11}$ = ____________ $\frac{1}{9}$ = ____________

$\frac{19}{15}$ = ____________ $\frac{6}{9}$ = ____________ $\frac{1}{3}$ = ____________

$\frac{3}{11}$ = ____________ $\frac{8}{15}$ = ____________ $\frac{2}{9}$ = ____________

Write each fraction as a decimal. Divide until the remainder is zero.

$\frac{1}{5}$ = ____________ $\frac{1}{2}$ = ____________ $\frac{7}{8}$ = ____________

$\frac{12}{15}$ = ____________ $\frac{3}{4}$ = ____________ $\frac{1}{10}$ = ____________

$\frac{5}{8}$ = ____________ $\frac{4}{5}$ = ____________ $\frac{9}{10}$ = ____________

7 **Place the decimal numbers in the boxes below in order from least to greatest.** Connect the points in the drawing below in the order you have given.

0.021	1.01	0.89	0.1	1.1	0.22	0.9	0.456	1.075
1.125	0.3	0.544	0.8	0.99	0.801	0.92	0.2	.41

________ ________ ________ ________ ________ ________

________ ________ ________ ________ ________ ________

________ ________ ________ ________ ________ ________

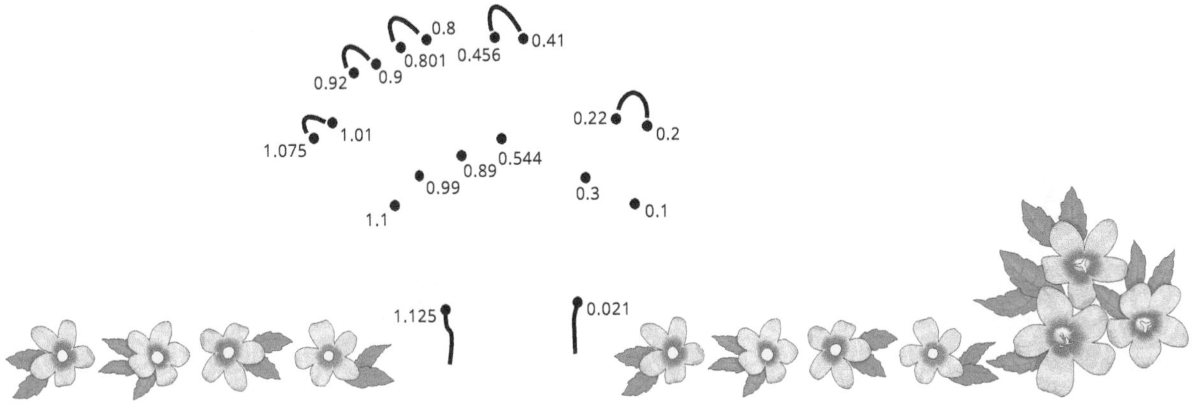

You obey the law of Christ when you offer each other a helping hand.

Galatians 6:2 (CEV)

Measuring Angles in Circles

We can use a protractor to measure angles in a circle. The sum of the measures of the angles will equal 360 degrees.

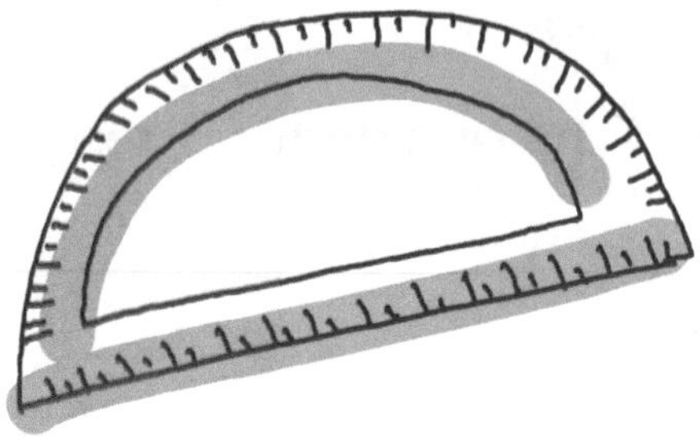

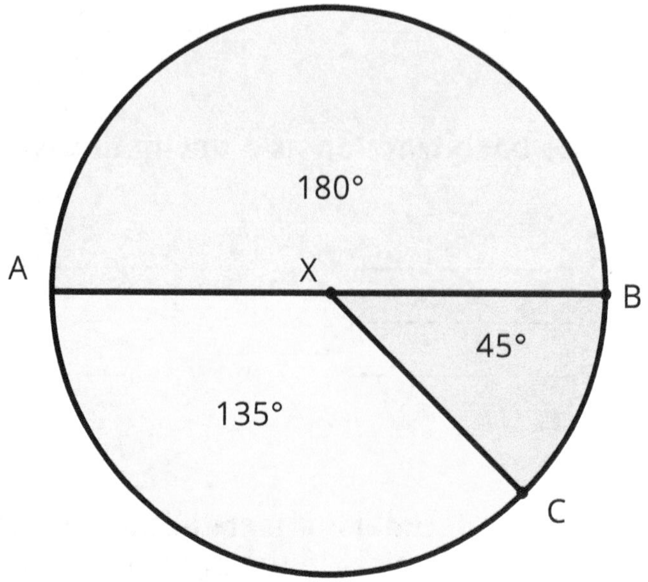

∠AXB + ∠BXC + ∠CXA = 360°

<u>180°</u> + <u>45°</u> + <u>135°</u> = 360°

1 **Use a protractor to measure the angles in the circle. Write the measurement on the lines provided.**

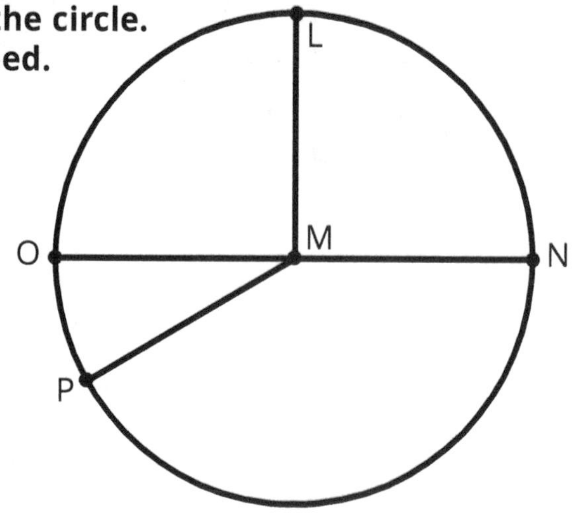

∠LMN = ____________

∠NMP = ____________

∠PMO = ____________

∠OML = ____________

∠LMN + ∠NMP + ∠PMO + ∠OML = 360°

_______ + _______ + _______ + _______ = 360°

2 **Use a protractor to measure the angles. You may need to extend the lines to get an accurate reading.**

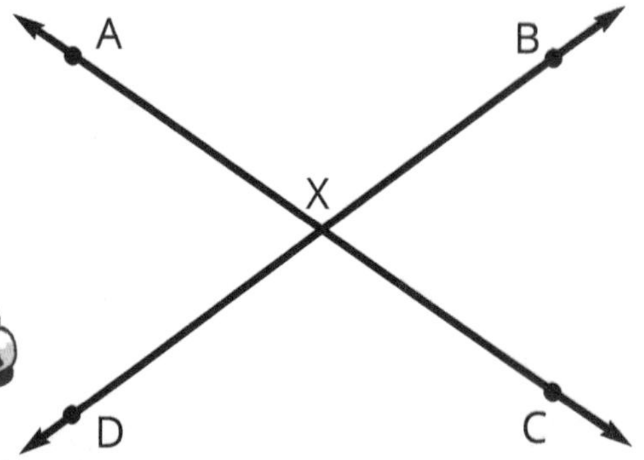

∠AXB = ____________

∠DXC = ____________

∠AXD = ____________

∠CXB = ____________

∠EKF = ____________

∠GKH = ____________

∠EKG = ____________

∠FKH = ____________

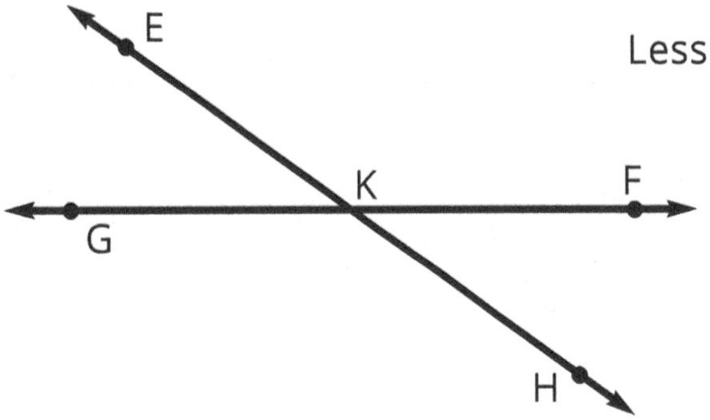

Based on the examples above, choose the correct word to complete the following statement: When two lines intersect, they form opposite angles that are (congruent / not congruent) ________________ .

3 **Use the information on the sign to answer the questions below.**

Ben's Skate Rental

Roller Skates	*$5.00 hourly*	*$15.00 half day*	*$25.00 all day*
In-Line Skates	*$7.50 hourly*	*$20.00 half day*	*$30.00 all day*
Helmet	*$2.00 hourly*	*$ 3.00 half day*	*$ 4.00 all day*
Pads	*$2.00 hourly*	*$ 3.00 half day*	*$ 4.00 all day*

Angelo and his four friends are going skating,

a. How much will it cost in total if they all spend a half-day roller skating?

b. How much will it cost in total if they all spend a half-day in-line skating?

c. How much will it cost in total if they roller skate all day and rent helmets all day, but not pads?

d. How much will it cost in total if they in-line skate all day and rent helmets and pads all day?

e. If Angelo brought $40.00 and he rented in-line skates all day and a helmet and pads all day, would he have enough left over to buy a soda for seventy-five cents?

4 **Divide each of these fractions. Write the answers as repeating decimals.**

$\frac{4}{9}$ = ____________ $\frac{4}{11}$ = ____________ $\frac{23}{30}$ = ____________

$\frac{5}{9}$ = ____________ $\frac{7}{15}$ = ____________ $\frac{1}{6}$ = ____________

$\frac{3}{11}$ = ____________ $\frac{8}{9}$ = ____________ $\frac{2}{11}$ = ____________

5 **If it is 2:00 P.M. in Des Moines, Iowa, what time is it in:**

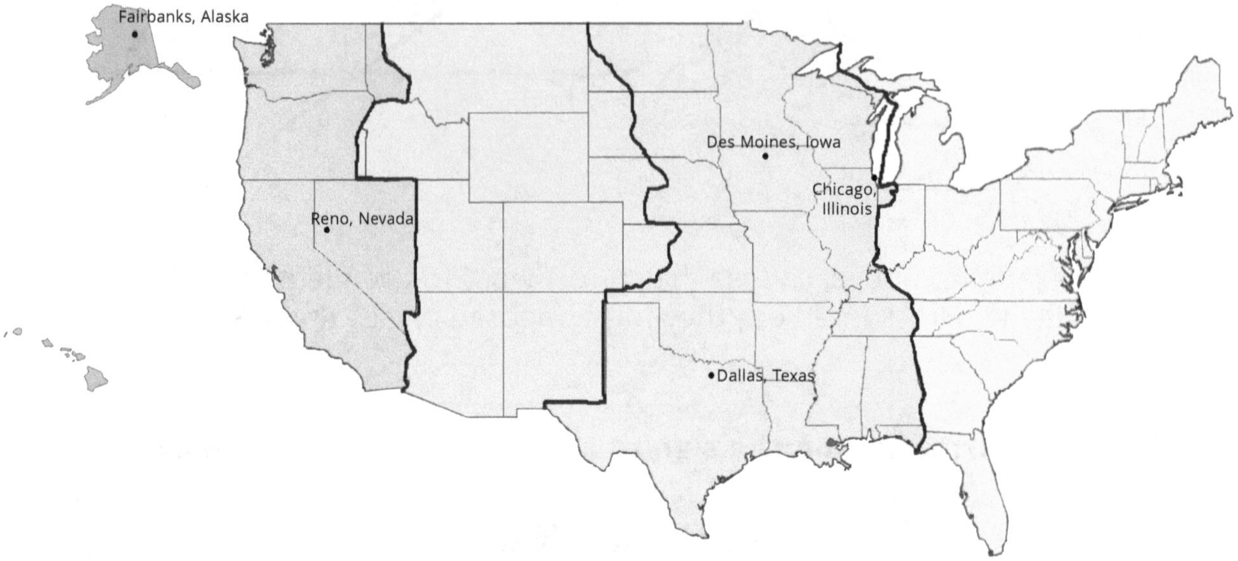

a. Reno, Nevada? ______________ b. Dallas, Texas? ______________

c. Chicago, Illinois? ______________ d. Fairbanks, Alaska? ______________

6 **Find your way through the maze with prime numbers. You may move vertically, horizontally, or diagonally.**

4	12	16	20	10	16	22	5	← Begin
4	81	18	25	36	2	11	3	
12	6	10	14	15	67	43	32	
45	36	35	50	45	19	12	16	
18	24	20	44	24	53	42	55	
6	8	42	34	31	67	28	10	
13	29	41	89	79	6	16	50	

End ↑

Constructing Angles

Draw an angle of 45° using $\overrightarrow{XY}$ as one side.

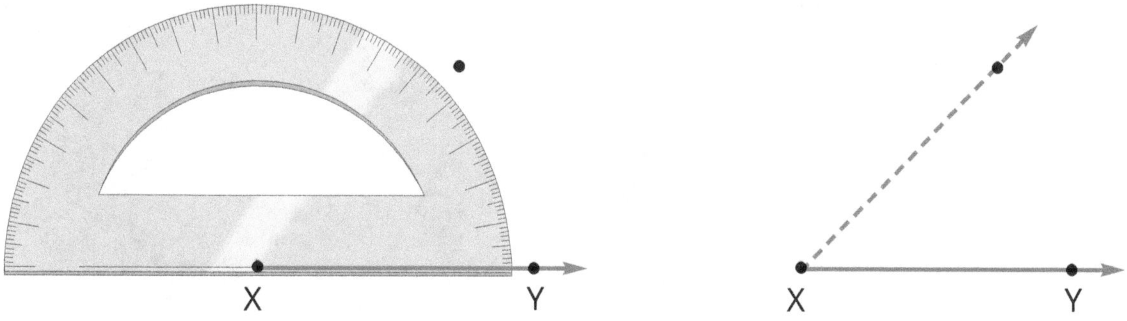

Here's how:

1. Place the center of the protractor at the vertex of the angle, with the edge of the protractor along $\overrightarrow{XY}$.
2. Place a point above the 45° mark on the protractor.
3. Remove the protractor and draw a straight line from the vertex to the new point. Label the point Z.
4. ∠ZXY measures 45°.

(1) Draw the angles indicated using the given side.

90° angle; label it ∠ABC

120° angle; label it ∠LMN

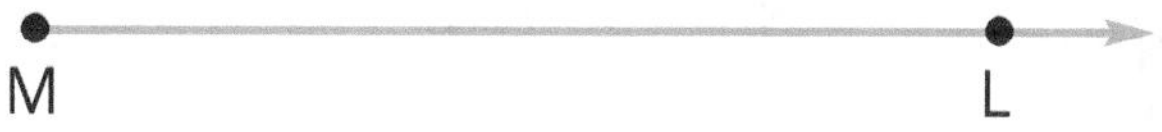

10° angle; label it ∠DEF

2 **Use a protractor to measure the angles in the circle. The sum of the measures of the angles will equal 360 degrees.**

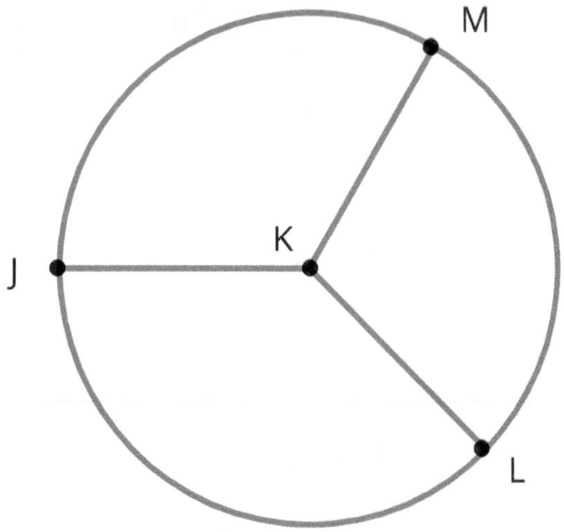

∠JKM + ∠MKL + ∠LKJ = 360°

_____ + _____ + _____ = 360°

3 **Use the information on the sign to solve the problems.**

Jan, Lori, and Nancy are selling items at the ballpark to help raise money for their track team. Use your calculator to help them determine how much to charge for each purchase and how much change to give back.

Souvenirs for Sale

T-shirts	$15.99
Caps	$12.50
Programs	$5.29
Banners	$5.45

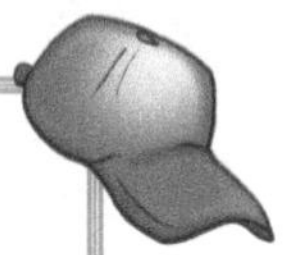

a. Items purchased: 1 Cap, 2 Banners
Payment: $25.00

Total bill: ____________ Amount of change: ____________

b. Items purchased: 1 T-shirt, 1 Program
Payment: $25.00

Total bill: ____________ Amount of change: ____________

c. Items purchased: 1 T-shirt, 1 Cap
Payment: $40.00

Total bill: ____________ Amount of change: ____________

d. Items purchased: 1 T-shirt, 1 Program, 1 Cap, 1 Banner
Payment: $40.00

Total bill: ____________ Amount of change: ____________

4 **Complete the table. The first one is done for you.**

	Factors	Product	Exponent	Number of Zeros
7^2	7×7	49	2	0
		10,000		
2^4		16		
	$10 \times 10 \times 10 \times 10 \times 10$			
3^6				

5 **Divide. You may need to extend the dividend.**

$4.7\overline{)42.3}$ $2.5\overline{)10}$ $2.2\overline{)6.6}$

$0.6\overline{)3}$ $1.5\overline{)9}$ $4.5\overline{)90}$

6 **Draw a circle around the best estimate.**

10 oz

100 lbs

1 ton

1 lb

4 oz

1 ton

12 lbs.

12 tons

12 ounces

2 oz

1 ton

1 lb

Constructing a Perpendicular Bisector

When two lines intersect to from four congruent right angles, the two lines are perpendicular. Given line AB, we are going to use a compass and straightedge to draw another line that bisects line AB and forms four congruent right angles.

1. Set the compass to any size you choose but it must be more than $\frac{1}{2}$ the distance from A to B.
2. Put the point of your compass on point A. Draw two arcs, one above line AB and one below line AB using the same compass setting.
3. Using the same compass setting put the point of your compass on point B. Draw two more arcs one above and one below the line that intersect the arcs made in step 2. Label the points where the arcs intersect L and M.
4. With a straightedge draw line LM which is the perpendicular bisector of line AB.

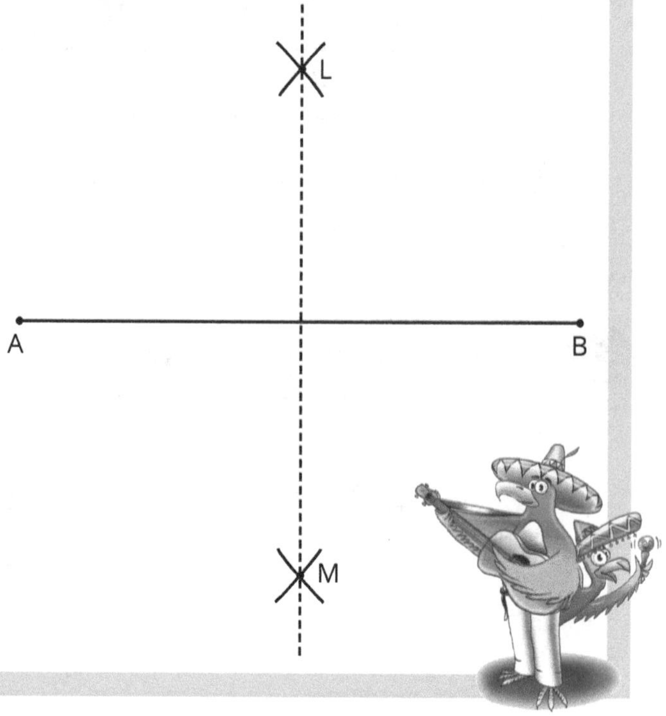

(1) **Use a compass and straightedge to construct perpendicular bisectors to line CD. Label it line EF.**

Use a compass and straightedge to construct perpendicular bisectors to line UV. Label it line JK.

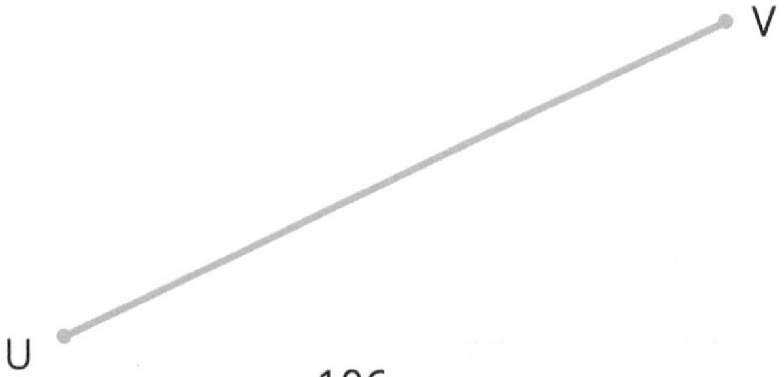

(2) **Draw the angles indicated using the given side.**

30° angle; label it ∠ABC

130° angle; label it ∠EFG

(3) **Use a protractor to measure the angles in the circle. Write the measurement on the lines provided.**

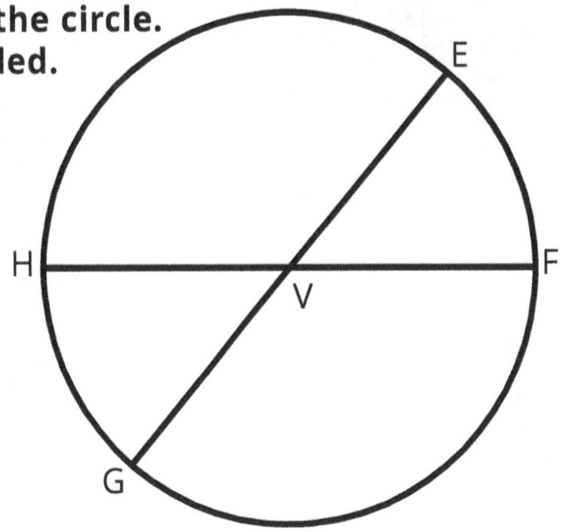

∠EVF = ______________

∠EVH = ______________

∠GVH = ______________

∠GVF = ______________

∠EVF + ∠EVH + ∠GVH + ∠GVF = 360°

________ + ________ + ________ + ________ = 360°

(4) **Give the measure of each angle. You may need to extend the sides of the angle for easier reading.**

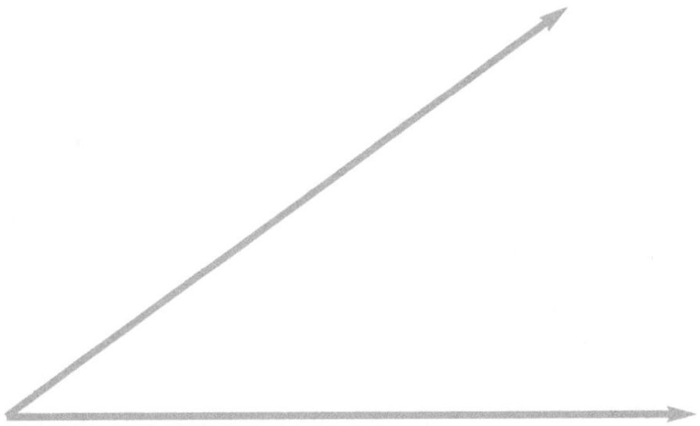

5 **In the message below, find the product of each number with an exponent.**

If the product is between 1 and 100, replace the number with an A.
If the product is between 101and 200, replace the number with and E.
If the product is between 201 and 300, replace the number with and I.
If the number is between 301 and 400, replace it with an O.
If the number is between 401 and 500, replace it with a U.
Write the message on the line provided.

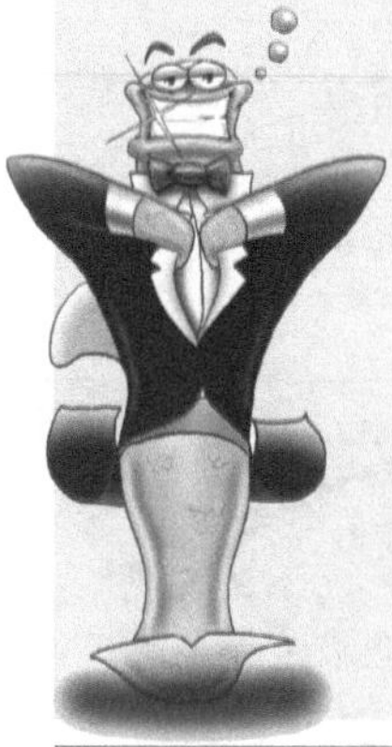

Wh(2^4)t   d(7^3)   y(18^2)(21^2)   c(3^2)ll

(4^2)   f(2^8)sh   th(5^2)t   pl(2^3)ys

p(19^2)k(11^2)r?

(3^4)   c(4^3)rd   sh(9^2)rk!

_____ _____ _____ _____   _____ _____   _____ _____ _____

_____ _____ _____ _____   _____   _____ _____ _____ _____

_____ _____ _____ _____   _____ _____ _____ _____ _____

_____ _____ _____ _____ _____?

_____   _____ _____ _____ _____   _____ _____ _____ _____ _____!

6 **Divide. You may need to extend the dividend.**

$2.5\overline{)20}$ $0.8\overline{)4}$

$3.5\overline{)70}$ $0.12\overline{)48}$

Constructing Bisectors of an Angle

When we divide an angle into two congruent angles using a protractor or a compass, we have bisected the angle. Look at the example below.

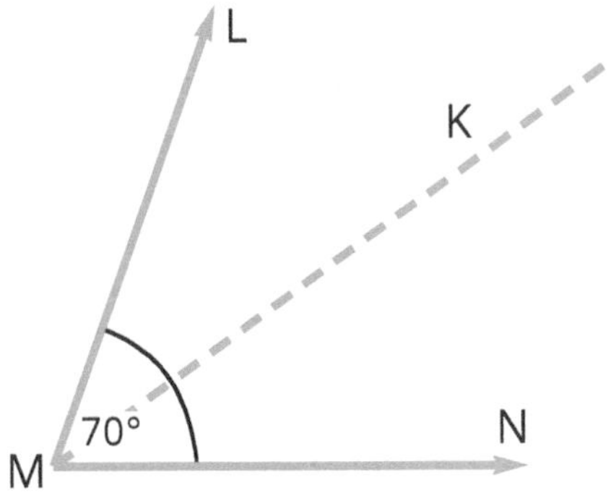

It is easy to bisect an angle using a protractor.

1. Place the protractor on the vertex of the angle with the zero edge on one side of the angle.
2. Measure the angle. (70°)
3. Divide the measurement by 2. (70° ÷ 2 = 35).
4. Place a point at the 35° mark on the protractor and label it K.
5. Remove the protractor and draw a straight line from vertex M to point K.

∠NMK is congruent to ∠KML

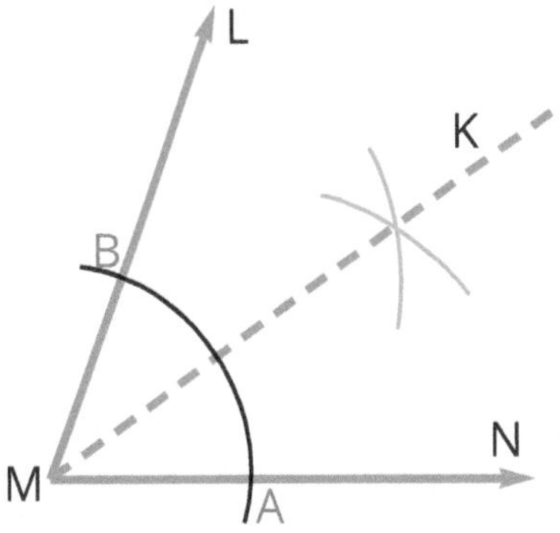

You can also bisect an angle with a compass and a ruler.

1. Set the compass to any size you choose. Place the sharp point of your compass at vertex M. Draw an arc that intersects both sides of the angle.
2. Place points where the arc and each side of the angle intersect and label them A and B.
3. Use AB as the radius by placing the sharp point of your compass on point A. Open your compass until the pencil point touches point B. Leave the sharp point of your compass on point A and draw an arc as shown in the picture above.
4. With the compass set to the same size do the same thing on the other side of the angle by placing the sharp point of your compass on point B.
5. Label the point where the two arcs intersect point K.
6. Use a straightedge to draw a line from vertex M to point K. This line bisects the angle.

∠NMK is congruent to ∠KML

(1) **Bisect each angle using a protractor.**

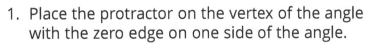

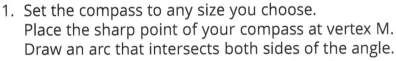

Bisect each angle using a compass and straightedge.

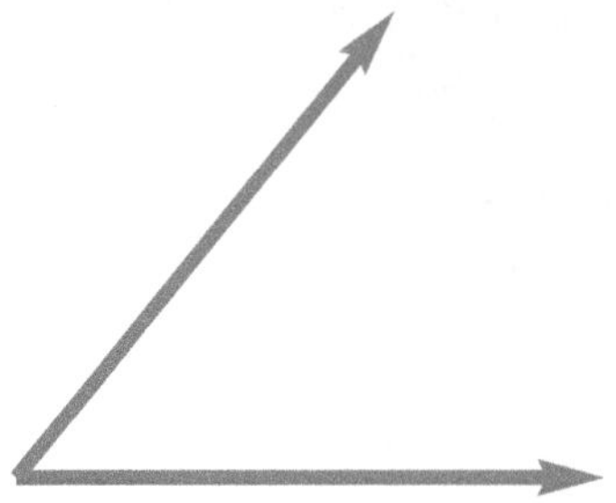

2 **Construct a perpendicular bisector of each side of the triangle.**

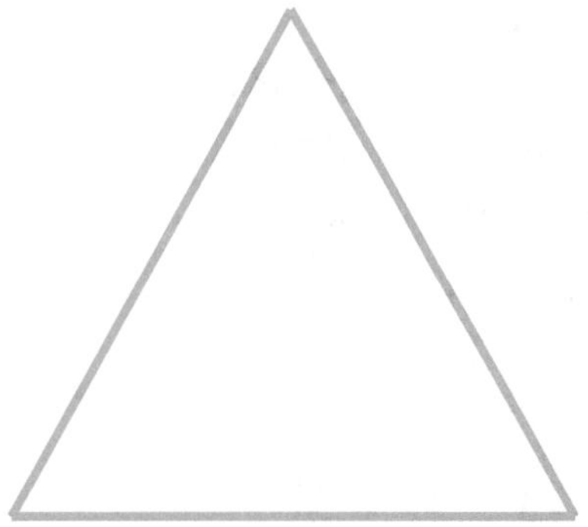

3 **Draw the angles indicated using the given side.**

10° angle; label it ∠ABC

180° angle; label it ∠QRS
This angle is called a straight angle.

95° angle; label it ∠UVW

4 **Use a protractor to measure the angles in the circle. Write the measurement on the lines provided.**

∠CDE = ____________

∠EDF = ____________

∠CDF = ____________

∠CDE + ∠EDF + ∠CDF = 360°

_______ + _______ + _______ = 360°

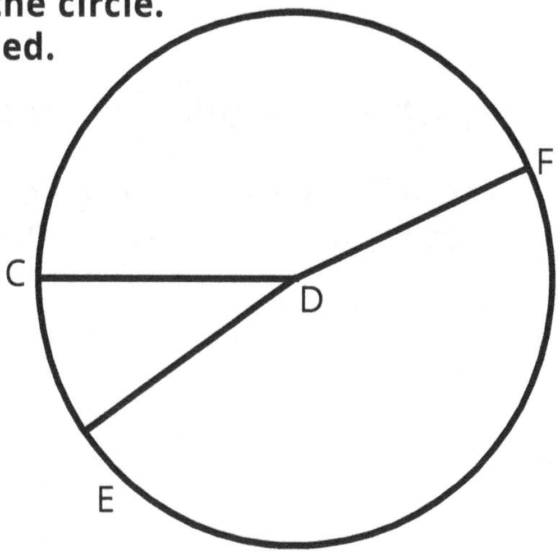

5 **Pair each number with its square root. The first one has been done for you.**

25	11
121	5
196	12
64	8
144	14

361	15
81	25
225	19
400	20
625	9

6 **Place numbers on the lines so that each number sentence is true. The first one has been done for you.**

5 cm = 50 mm

40 mm = ________ cm

4 m = ________ cm

4000 m = ________ km

9 cm = ________ mm

700 mm = ________ cm

8 m = ________ cm

2000 m = ________ km

Constructing a Hexagon

A hexagon is a six-sided figure.
A regular hexagon is a six-sided figure with all sides and angles equal.

We can draw any size regular hexagon using a compass where the length of one side is given. Look at the example below.

length of one side

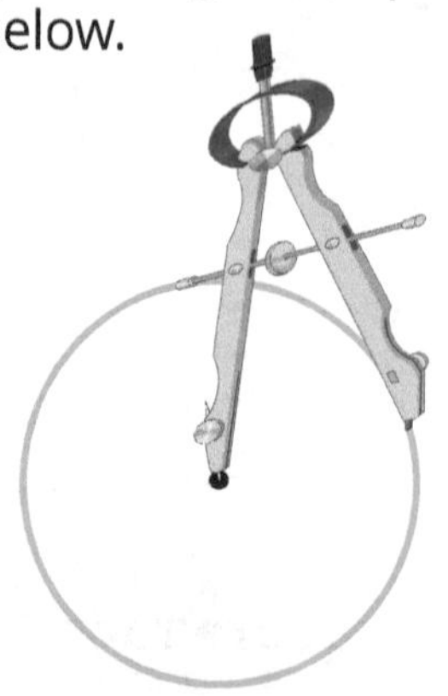

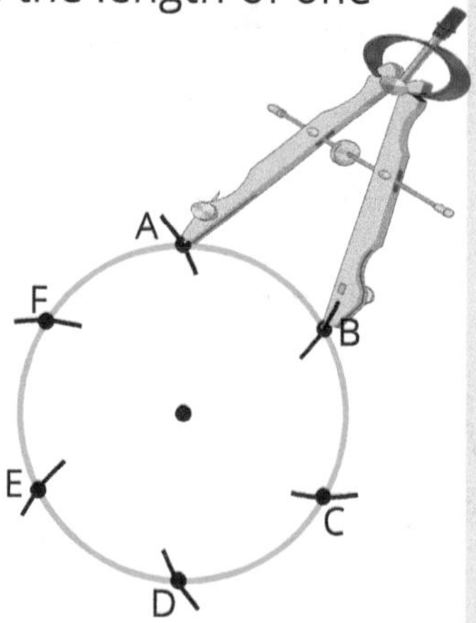

1. Construct a circle with a radius the same length as the length of one side of the hexagon you wish to draw.
2. Place a point on the circle and name it point A. Keep your compass open the same width as the radius of the circle and place the sharp side of your compass on point A. Draw an arc that crosses the circle. Place a point where the arc and the circle intersect and label it point B.
3. Place the sharp side of your compass on point B. Draw an arc that crosses the circle and label it point C. Continue this pattern around the circle until you return to point A.
4. Draw straight lines between point A and point B; point B and point C; point C and point D; point D and point E; point E and point F; point F and point A.

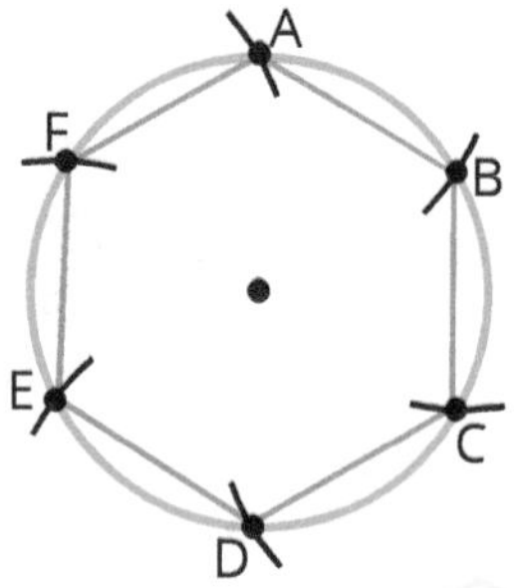

(1) Draw a regular hexagon using a compass and straightedge. Using the segment length given.

3 cm

(2) **Bisect each angle using a compass and straightedge.**

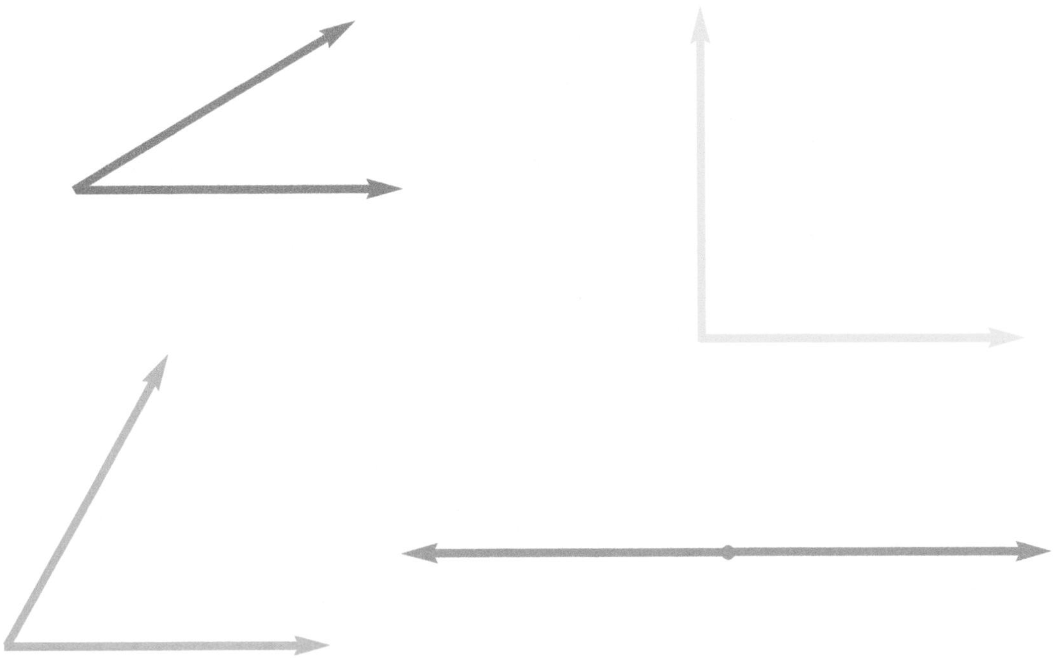

(3) **Construct a perpendicular bisector of line EF. Label the new line GH.**

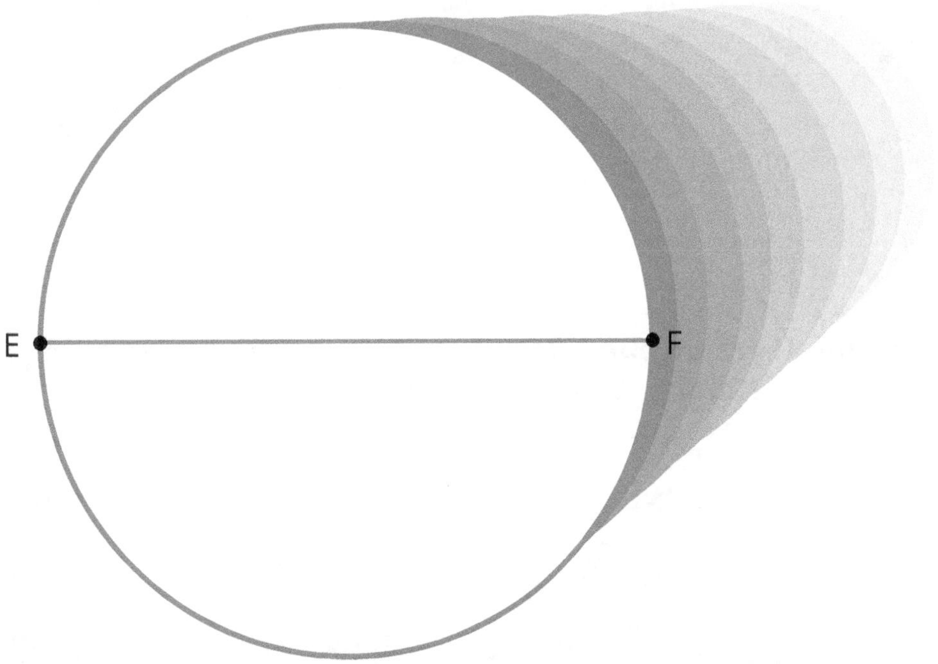

If the endpoints for line GH end on the circle, which statement is true?
Circle the true statement.

$\overline{EF} = \overline{GH}$ or $\overline{EF} \neq \overline{GH}$

4 **Draw the angles indicated using the given side.**

17° angle; label it ∠UVW

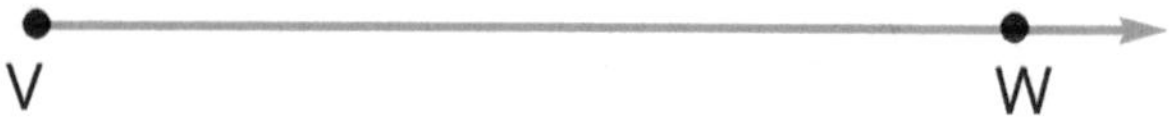

150° angle; label it ∠QRS

5 **Find the square root for each number.**

121	______	4	______	16	______
9	______	64	______	36	______
169	______	81	______	25	______
100	______	144	______	49	______

6 **Place numbers on the lines so that each number sentence is true. The first one has been done for you.**

11 cm	=	110 mm	8 cm	=	______ mm
4.5 m	=	______ cm	3.85 m	=	______ cm
4.77 cm	=	______ mm	11.8 mm	=	______ cm
7000 m	=	______ km	230 m	=	______ km

Constructing Equilateral Triangles

An equilateral triangle is a triangle with all three sides the same length and all three angles the same measure.

We can construct an equilateral triangle using a compass and straightedge.

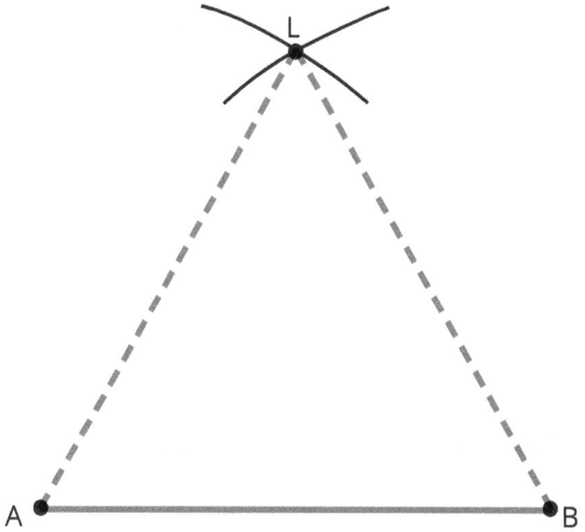

1. Place the point of your compass on point A and the pencil on point B to adjust the width of your compass.
2. Leave the point of your compass on point A draw an arc above line AB.
3. Place the point of your compass on point B and draw an arc that intersects the other arc. Label the point of intersection point L. If you did not change the size of your compass the distance from B to L and the distance from A to L will be the same.
4. With a straightedge draw a line from point A to point L and a line connecting point b and point L.

   ΔALB is an equilateral triangle.

(1) **Construct an equilateral triangle using a compass and straightedge. Use line GH as one side of the triangle. Label the triangle ΔFGH.**

(2) **Draw a regular hexagon using a compass and straightedge. The side of the hexagon is 4 centimeters.**

(3) **Bisect each angle using a protractor.**

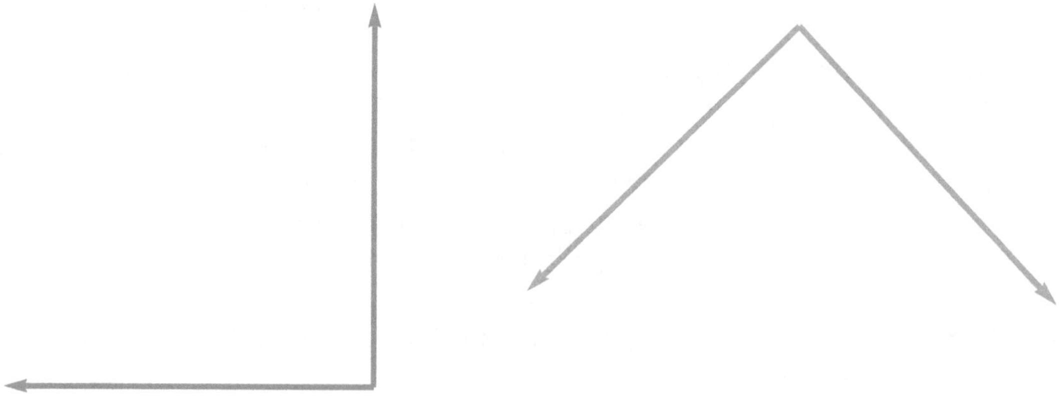

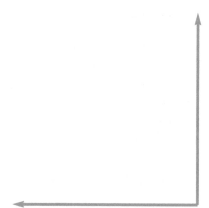

(4) **Bisect each angle using a compass and straightedge.**

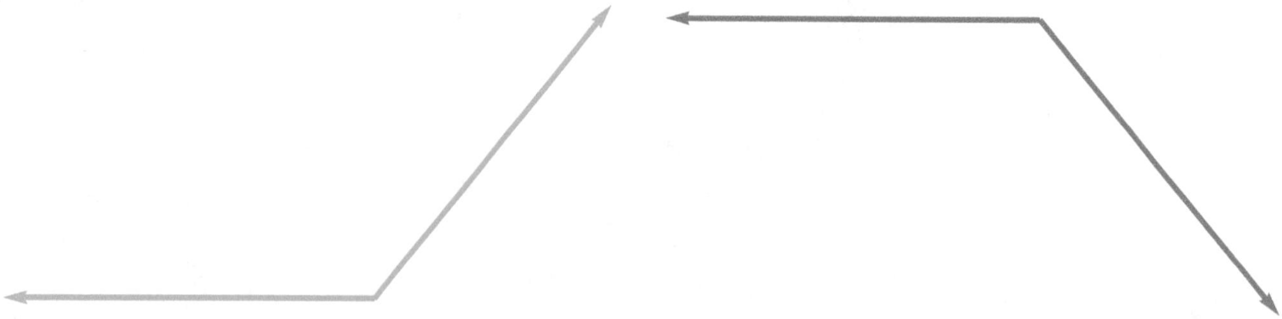

(5) Write each number in exponent form.

10,000,000,000 = __________ 100 = __________

1000 = __________ 10,000 = __________

Write each number in standard form.

3×10^2 = __________ 5×10^3 = __________

7×10^5 = __________ 9×10^4 = __________

(6) Complete the crossword puzzle.

Across

1. 426 × 8 = __________
3. 63 × 12 = __________
4. 193 × 30 = __________
5. 67 × 9 = __________
7. 205 × 12 = __________
8. 117 × 5 = __________

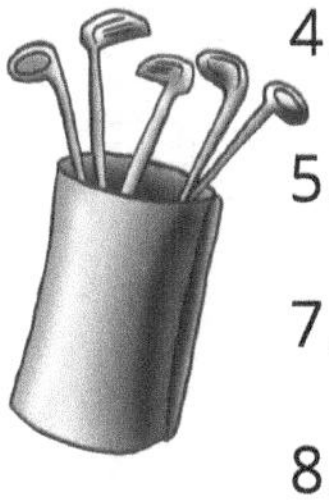

Down

2. 569 × 15 = __________
3. 3,526 × 2 = __________
5. 103 × 6 = __________
6. 113 × 8 = __________

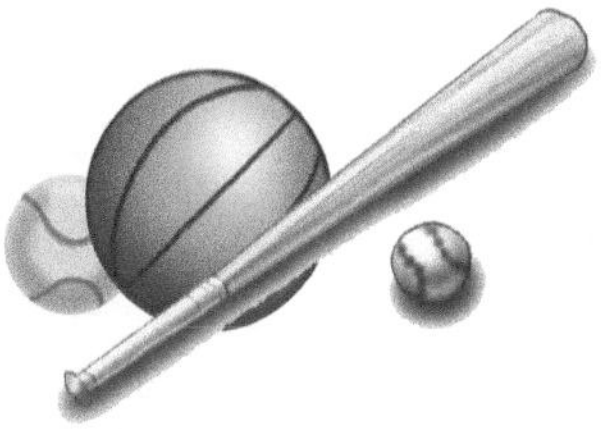

Constructing Right Triangles

A right triangle is a three-sided figure with one right angle.

We can draw a right triangle with line AB as one side of the triangle using a compass and straightedge.

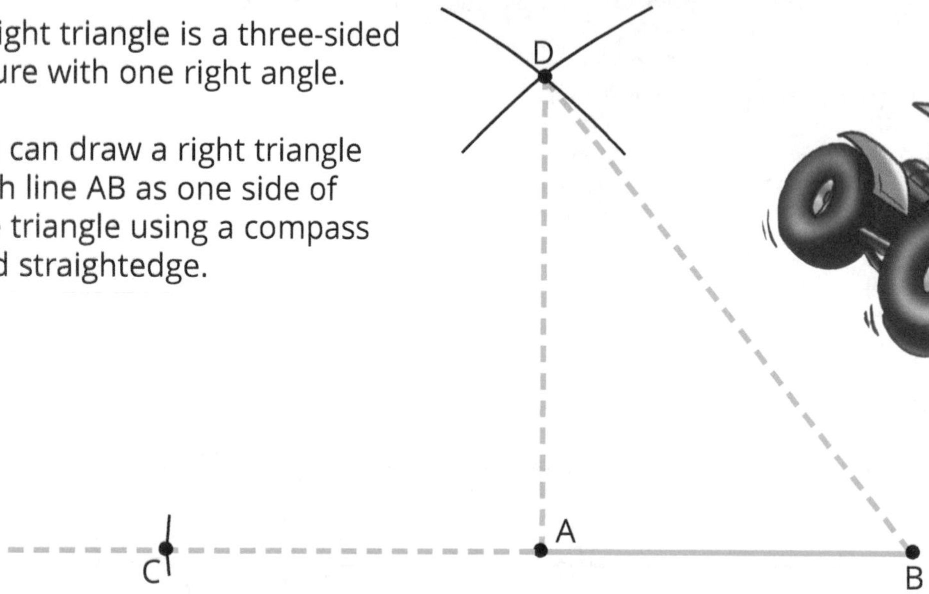

1. Extend line AB to the left. Set the compass to the length of segment AB by placing the point on point A and pencil on point B. Leave the point of the compass on point A and make an arc to the left of A that intersects the line. Label the new point C.
2. Open the compass up a little and place the point of the compass at point B and make an arc above the line. Use the same compass setting and place the point of the compass on point C and make an arc above the line that intersects the other arc. Label the intersections point D.
3. Use a straightedge to connect point A and point D. Use the straightedge to connect point D and point B.

   ΔDAB is a right triangle.

(1) Construct a right triangle using a compass and straightedge. Use line JK as one side of the triangle. Label the triangle ΔIJK.

2 **Construct an equilateral triangle using a compass and straightedge.**
Use line QR as one side of the triangle. Label the triangle ΔPQR.

3 **Construct a hexagon using the radius of your choice.**
Many quilt patterns have been designed using the regular hexagon shape. A few have been included here. Using the hexagon you constructed as a base, create a new quilt pattern.

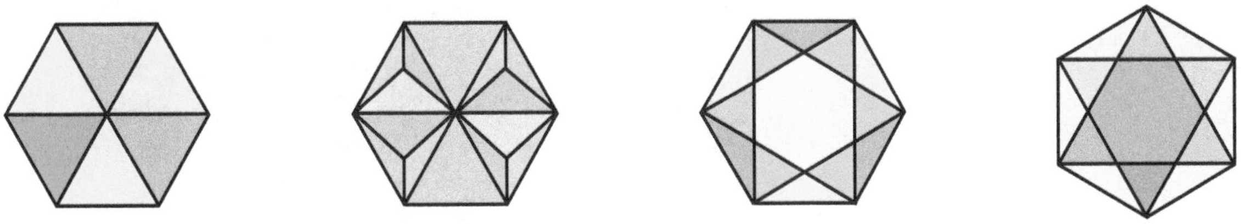

4 **Bisect each angle using a compass and straightedge.**

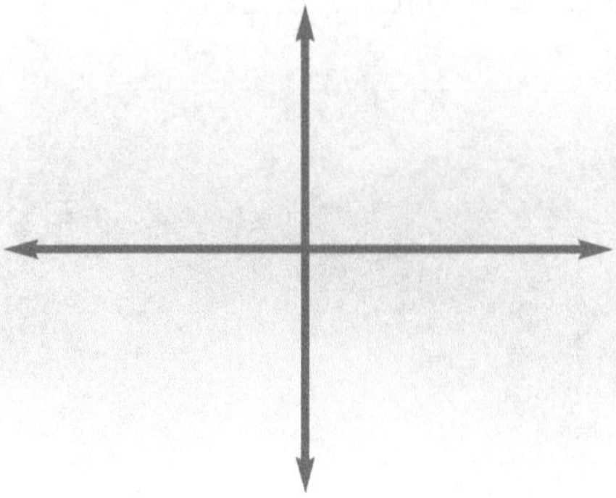

5 **Write in standard form. The first two have been done for you.**

$8.34 \times 10^3 = 8{,}340$ **$2.7 \times 10^6 = 2{,}700{,}000$**

$1.06 \times 10^4 =$ ________ $9.9 \times 10^5 =$ ________

$6.1 \times 10^2 =$ ________ $5.1 \times 10^3 =$ ________

$1.11 \times 10^5 =$ ________ $4.23 \times 10^6 =$ ________

$9.612 \times 10^4 =$ ________ $8.3 \times 10^2 =$ ________

6 **Multiply. Find your answer in the code box.**
Write the corresponding letter on the line at the bottom of the page to find the solution to this riddle: Why couldn't the math teacher find any shoes to fit?
The first one has been done for you.

1,095	1,936	4,035	2,068	4,564	1,536	4,740	1,701
A	E	F	Q	R	S	T	U

1. 192×8 = 1,536
2. 517×4
3. 189×9
4. 365×3
5. 652×7
6. 242×8
7. 807×5
8. 484×4
9. 968×2
10. 790×6

She had ... S (1.) ___ (2.) ___ (3.) ___ (4.) ___ (5.) ___ (6.)   ___ (7.) ___ (8.) ___ (9.) ___ (10.)

Construct a Square

A square is a quadrilateral with four sides and all angles the same length.
We can construct a square using a compass and straightedge.

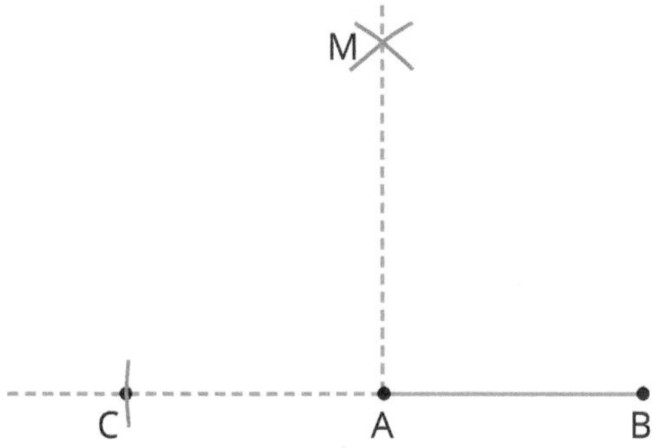

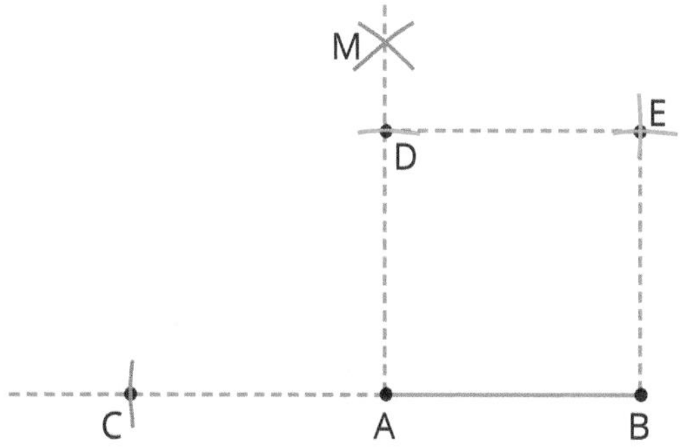

1. Draw a line the desired length of one side and label it AB. Extend line AB to the left. Place the compass at point A and then open it up until the pencil is at point B. Spin the compass around and draw an arc to the left of point A. Label the intersection of the line and the arc point C.
2. Since segment CA and segment AB are the same length, point A is the midpoint of segment CB. Next make a perpendicular at point A by placing the point of the compass at point B and make an arc above the line. (You will need to open the compass up some before making this arc.)
   Place the point of the compass on point C and make an arc above the line that intersects the other arc. Label the intersection point M. Use your straightedge to draw a line from point A through point M.
3. Open your compass to the length of one side of the square. (Place the compass point on point A and the pencil end on point B.) Leave the point of the compass on point A and make an arc that intersects line AM. Label the point D. Place the compass point on point D and draw an arc above line CB and to the right of line AD. Place the compass on point B and draw an arc intersecting the arc above it. Label the intersection point E.
4. With a straightedge draw a line connecting point D and point E; draw a line connecting point E and point B.
5. Figure ADEB is a square.

(1) **Construct a square using line XY as one side.**
Label the square VWXY.

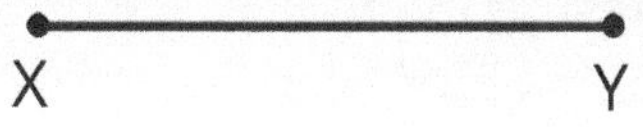

2 **Construct a right triangle using a compass and straightedge. Use line MN as one side of the triangle. Label the triangle ΔMNO.**

3 **Construct an equilateral triangle using a compass and straightedge. Use line JK as one side of the triangle. Label the triangle ΔJKH.**

4 **Average the numbers and round the average to the nearest whole number.**

34, 88, 27, 69

12, 18, 17, 19, 11

781, 900, 843

72.3, 89.4, 66.2

988, 534, 678

1,098, 6,981

5 **Multiply.**

902 × 30	812 × 14	451 × 58	722 × 47
402 × 51	129 × 84	599 × 37	688 × 19
359 × 21	317 × 52	691 × 65	297 × 86

6 **Use the chart to solve the following.**

1 cup (c) = 8 fluid ounces (fl oz)	1 quart (qt) = 32 fluid oz 4 cups 2 pints 
1 pint (pt) = 16 fluid ounces 	1 gallon (gal) = 128 fluid oz 16 cups 8 pints 4 quarts

7 gal = ____ qt

8 pt = ____ gal

32 c = ____ qt

7 pt = ____ c

7 gal = ____ oz

12 pt = ____ c

9 c = ____ oz

10 pt = ____ c

Constructing a Parallelogram

A parallelogram is a quadrilateral with opposite sides that are parallel.
Look at these three examples.

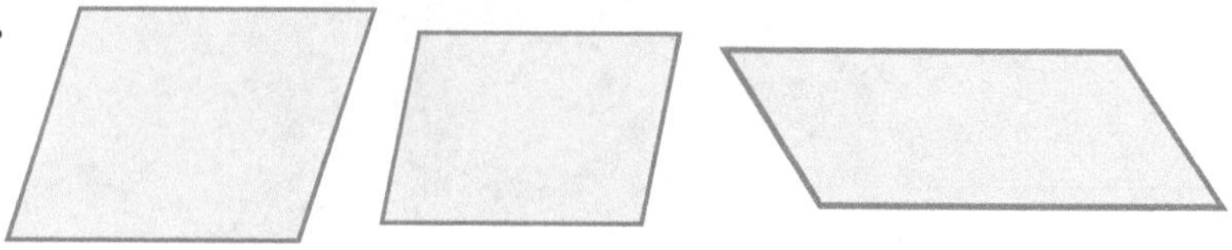

We can construct a parallelogram given the length of two sides and one angle. One side of the parallelogram equals 6 cm, the other side equals 3 cm. The measure of one angle is 45°.

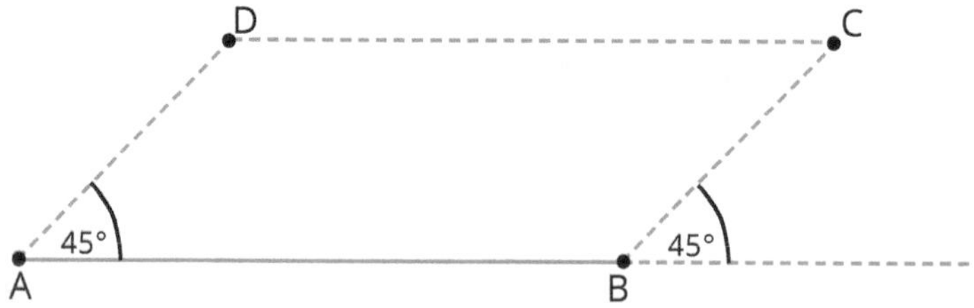

1. Draw a line 6 cm long. Place point A on one end of the line and point B on the other end.
2. Place the arrow of the protractor on point A and the zero edge on line AB. Measure a 45° angle.
3. Draw a straight 3 cm long line from point A at a 45° angle. Label the endpoint point D.
4. Attach a work line to the end of line AB.
5. Place the arrow of the protractor on point B and the zero edge on the work line. Measure a 45° angle.
6. Draw a straight 3 cm long line from point B at a 45° angle. Label the endpoint point C.
7. Draw a straight line connecting point C and point D.
8. Figure ABCD is a parallelogram.

(1) **Construct a parallelogram with the length of one side 5 cm and the length of the other side 3 cm. The measure of the angle is 60°. The length of one side has been drawn for you. Label the parallelogram EFGH.**

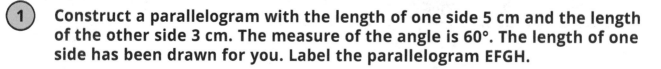

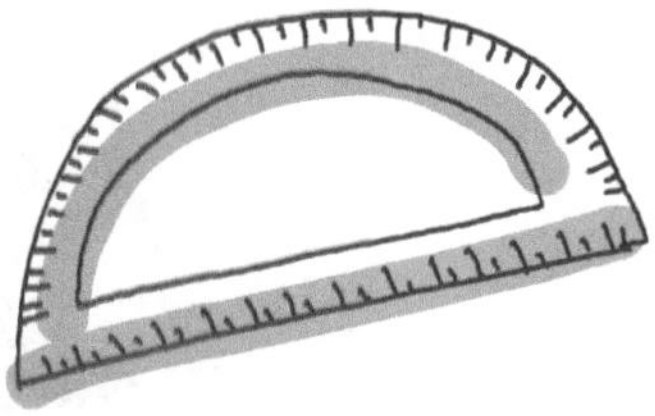

(2) **Construct a square using line OP as one side.**
Label the square OPQR.

(3) **Construct a right triangle using a compass and straightedge.**
Use line ST as one side of the triangle.
Label the triangle ΔSTU.

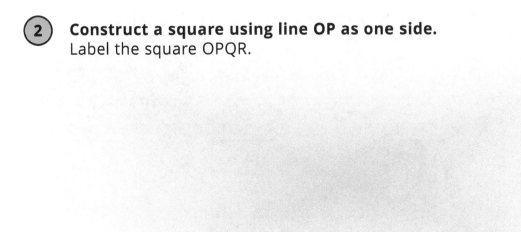

(4) **Construct an equilateral triangle using a compass and straightedge.**
Use line HI as one side of the triangle.
Label the triangle ΔHIJ.

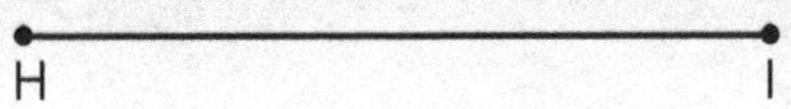

5 **Multiply. Place the answers (along with their corresponding letters) in order from least to greatest. The corresponding letters will solve this riddle:**

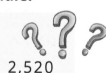

What kind of tile do you NOT want on your kitchen floor?

1,811 × 20	4,812 × 12	3,451 × 91	2,520 × 34
A	R	E	E
4,990 × 22	6,423 × 40	8,441 × 28	5,121 × 30
P	L	I	T

1. ______________ ______

2. ______________ ______

3. ______________ ______

4. ______________ ______

5. ______________ ______

6. ______________ ______

7. ______________ ______

8. ______________ ______

6 **Use the chart to solve the following problems.**

Just a Reminder:
12 inches = 1 foot
3 feet = a yard
5,280 feet = 1,760 yards = 1 mile

84 inches = ______________ ft

42 yards = ______________ ft

5 miles = ______________ ft

12 miles = ______________ yd

17 feet = ______ yd ______ ft

88 feet = ______ yd ______ ft

79 inches = ______ ft ______ in

219 inches = ______ ft ______ in

Test 12

32 points total   Lessons 106-115

① Find the volume of each cylinder. Round the answer to the tenths. 2 pts.

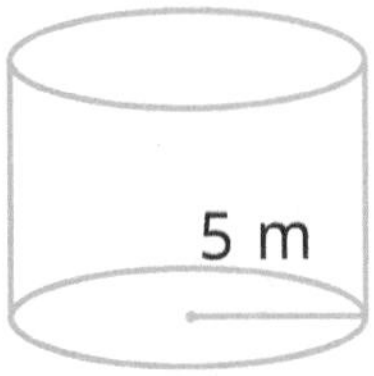

Volume = ____________ m^3

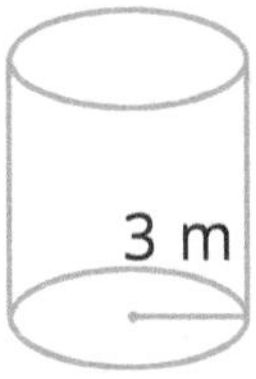

Volume = ____________ m^3

② Find the surface area of the figure below. 1 pt.

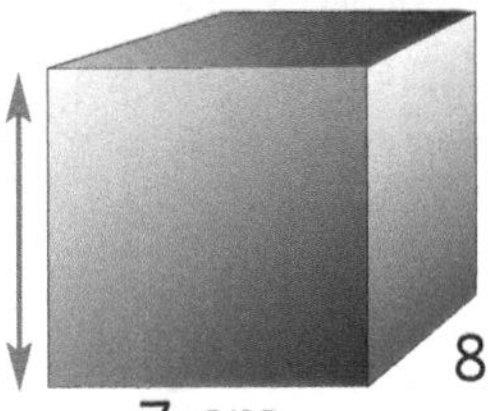

Surface area = ____________

③ Find the volume of each figure. 2 pts.

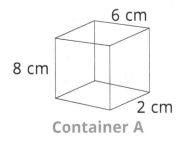

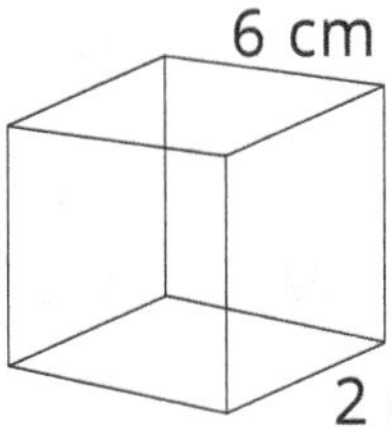

Container A

Volume = __________

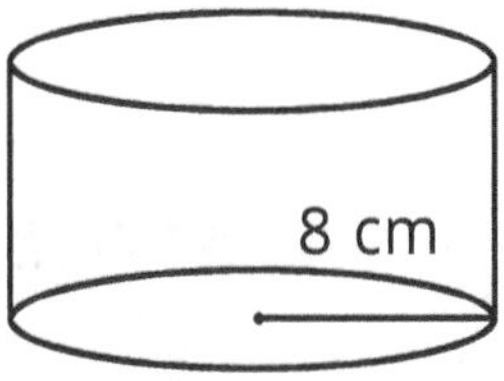

Container B

Volume = __________

④ Answer the questions below. 4 pts.

When you cross one individual time zone going west, the clocks are one hour ______________.

When you cross one time zone going east, the clocks are one hour __________________.

From April to October many regions use Daylight Saving Time. The clocks are set one hour ______________ of the standard time for that zone.

There are 24 time zones in the world. Twelve zones are east of the ______________________________________ and twelve zones are west of it.

⑤ Read each word problem and identify the two operations required to solve the problem. Then solve the problems. 8 pts.

1. Simon had $3\frac{6}{8}$ bag of candy to give to his baseball team. Each full bag of candy has 16 pieces in it. If there are 30 players on his team, how much candy does each player get?
2. Katrina has $98.00 in her savings account. She is going to withdraw $17.89 for a watch and $9.98 for a game. How much will she have in savings after her withdrawals?

6 **Give the measure of each angle.** You may need to extend the angle for easier reading. 2 pts.

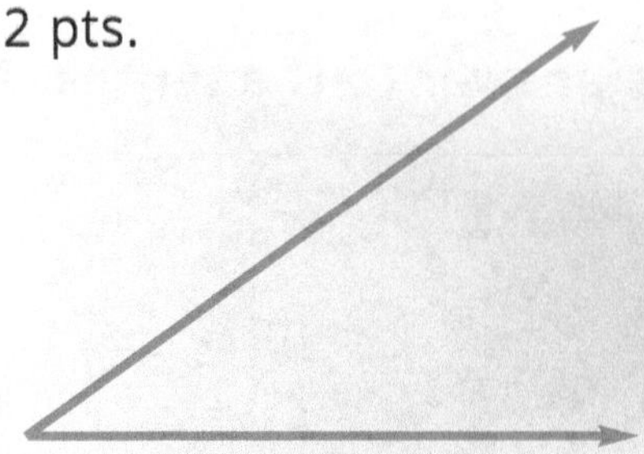

7 **Use a protractor to measure the angles in the circle. Write the measurements on the lines provided.** 8 pts.

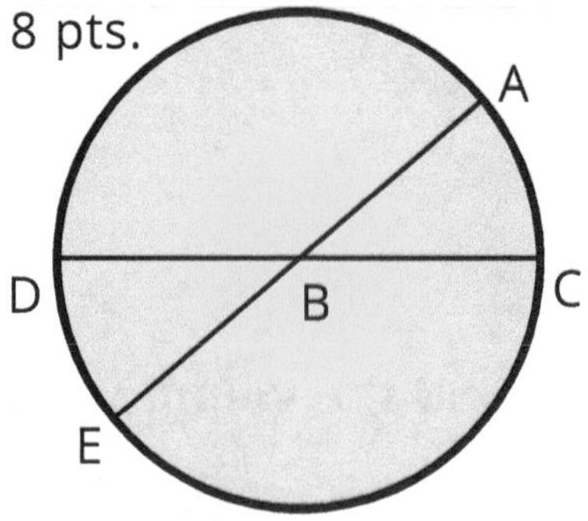

∠ABC = ________

∠CBE = ________

∠EBD = ________

∠DBA = ________

∠ABC + ∠CDE + ∠EBD + ∠DBA = 360°

________ + ________ + ________ + ________ = 360°

8 **Draw a 40° angle using the given side. Label it ∠LMN.** 1 pt.

9 **Given line AB, draw another line that bisects line AB and forms four congruent right angles. Label the new line, the perpendicular bisector, CD.** 1 pt.

10 **Bisect the angle using a compass and straightedge. Label the bisector QU.** 3 pts.

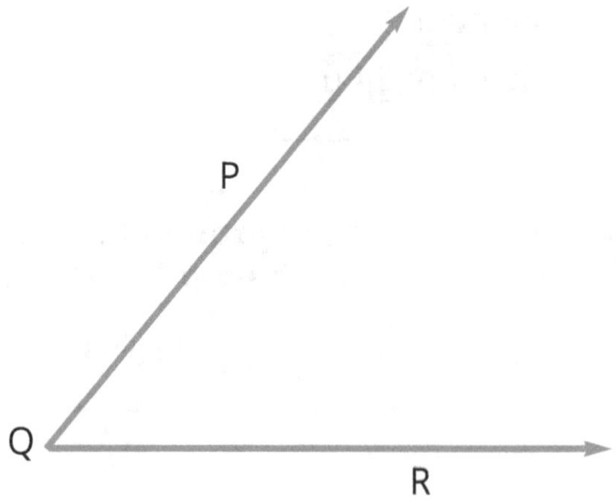

∠ PQU measures ________ degrees.
∠ RQU measures ________ degrees.

Writing Ratios to Compare Numbers

10 out of 23 children in Mrs. Fowler's class like chocolate ice cream. You can write a ratio to compare these numbers. The ratio of children who like chocolate ice cream to the total number of student is 10 to 23.

We write: 10 to 23, or 10:23, or $\frac{10}{23}$

We read: ten to twenty-three

Try these examples.

What ratio of the houses are green?

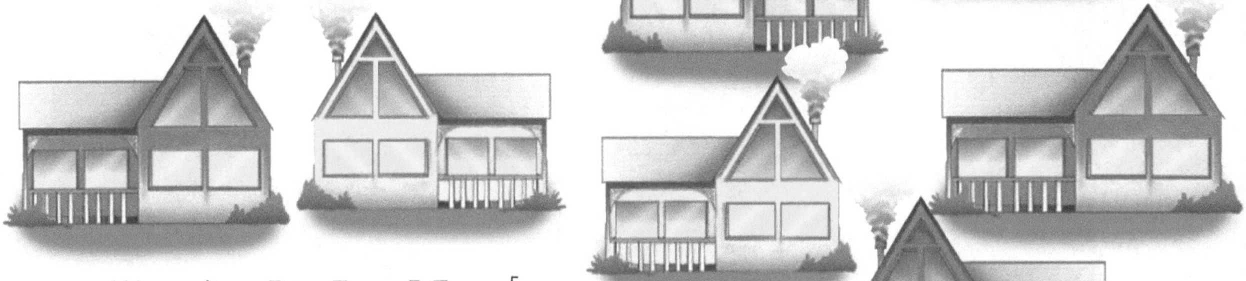

We write: 5 to 7, or 5:7, or $\frac{5}{7}$

We read: five to seven

What ratio of the shapes are quadrilaterals?

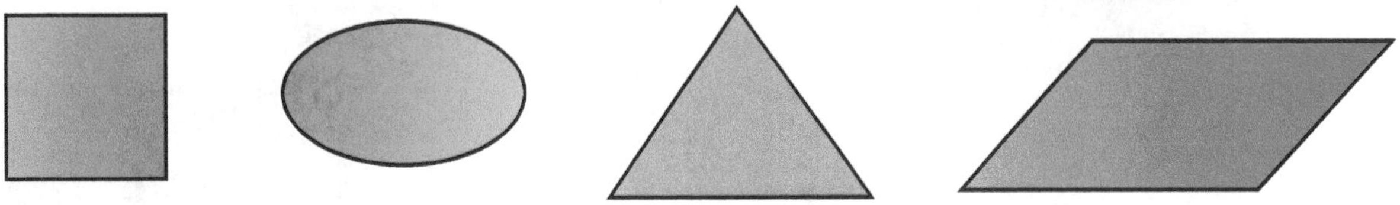

We write: 2 to 4, 2 : 4, or $\frac{2}{4}$ We read: two to four

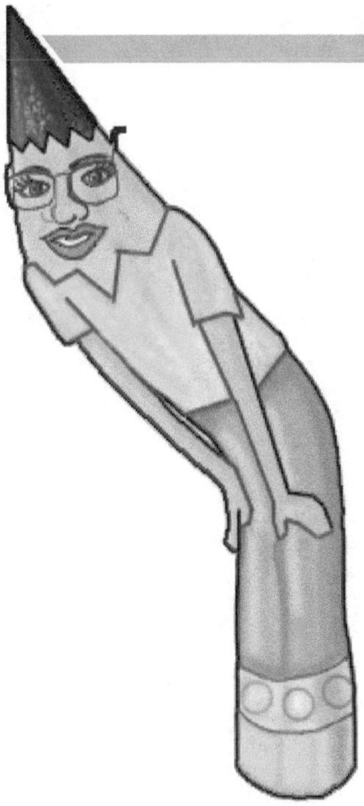

1 **Write the ratio.**

Tissue paper is sold 25 sheets for $1.25.

A package of 15 pencils costs $1.69.

5 sheets of poster board costs $2.35.

27 students are in Mrs. Hawkins' class:

15 of them are girls.

10 of them bring their lunch from home every day.

3 of them walk to school.

5 of them are already 11 years old.

(2) Add.

723.1 + 10.2 + .03 =	405.6 + 0.007 + 72.9 =
1.003 + 6.3 + 304 =	9.08 + .045 + 25 + 1.2 =
96 + .20 + 5 + .99 =	129.33 + 4.3 + 12.16 + .03 =

(3) Match.

$\frac{33}{44} - \frac{1}{44} =$	$\frac{33}{44}$
$\frac{36}{98} + \frac{14}{98} =$	$\frac{36}{98}$
$\frac{26}{47} + \frac{25}{47} =$	$\frac{32}{44}$
$\frac{47}{98} - \frac{11}{98} =$	$\frac{51}{47}$
$\frac{23}{44} + \frac{10}{44} =$	$\frac{5}{47}$
$\frac{15}{47} - \frac{10}{47} =$	$\frac{50}{98}$

(4) Find the area.

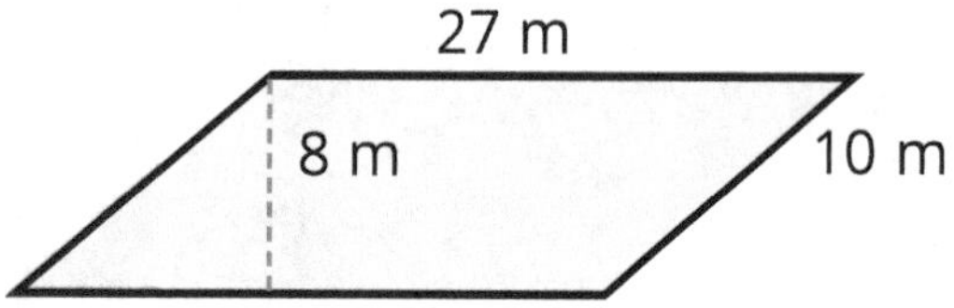

Area =

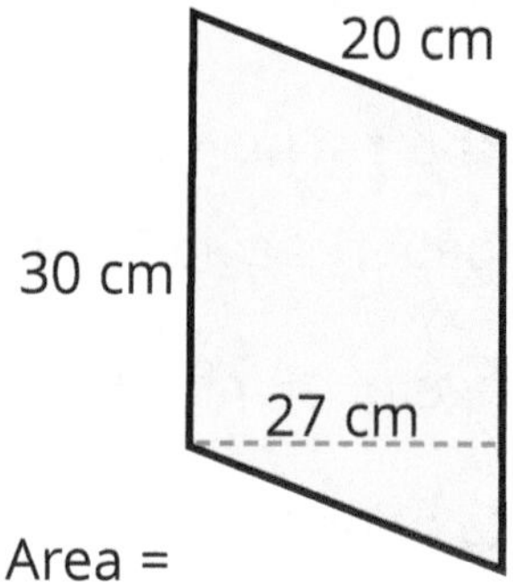

Area =

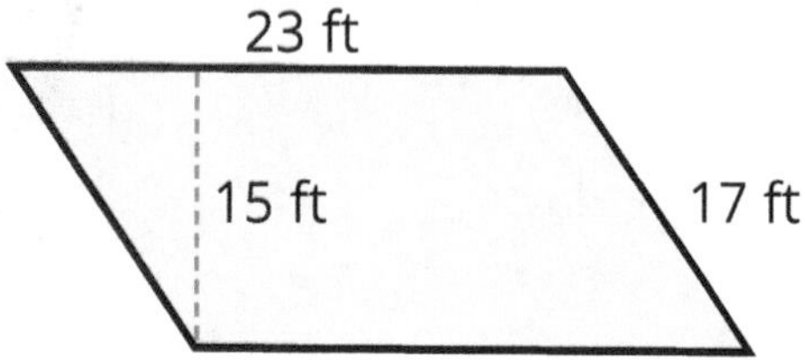

Area =

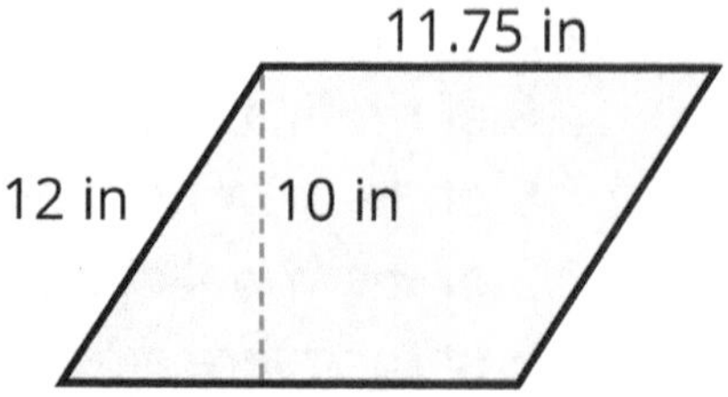

Area =

5 **Solve.**

James purchased $225.98 worth of supplies at the local hardware store.
If he paid the cashier in $50.00 bills, how many did he give her and how much change did he receive?

Hannah purchased 4 lemons for $0.98 at the grocery store.
How much would she pay for 16 lemons?

Joe needs 48 cookies. A package of 12 fresh homemade cookies costs $2.95.
How much will it cost him to purchase the amount he needs?

Kelly earned $295.00 working for her father. She owes him $169.00 for an advance on her allowance. How much money will she receive?

6 **Solve.**

Hughes department store is having a holiday sale. Everything is to be marked down by 20%. Complete the chart below to show the new price of each item.

Remember: When finding a discount, you multiply the regular price by the percentage discount. Look at the example below:

A pair of children's shoes is on sale for 20% off. The regular price is $19.98. To find the amount of the discount, you multiply 20% (change to a decimal before multiplying 0.20) by $19.98.

$0.20 \times \$19.98 = 3.996$ which rounds to $4.00.

The discount amount is $4.00.

To calculate the **new sale price** just subtract the discount amount from the regular price. $19.98 – $4.00 = $15.98 The shoes will cost $15.98 after the discount.

ITEM	*REGULAR PRICE*	*20% DISCOUNT*	*NEW PRICE*
WALLET	$35.00		
GOLD EARRINGS	$98.25		
NECKLACE	$198.99		
JEANS	$45.00		
TODDLER SWEATER	$25.00		
MEN'S COAT	$235.00		
WOMAN'S DRESS	$75.50		

7 **Find the sum. Unscramble the message.**

51,560 **T**	54,081 **O**	12,369 **S**	26,549 **L**
+ 61,581	+ 34,752	+ 79,008	+ 34,930

Order the answers from smallest to largest.

Luke 15:32

Using Ratio Tables

Suzanne and Sherea are baking cupcakes for the entire grade level. For every package of cupcake mix, they need 2 tablespoons of oil and 3 eggs. How much oil and how many eggs will they need for 6 boxes of cupcake mix?

Ratio tables can help solve problems like this one. Remember, we can make ratio tables by finding equivalent fractions. We find equivalent fractions by multiplying each term by the same number.

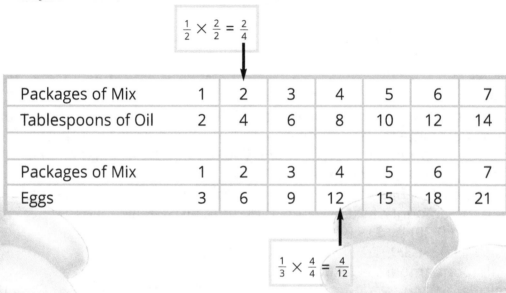

$\frac{1}{2} \times \frac{2}{2} = \frac{2}{4}$

Packages of Mix	1	2	3	4	5	6	7
Tablespoons of Oil	2	4	6	8	10	12	14
Packages of Mix	1	2	3	4	5	6	7
Eggs	3	6	9	12	15	18	21

$\frac{1}{3} \times \frac{4}{4} = \frac{4}{12}$

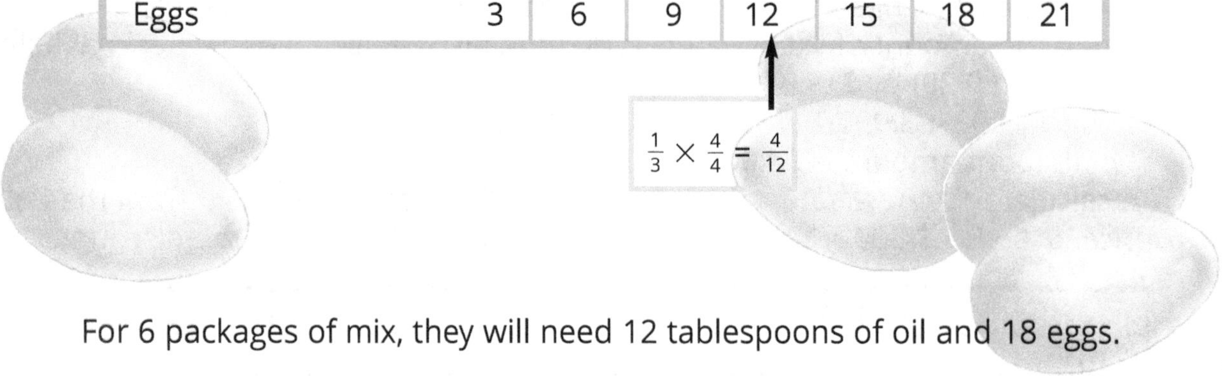

For 6 packages of mix, they will need 12 tablespoons of oil and 18 eggs.

1 **Complete each ratio table.**

Drink Mix	3 scoops	6	9					
Water	1 cup	2	3					

Fertilizer Mix	2 tbs	4						
Water	1 gal	2						

Milk	1 cup	2						
Eggs	2	4						

2 **Write the ratio.**

Push Pins: 5 for $0.25

Ratios:

cents to pins ______

pins to cents ______

blue pins to green pins ______

red pins to total pins ______

red pins to blue pins ______

green and red pins to blue pins ______

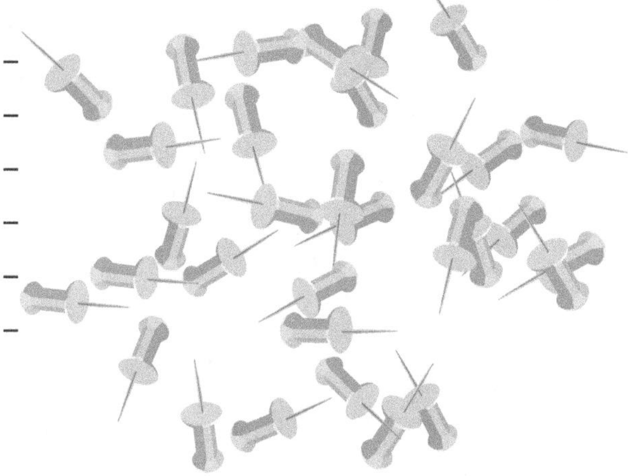

3 **Find the value of each word by adding the value of each number.**

A 665.3	B 54.6	C 21.3	D 0.02	E 1.56	F 0.007
G 89.006	H 2.08	I 61.71	K 60.28	L 6.19	N 45.98
O 45.9	P .33	R 12.86	S 26.46	T 9.15	U 50.47

B
O
O
+ K
______

B
I
B
L
+ E
______

T
R
U
S
+ T
______

F
A
I
T
+ H
______

4 **Fill in the missing numbers and solve.**

$$\frac{3}{8} = \frac{N}{8} \qquad + \frac{1}{4} = \frac{N}{8}$$
______

$$\frac{7}{10} = \frac{7}{10} \qquad - \frac{1}{5} = \frac{N}{N}$$
______

$$\frac{1}{12} = \frac{N}{N} \qquad + \frac{3}{4} = \frac{9}{N}$$
______

$$\frac{3}{5} = \frac{12}{N} \qquad - \frac{1}{4} = \frac{N}{N}$$
______

5 **Find the area of each parallelogram.**

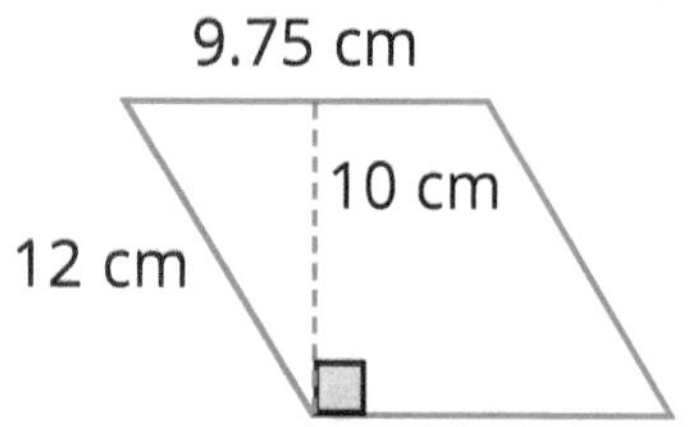

Area =

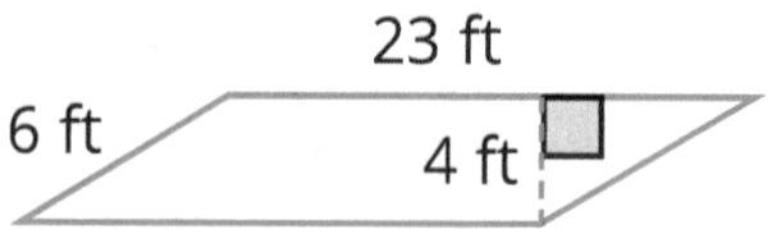

Area =

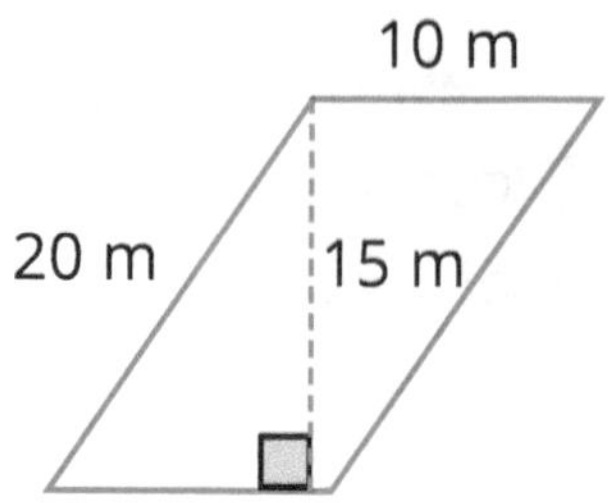

Area =

6 **Solve.**

Sabrina made $400 working over Christmas vacation. How much will her 10% tithe be on Sunday?

If Sabrina tithes 15% instead of 10%, off of the $400, how much will she give on Sunday?

Brett is saving $25.00 a week to buy a stereo for his car. He already has $150.00 saved. If the stereo system costs $398.00, how many more weeks will it be before he has enough money to purchase the equipment?

There are 75 students in Loganville Christian Academy. If every student purchases 2 slices of pizza at a cost of $1.50 per slice, how much money will the school collect?

For a special occasion, the local preschool ordered 198 chicken sandwich meals from the local restaurant. If each meal cost $3.25, how much was the total purchase?

7 **Complete the chart.**

Item	*Regular Price*	*20% Discount*	*New Price*
Purse	$75.00		
Engagement Ring	$3,198.25		
Sweater	$98.99		
Pants	$35.00		
Perfume	$55.00		
Wide Screen TV	$2,235.00		
Comforter Set	$175.50		

Using Ratio Tables

Mr. Holmes bought bags of candy for the church carnival. The store was selling 25 bags of candy for $5.00. If Mr. Holmes purchased 225 bags of candy and paid $45.00, was Mr. Holmes charged the correct amount?

We need to determine if the ratios are equal.

$$\frac{225}{\$45} = \frac{25}{\$5}$$

Remember, we can either multiply or divide to find equal ratios.

$$\frac{225}{\$45} \div \frac{9}{9} = \frac{25}{\$5}$$

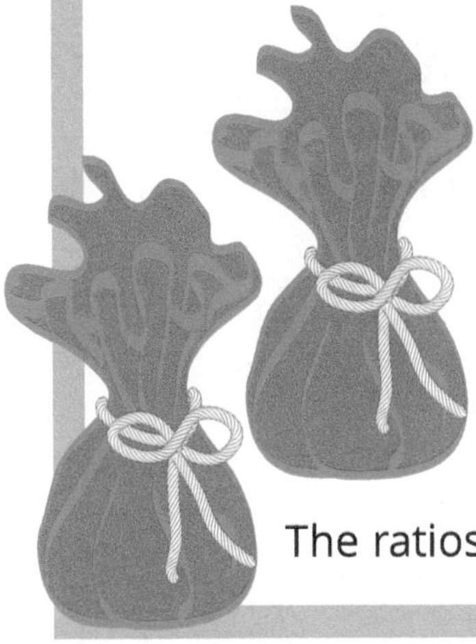

The ratios are equal. Mr. Holmes was charged the correct amount.

1 **Divide. Write two equal ratios for each.**

$\frac{20}{30} =$ $\frac{40}{300} =$ $\frac{320}{160} =$ $\frac{12}{42} =$

$\frac{18}{30} =$ $\frac{80}{10} =$ $\frac{550}{150} =$ $\frac{988}{428} =$

② Complete the ratio charts.

Cups of Peanut Butter	2		6			
# of Cookies	24					

Cookies	3	6				
Scoops of Ice Cream	1					

Eggs	48					
Cartons	4	5				

③ Use this list of books of the Bible to write each ratio.

Books	Questions
Exodus Matthew	What is the ratio of Old Testament books to New Testament books?
John Psalms	What is the ratio of New Testament books to total books listed?
Job Revelation	What is the ratio of Old Testament books to total books listed?
James Malachi	What is the ratio of "gospel" books to total New Testament books?
Hebrews Ephesians	What is the ratio of "poetry" books to total Old Testament books?
Nehemiah Song of Solomon	What is the ratio of "history" books to "poetry" books?

④ Find the difference.

$$\begin{array}{r} 12.24 \\ -\ 7.20 \\ \hline \end{array} \qquad \begin{array}{r} 11.41 \\ -\ 8.40 \\ \hline \end{array} \qquad \begin{array}{r} 62.53 \\ -11.92 \\ \hline \end{array}$$

$$\begin{array}{r} 104.80 \\ -75.80 \\ \hline \end{array} \qquad \begin{array}{r} 7.58 \\ -\ 3.25 \\ \hline \end{array} \qquad \begin{array}{r} 41.26 \\ -24.14 \\ \hline \end{array}$$

5 **Write each fraction in lowest terms.**
Match your answer with the fraction below.
Place the appropriate letter on the line and read the mystery message.

$\frac{18}{81}$ = ______ D	$\frac{5}{145}$ = ______ T	$\frac{50}{100}$ = ______ I
$\frac{15}{20}$ = ______ R	$\frac{8}{96}$ = ______ P	$\frac{70}{100}$ = ______ O
$\frac{35}{42}$ = ______ H	$\frac{12}{96}$ = ______ E	$\frac{100}{100}$ = ______ S
$\frac{12}{15}$ = ______ L	$\frac{25}{100}$ = ______ A	

___	___	___	___	___	___	___	___	___	___	___	___	___	___!
$\frac{1}{12}$	$\frac{3}{4}$	$\frac{1}{4}$	$\frac{1}{2}$	1	$\frac{1}{8}$	$\frac{1}{29}$	$\frac{5}{6}$	$\frac{1}{8}$	$\frac{4}{5}$	$\frac{7}{10}$	$\frac{3}{4}$	$\frac{2}{9}$	

Psalms 112:1a

6 **Find the area.**

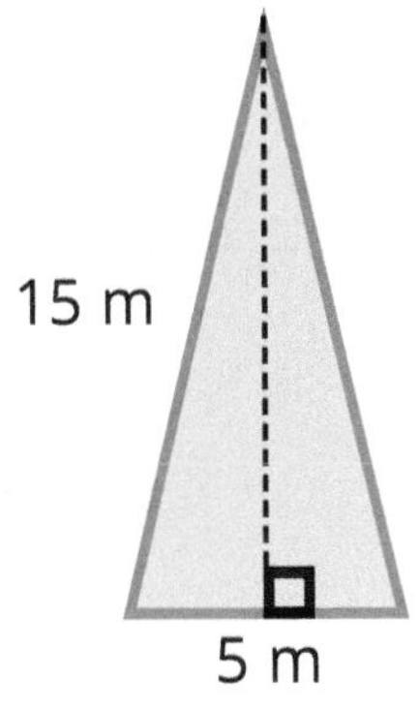

Area =

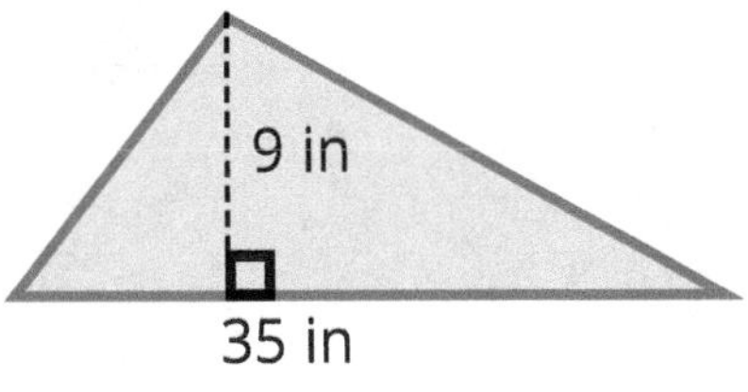

Area =

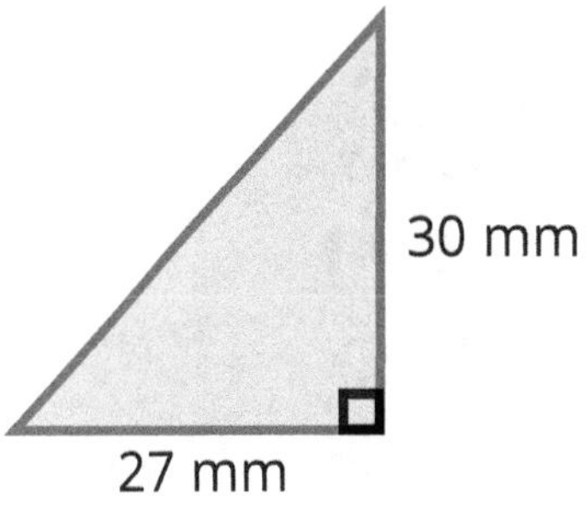

Area =

Proportions and Equal Ratios

Tom is planning to build a miniature replica of his house for a math project. The model should be $\frac{1}{10}$ the size of the real house. This means that every part of the model will be $\frac{1}{10}$ the size of the same part of the real house.
The equation shown below is called a **proportion**. A proportion states that two ratios are equal. We can use cross products to tell if ratios are equal.

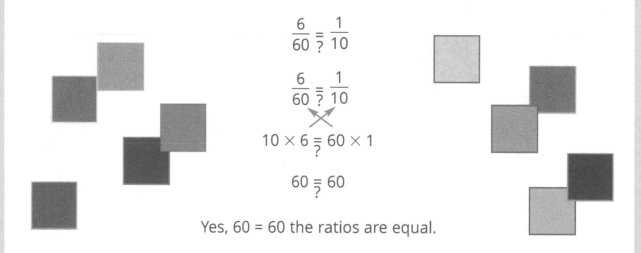

$$\frac{6}{60} \overset{?}{=} \frac{1}{10}$$

$$\frac{6}{60} \overset{?}{=} \frac{1}{10}$$

$$10 \times 6 \overset{?}{=} 60 \times 1$$

$$60 \overset{?}{=} 60$$

Yes, 60 = 60 the ratios are equal.

Once you find the cross products, look at them carefully. If they are equal, then the ratios are equal. Another way of stating this is by saying that the ratios are equivalent fractions.

1 **Use the cross-products method to see if the ratios are equal. Circle the ratios that are equal.**

$\frac{2}{8}$ $\frac{5}{10}$ $\frac{10}{20}$ $\frac{1}{2}$ $\frac{12}{15}$ $\frac{4}{5}$ $\frac{6}{21}$ $\frac{5}{7}$

$\frac{4}{18}$ $\frac{2}{9}$ $\frac{300}{600}$ $\frac{1}{2}$ $\frac{6}{36}$ $\frac{1}{3}$ $\frac{3}{7}$ $\frac{99}{231}$

2 **Divide. Write two equal ratios for each.**

$\frac{180}{140} =$ $\frac{130}{170} =$ $\frac{1110}{1150} =$ $\frac{250}{175} =$

3 **Write *yes* if the ratios are equivalent. Write *no* if the ratios are not equivalent.**

20 to 30 and 4 to 6 ______ 15 to 45 and 35 to 60 ______

1 to 2 and 15 to 30 ______ 1 to 7 and 12 to 85 ______

10 to 40 and 2 to 8 ______ 9 to 63 and 1 to 7 ______

13 to 39 and 11 to 33 ______ 25 to 75 and 12 to 48 ______

4 **Write a simple ratio for each.**

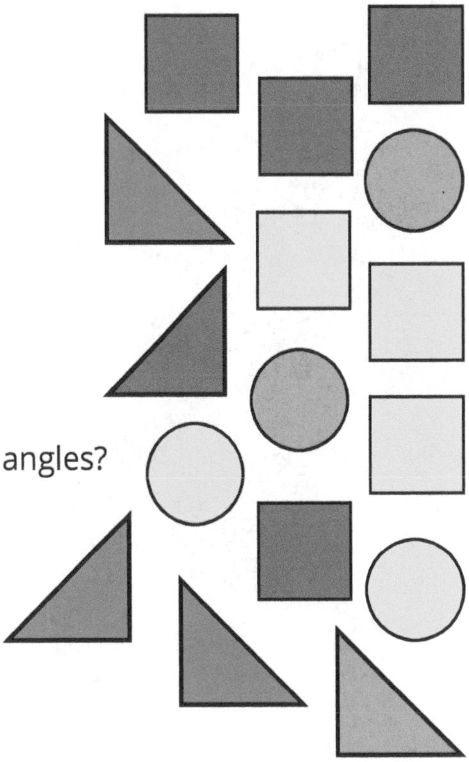

What is the ratio of blue triangles to green triangles?

What is the ratio of blue squares to yellow circles?

What is the ratio of pink circles to pink triangles?

What is the ratio of yellow squares to pink squares?

What is the ratio of yellow circles and squares to green triangles?

What is the ratio of triangles to squares?

What is the ratio of circles to triangles?

What is the ratio of pink figures to blue figures?

5 **Multiply to find the numerator or denominator.**

$\frac{1}{5} = \frac{}{10} = \frac{4}{} = \frac{8}{}$

$\frac{3}{11} = \frac{6}{22} = \frac{9}{} = \frac{12}{44} = \frac{}{55} = \frac{}{66}$

$\frac{1}{} = \frac{4}{16} = \frac{}{32} = \frac{12}{}$

6 **Number all the different triangles that can be found in the diagram. Find the area of each triangle.**

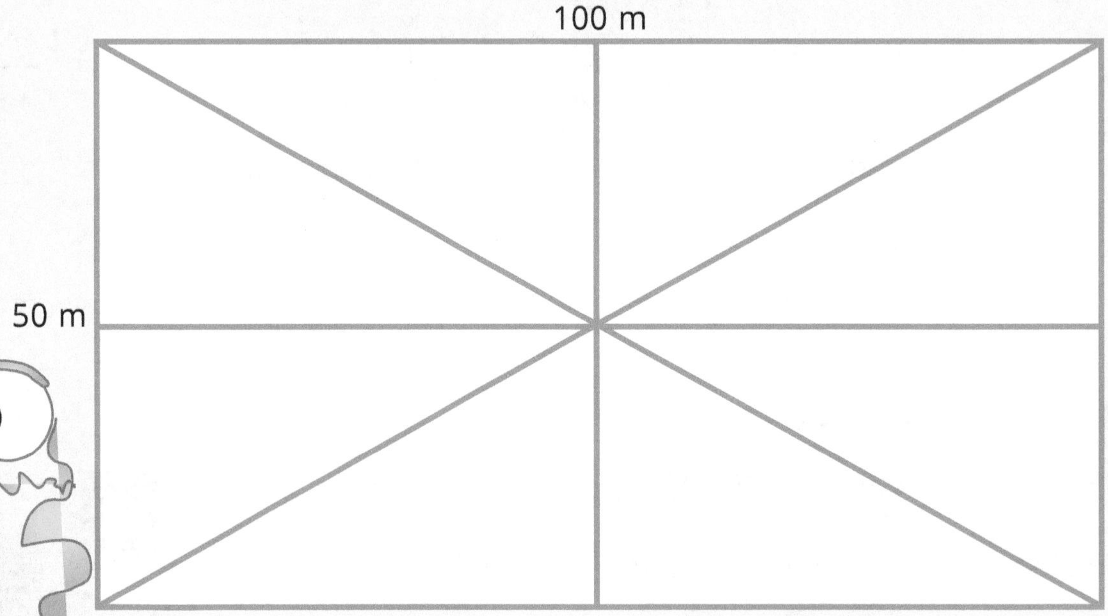

1.
2.
3.
4.
5.
6.
7.
8.
9.
10.
11.
12.
13.
14.
15.
16.

Using Cross-Products to Solve for N

Old newspapers may be purchased at a rate of 5 for \$2.00.
How many papers can be purchased for \$16.00? Use cross products to solve for N.

$$\frac{5}{\$2} = \frac{N}{\$16}$$

Think: $5 \times 16 = 80$, so an equal ratio would be made by solving $2 \times N = 80$.

Divide both sides by 2.

$$\frac{2 \times N}{2} = \frac{80}{2}$$

$$N = 40$$

$$\frac{5}{\$2} = \frac{40}{\$16}$$

40 newspapers may be purchased with \$16.00.
You can use cross products to find missing information in proportions.

(1) Use cross-products to solve each equation.

$\frac{N}{36} = \frac{6}{8}$ $\frac{10}{12} = \frac{15}{N}$ $\frac{16}{32} = \frac{N}{20}$ $\frac{5}{N} = \frac{1}{3}$

$\frac{7}{35} = \frac{6}{N}$ $\frac{4}{6} = \frac{N}{9}$ $\frac{50}{10} = \frac{10}{N}$ $\frac{2}{20} = \frac{6}{N}$

2 **Complete the charts.**

Runners	90	81			
Teams	20			14	

Cheese Slices	2		6		
Meat Slices	5	10			

Bananas						12	14
Scoops of ice cream				12			21

Cups of ice	7	6	5				
Squirts of flavoring	21	18					

3 **Place the fractions in order from least to greatest.**
When the fractions are in the correct order, they spell a message.

$\frac{1}{18}$ R $\frac{5}{9}$ N $\frac{2}{18}$ E $\frac{7}{9}$ T $\frac{1}{3}$ P $\frac{1}{2}$ E

____ ____ ____ ____ ____ ____

Acts 2:38

4 **Find the area. (Round to the nearest tenth.)**

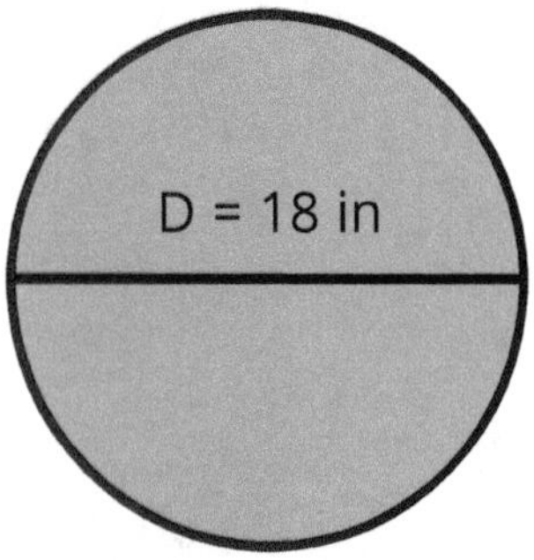

Area = _____

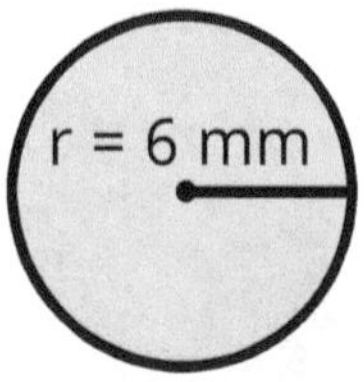

Area = _____

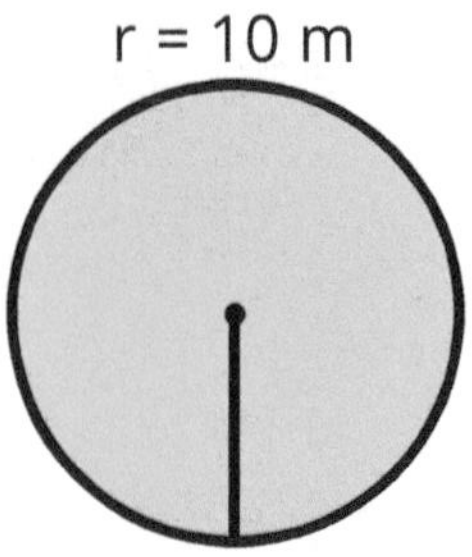

Area = _____

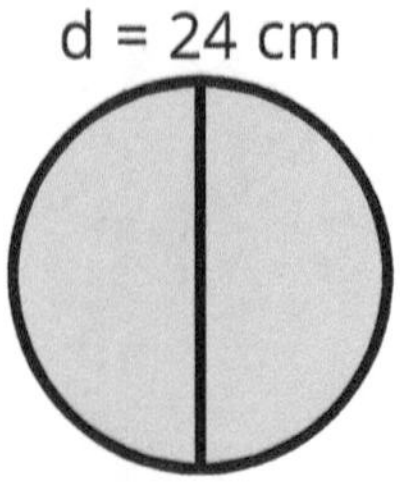

Area = _____

5. **Draw a thermometer that shows the indicated temperature.**

- 4° C	*13° C*	*freezing point (C)*	*boiling point (C)*	*55° C*

6. **Solve.**

Kimberly, Benjamin, Lorraine, Brett, and Bryce want to ride in pairs on Go Carts that accommodate two people. How many different rides will be taken if every different possible pair go for a ride? Hint: Make an organized list.

	Kimberly	Benjamin	Lorraine	Brett	Bryce
Kimberly					
Benjamin					
Lorraine					
Brett					
Bryce					

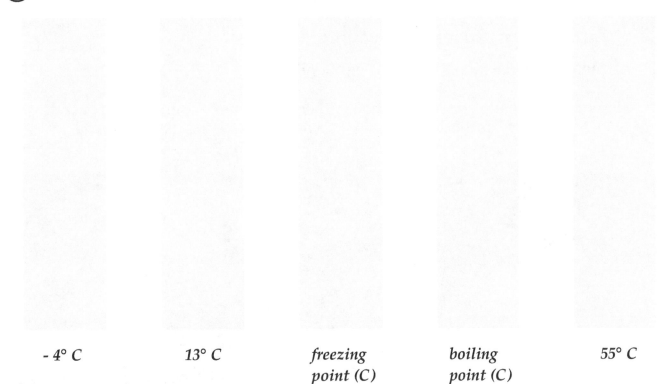

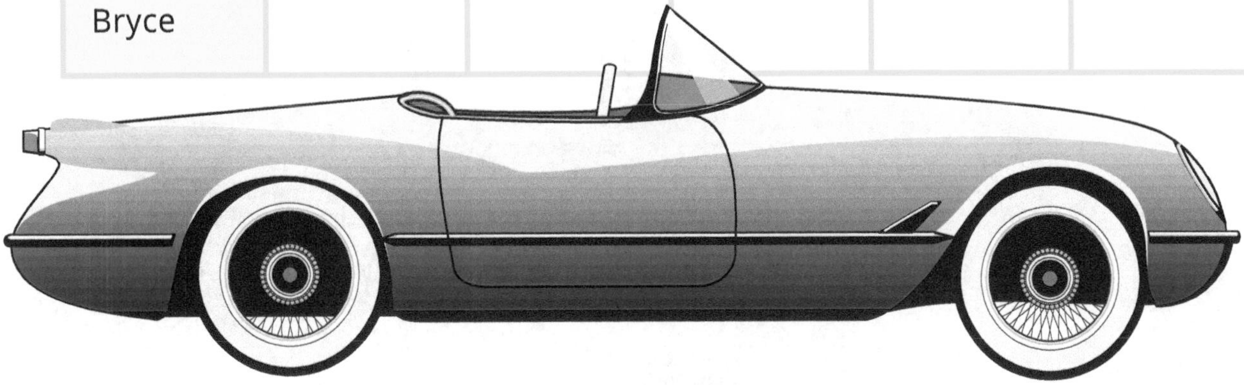

Percentages - Ratios per Hundred

Percent is a special ratio that means per hundred.

Allison threw the basketball at the hoop 10 times. 9 times Allison made a basket. Write the ratio of baskets to throws. Then write the percent of baskets made.

$$\frac{9}{10} = \frac{n}{100}$$

n **= 90**

$$\frac{90}{100} = \mathbf{90\%}$$

Allison made 90% of the shots she made.

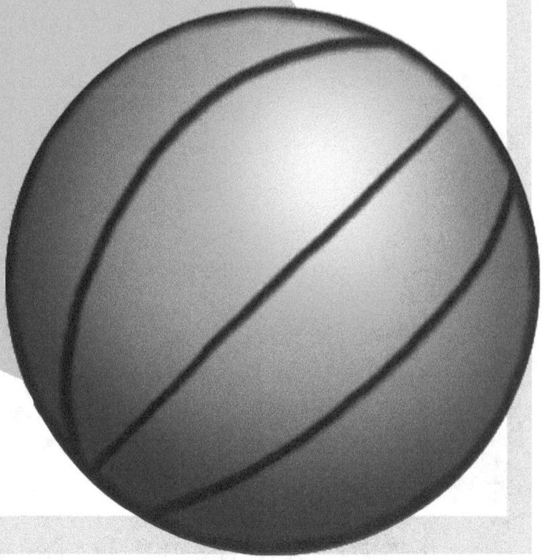

1 Complete.

$\frac{27}{50}$ = ___ %	$\frac{21}{25}$ = ___ %	$\frac{4}{5}$ = ___ %	$\frac{3}{20}$ = ___ %
$\frac{1}{5}$ = ___ %	$\frac{2}{8}$ = ___ %	$\frac{1}{10}$ = ___ %	$\frac{2}{4}$ = ___ %
$\frac{3}{6}$ = ___ %	$\frac{9}{10}$ = ___ %	$\frac{75}{100}$ = ___ %	$\frac{50}{200}$ = ___ %

(2) Use cross-products to find N.

$\frac{N}{8} = \frac{10}{16}$ $\frac{5}{N} = \frac{40}{72}$ $\frac{N}{15} = \frac{16}{6}$ $\frac{27}{24} = \frac{36}{N}$

$\frac{35}{N} = \frac{14}{50}$ $\frac{27}{9} = \frac{N}{35}$ $\frac{15}{21} = \frac{N}{49}$ $\frac{12}{84} = \frac{56}{N}$

(3) Divide to find an equal ratio.

$\frac{96}{80} =$ _____ $\frac{38}{86} =$ _____ $\frac{200}{400} =$ _____ $\frac{15}{24} =$ _____

$\frac{40}{12} =$ _____ $\frac{8}{18} =$ _____ $\frac{24}{16} =$ _____ $\frac{22}{20} =$ _____

(4) Compare using the correct sign (< > =).

$\frac{5}{8}$ _____ $\frac{7}{8}$ $\frac{7}{15}$ _____ $\frac{10}{12}$ $\frac{3}{4}$ _____ $\frac{1}{2}$

$\frac{1}{3}$ _____ $\frac{2}{6}$ $\frac{5}{9}$ _____ $\frac{3}{8}$ $\frac{4}{12}$ _____ $\frac{7}{14}$

$\frac{1}{4}$ _____ $\frac{2}{3}$ $\frac{4}{8}$ _____ $\frac{15}{30}$ $\frac{8}{14}$ _____ $\frac{9}{15}$

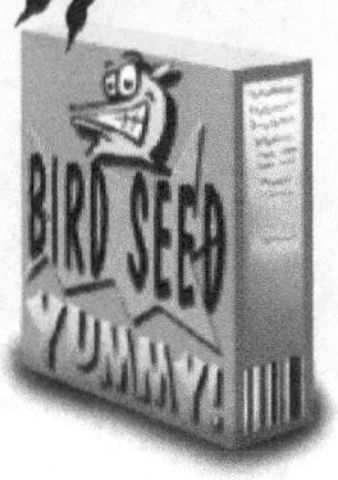

(5) **Find the area of each circle.**

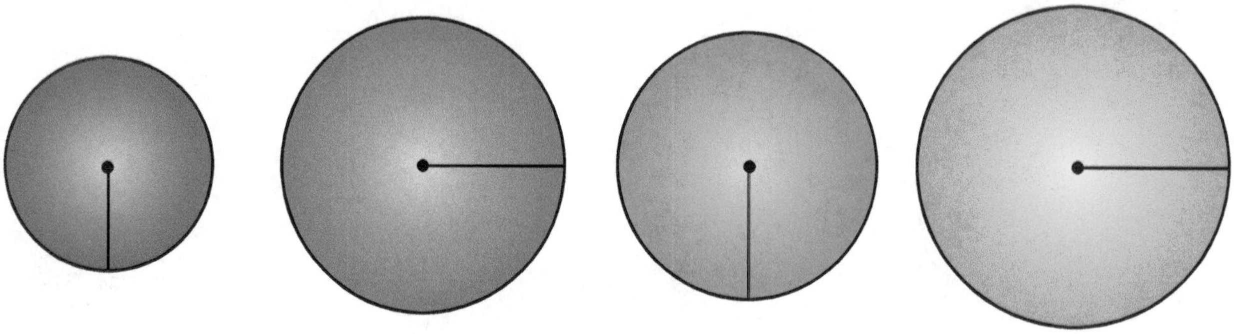

radius: 5 inches ______ radius: 15 feet ______ radius: 11 inches ______ radius: 20 feet ______

(6) **Match the Celsius temperature with the corresponding Fahrenheit temperature.**

_____ 100° C (boiling water) — **A.** 32° F (freezing)

_____ 37° C — **B.** 212° F

_____ 20° C (comfortable room temp.) — **C.** 98.6° F

_____ –10° C — **D.** 10° F

_____ 0° C — **E.** 70° F

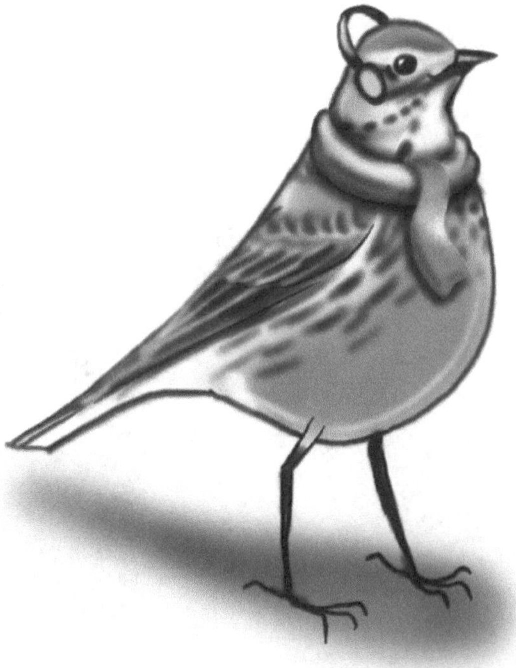

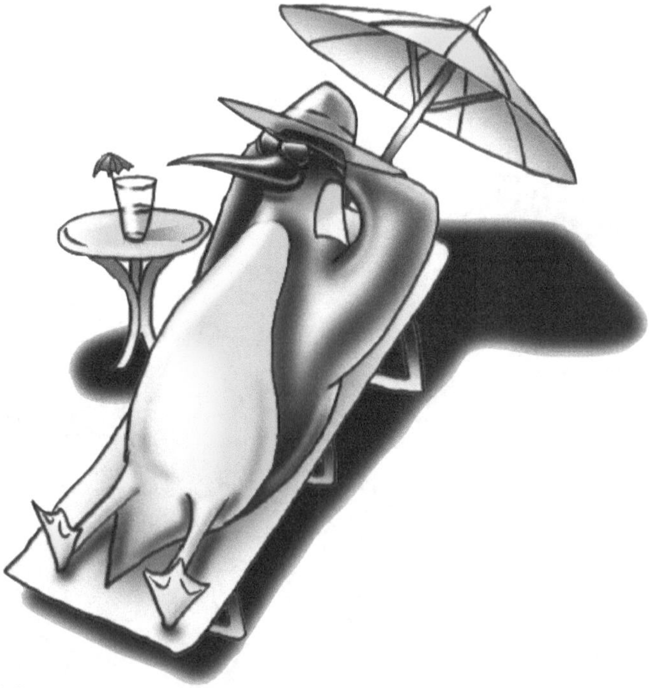

Probability - Chance that a Certain Event will Happen

Mrs. Carson's 1st Grade Class

Haley Hill	*Shelby Monda*
Tim Matthews	*Jarred Williams*
Mason Patrick	*Kyle Clayton*
Alice Smith	*Brett Fowler*
Katie Conners	*Daniel Smythe*
Brooke Henson	*Brooke Hope*

Mrs. Carson decided to give one of the children in her class the special privilege of using the computer during free time. In order to decide which child should get this job, she placed all the student names on individual pieces of paper and placed them in a hat. She then drew out one name. This process gives every one the same chance to be chosen provided that each name is placed in the box only one time, all the names are mixed well, and that the choice is made without looking.

If there are 12 children in the class, what is the **probability** Katie's name will be chosen?

Probability is the chance that a certain event will happen. In this case there is only one Katie in the class (look at the class list). If we want to know what chance she has of being chosen, it is 1 out of 12 or 1 in 12 or $(\frac{1}{12})$.

$$\text{Probability} = \frac{\text{Number of students named Katie in the class}}{\text{Total number of students in the class}} = \frac{1}{12}$$

What is the probability that a Brooke will be chosen? There a 2 students named Brooke in the class. Without specifying which Brooke we are talking about, there is a $\frac{2}{12}$ chance that a 'Brooke' will be chosen.

$$\text{Probability} = \frac{\text{Number of students named Brooke in the class}}{\text{Total number of students in the class}} = \frac{2}{12}$$

What is the probability of Mrs. Carson choosing a boy?

There are 6 boys in the class: $\frac{6}{12}$

1. **Use the spinner shown to answer the following probability questions.**

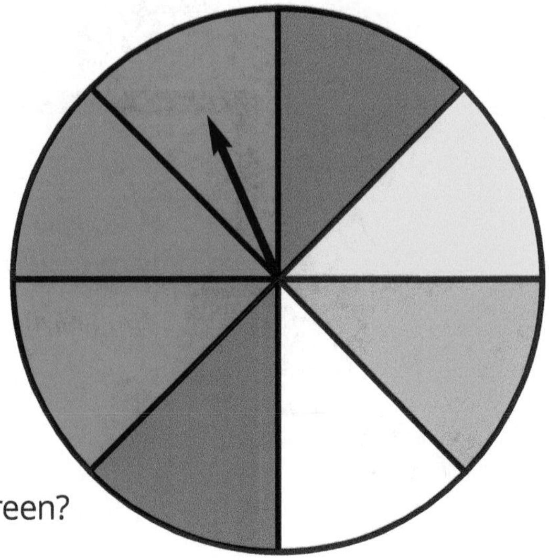

What is the probability of landing on orange?

What is the probability of landing on blue?

What is the probability of landing on green or red?

What is the probability of landing on white?

What is the probability of landing on blue, red or green?

2. **Write each ratio as a fraction, a decimal, and a percent.**

46 to 100   26 to 100   5 to 50   3 to 75   4 to 5

Write each decimal number as a percent.

0.7   0.96   0.05   .25   1.36

3. **Use the cross-products to solve for N.**

$\frac{12}{44} = \frac{9}{N}$ $\frac{N}{2} = \frac{25}{10}$ $\frac{3}{5} = \frac{N}{25}$

$\frac{15}{36} = \frac{N}{60}$ $\frac{7}{250} = \frac{N}{500}$ $\frac{16}{28} = \frac{N}{35}$

(4) Three of the problems below are incorrect. Circle them and then work them correctly.

$$\begin{array}{r} \frac{3}{8} = \frac{3}{8} \\ + \frac{1}{2} = \frac{4}{8} \\ \hline \frac{7}{8} \end{array} \qquad \begin{array}{r} \frac{7}{10} = \frac{7}{10} \\ - \frac{1}{5} = \frac{1}{10} \\ \hline \frac{8}{10} \end{array} \qquad \begin{array}{r} \frac{1}{6} = \frac{2}{6} \\ + \frac{2}{3} = \frac{2}{6} \\ \hline \frac{4}{6} \end{array} \qquad \begin{array}{r} \frac{1}{4} = \frac{2}{8} \\ - \frac{2}{8} = \frac{2}{8} \\ \hline \frac{4}{8} \end{array}$$

(5) Find the volume of each cylinder. (Round to the nearest tenth.)

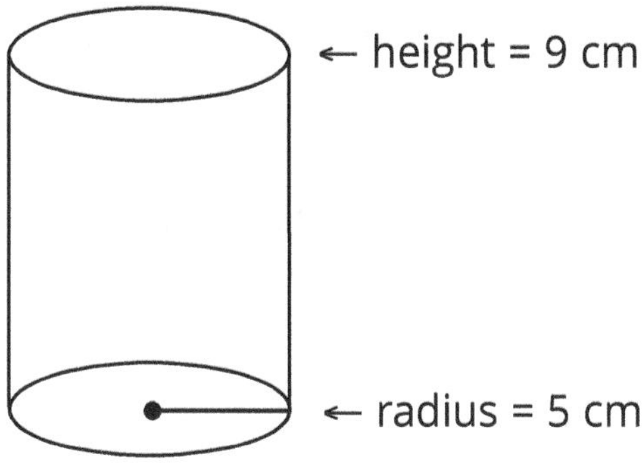

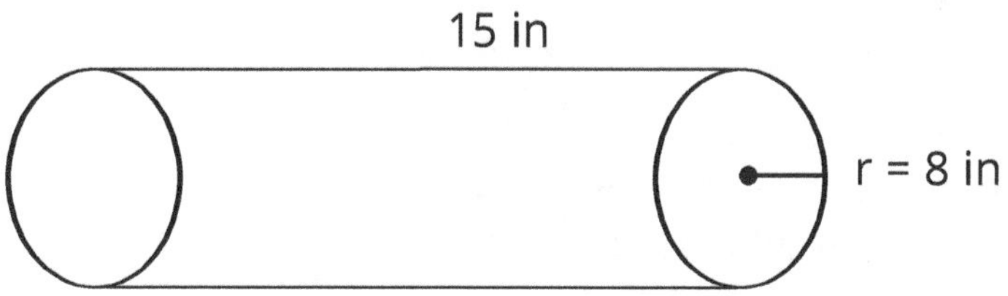

(6) Draw a vertical bar graph to show the following information.

Children enrolled in Bright Beginnings in 2018:

Toddlers:	8
2 year olds:	36
3 year olds:	44
4 year olds:	46
Kindergarten:	23

Outcome - The Result of a Probability Experiment

Mr. Salmon's class decided to have a probability center in his classroom. In one of the games, there are five cards that are to be turned over and shuffled. These cards are drawn below. What are the chances of drawing a card with a rectangle on it? $\frac{2}{5}$ because there are two cards with rectangles on them.
What is the probability of drawing a yellow card with an oval on it?
Only $\frac{1}{5}$ because there is only one yellow card with an oval on it.

When looking at probability problems, there are many things that can determine, or change, the **outcome**. An outcome is the result of a probability experiment.

Look at the cards again. What are the chances of drawing a blue or red card?

There are 2 blue cards and 1 red card so the probability is $\frac{3}{5}$. But what if I asked the probability of drawing a blue or red card with a rectangle on it? Then the probability would be only $\frac{1}{5}$.

What is the probability of picking a card with a black figure on it?

All of the cards have black figures on them so the answer would be $\frac{5}{5}$.

(1) **Use the diagrams to answer the questions.**

S A L V A T I O N

The letters to the word salvation are placed in a bag and one letter at a time is pulled back out of the bag.

What is the probability of getting a vowel?

What are the chances of pulling a consonant?

What is the probability of choosing a vowel on a pink background?

What is the probability of choosing a consonant on a blue background?

Now use a die to answer the questions.

What is the probability of landing on an even number?

What is the probability of landing on the number: one? ___ four ___ three ___

What is the probability of landing on any specific number?

2 **Look at the picture. Then name each as a ratio, as a fraction, as a ratio per hundred, as a decimal, and as a percent.** The first one has been done for you.

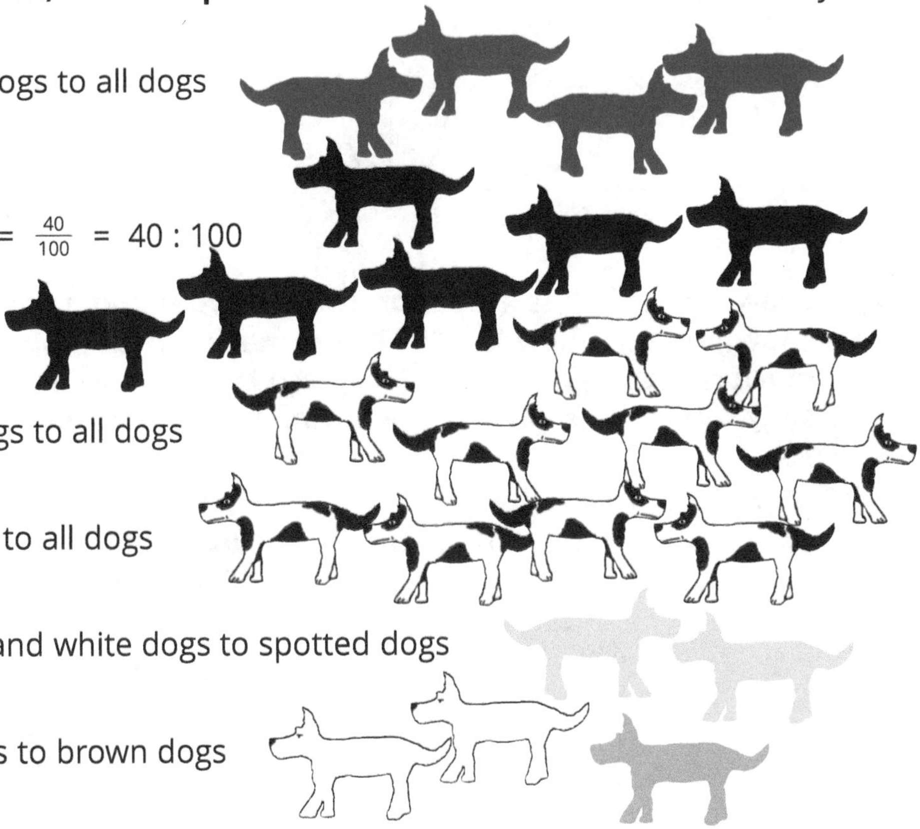

1. Ratio of spotted dogs to all dogs

ratio: 10:25

fraction: $\frac{10}{25}$

$\frac{\text{ratio}}{\text{fraction}}$ per 100: $\frac{10}{25} = \frac{40}{100} = 40 : 100$

decimal: $\frac{40}{100} = .40$

percent: $.40 = 40\%$

2. ratio of brown dogs to all dogs

3. ratio of gray dogs to all dogs

4. ratio of tan dogs and white dogs to spotted dogs

5. ratio of black dogs to brown dogs

3 **Use cross-products to solve for *N*.**

$\frac{N}{10} = \frac{4}{8}$	$\frac{3}{4} = \frac{15}{N}$	$\frac{7}{N} = \frac{21}{15}$	$\frac{9}{8} = \frac{N}{24}$
$\frac{1}{8} = \frac{N}{32}$	$\frac{30}{N} = \frac{6}{4}$	$\frac{N}{7} = \frac{9}{3}$	$\frac{N}{8} = \frac{3}{4}$

4 **Solve.**

$3\frac{1}{4} + 2\frac{1}{3} =$	$11\frac{3}{7} + 7\frac{2}{5} =$	$4\frac{5}{6} - 3\frac{1}{2} =$
$88\frac{3}{5} - 21\frac{2}{5} =$	$37\frac{1}{5} + 10\frac{2}{10} =$	$15\frac{7}{12} - 10\frac{1}{24} =$

5 **Find the volume.**

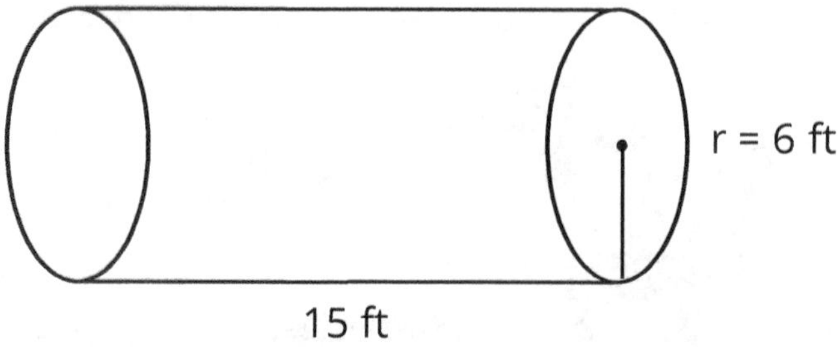

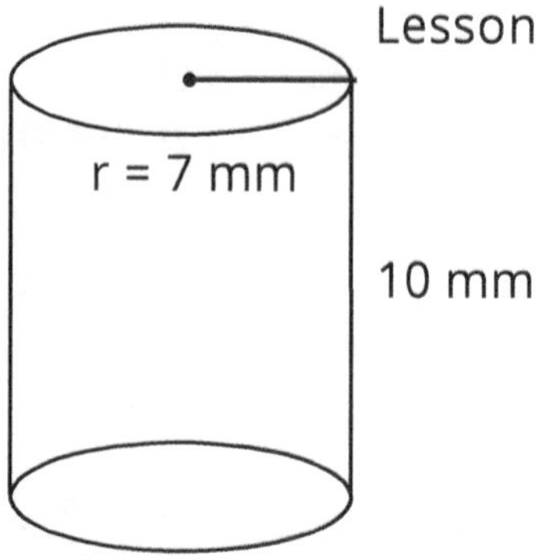

6 **Draw a double line graph, on the grid provided, to show the two sets of data shown below. Show the 2017 information with a pink line and the 2018 information with a green line. Complete the informational data which is not shown on the graph already (number of rooms and summer months).**

Number of rooms rented in 2017 during summer months at Round Ridge Mountain Inn

May	45
June	52
July	74
August	61

Number of rooms rented in 2018 during summer months at Round Ridge Mountain Inn

May	51
June	65
July	89
August	73

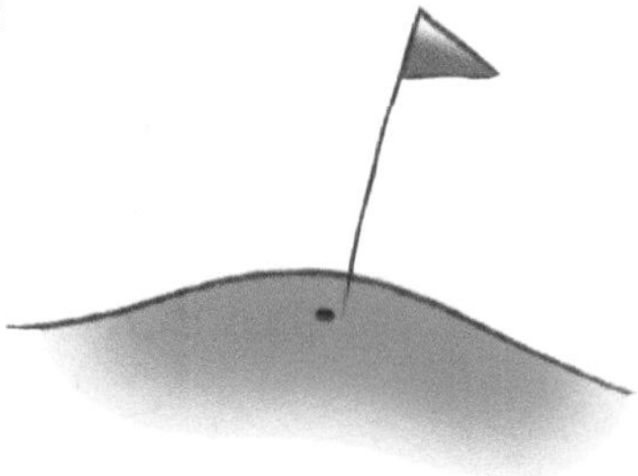

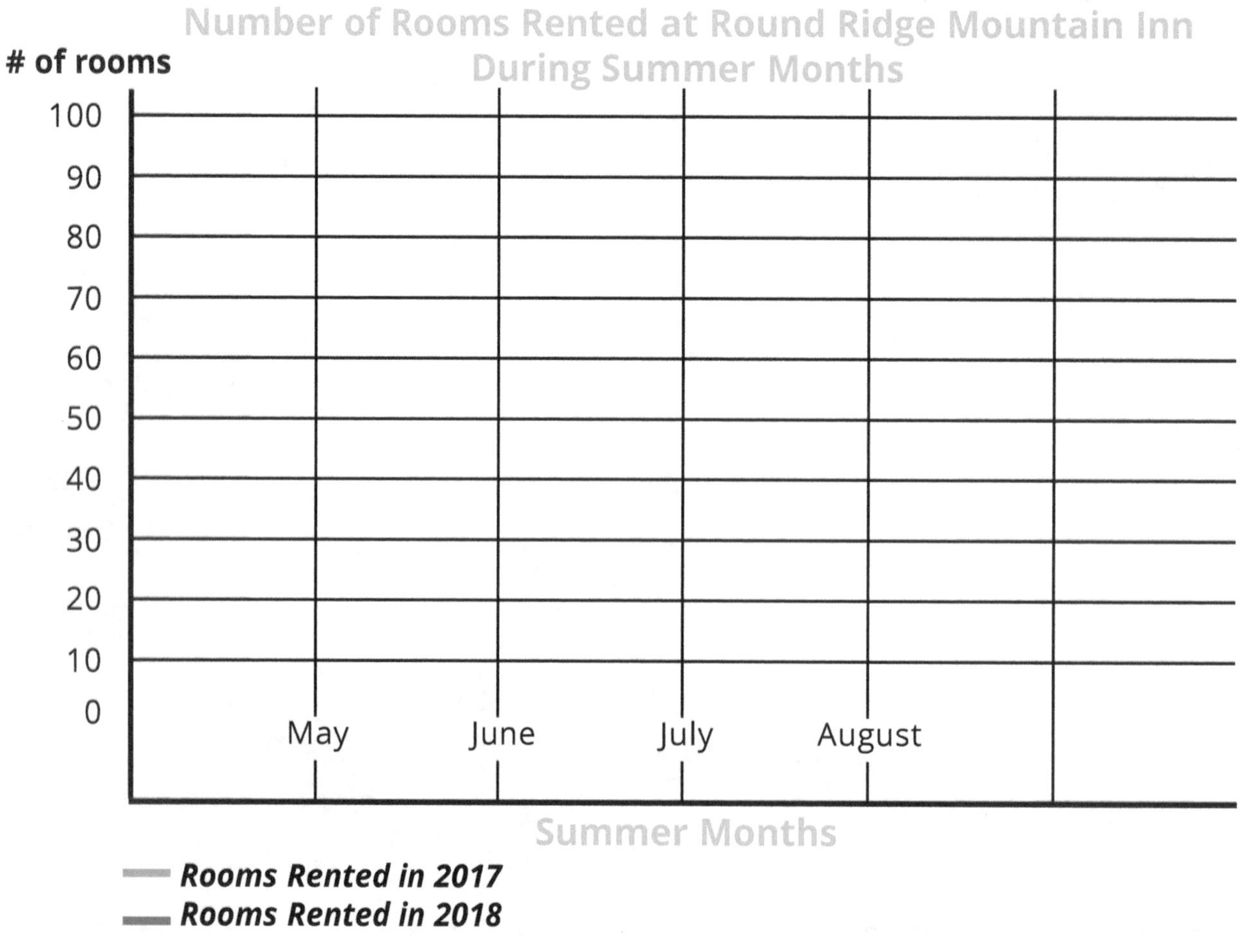

Using Division or Multiplication to find Ratio or Proportion

A factory produces 32 lawn tractors in 3 days. If the rate of production is constant, how many tractors can be produced in 12 days?

You can use division or multiplication to solve ratio or proportion word problems.

Step 1: Write the given ratio.

$$32 \text{ tractors to } 3 \text{ days} = \frac{32}{3}$$

Step 2: What is the new ratio?

$$\frac{32}{3} = \frac{N}{12}$$

Step 3: Find the missing value.

$$\frac{32}{3} = \frac{N}{12}$$

Think: $3 \times 4 = 12$, so $32 \times 4 = 128$

$$N = 128$$

Working at a constant speed, the factory can produce 128 tractors in 12 days.

(1) **Solve.**

A factory packs 1 semitrailer with 256 boxes of merchandise.
How many boxes of merchandise would be packed in 7 trailers?

The preschool bought 27 shirts for $850.00.
How many shirts could be purchased for $1,700.00?

Mr. Fowler bought 3 large cans of motor oil for $6.00.
How many cans can he purchase for $54.00?

The can factory produces 3,300 cans in 2 hours.
How long will it take to produce 26,400 cans?

The total weight of 4 toddlers is 112 pounds.
What is the average weight of one toddler?

2 **What are all the possible outcomes?** One card is drawn from each set.

A 1 A 2 A 3 ___

B 1 B 2 ___ ___

C 1 ___ ___ ___

___ ___ ___ ___

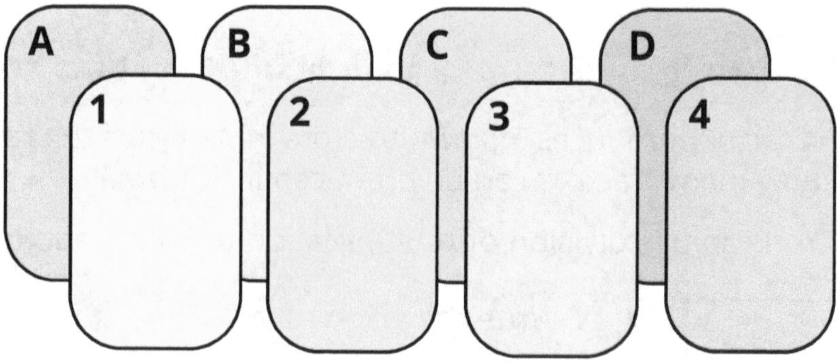

3 **Complete.**

Chet keeps batting statistics of each player on his softball team. Below is some of this data. Complete the chart to show each players batting ratio and percentage of hits. (Round averages to show the percentage answers as a whole number.)

Player	Hits	Times at Bat	Ratio	Hitting Percentage
Chet	23	26		
Brian	19	26		
Russell	21	25		
John	17	20		
Jeffrey	15	23		
Alan	18	22		
Mark	23	30		
Lynn	10	21		
Greg	9	15		
Jim	16	26		
Doug	8	17		

4 **Rename each mixed number.**

$5\,\frac{4}{3} = 6\,\frac{N}{3}$ $16\,\frac{3}{2} = 17\,\frac{N}{2}$ $101\,\frac{5}{4} = 102\,\frac{N}{4}$ $21\,\frac{6}{4} = 22\,\frac{N}{4}$

$125\,\frac{15}{10} = ?$ $9\,\frac{14}{11} = ?$ $8\,\frac{5}{3} = ?$ $320\,\frac{7}{6} = ?$

(5) **Solve.**

?35 + 258 = 793   6?9 + 379 = 998   279 + ?25 = 1,204

603 + ?48 = 1,051   ?4? + 247 = 896

(6) **Ratio and proportion can be used when drawing similar figures. Look at the triangles below. Figure 1 is similar to Figure 2 and Figure 3 is similar to Figure 4. Fill in the missing measurements. Some will require the use of ratio and proportion.**

Figure 1
Find the angle measurements of Figure 1

$\angle A = 32°$
$\angle B =$
$\angle C = 110°$

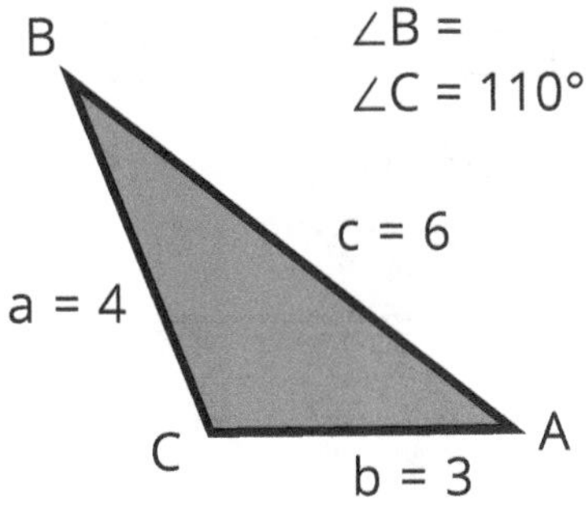

Figure 2
Label the proportional measurements for Figure 2

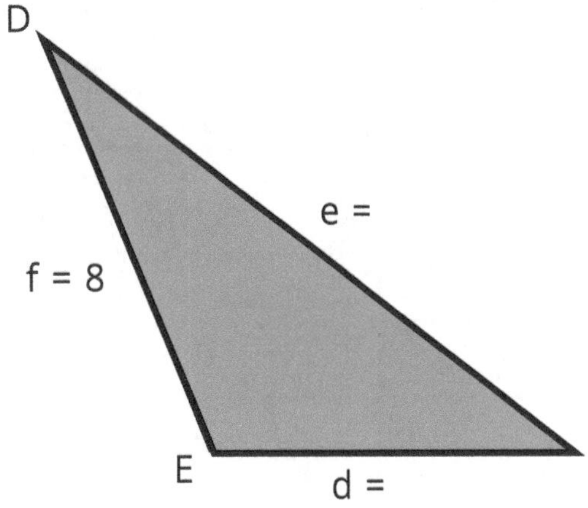

Figure 3
Find the proportional side measurement for Figure 3

x =
y =
z = 7

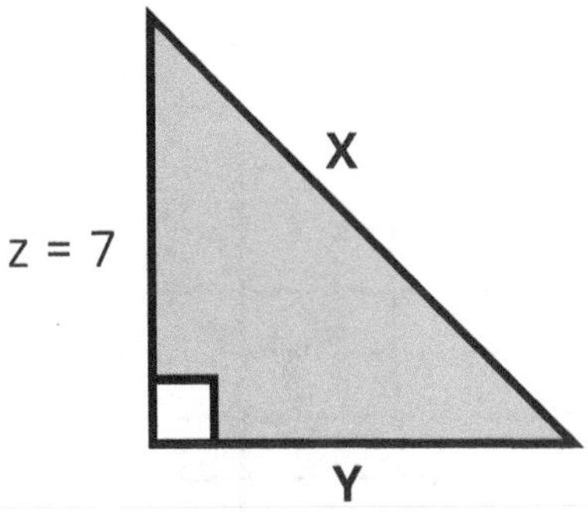

Figure 4
Find the angle measurements of Figure 4
Hint: Angles M & O have the same measurement.

$\angle M =$
$\angle N =$
$\angle O =$

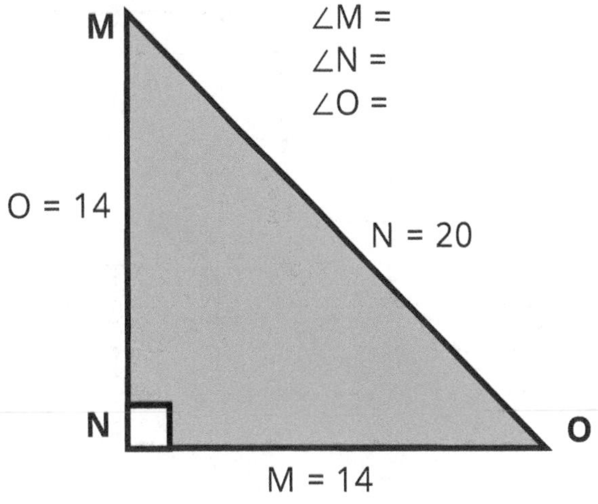

Patterns and Divisibility

Patterns can be found in many different mathematical concepts. Look at the number table below for an example. Several divisibility patterns are shown here.

All the columns that are shaded gray contain numbers that are divisible by 2. The numbers that are shaded yellow contain numbers that are divisible by 11.

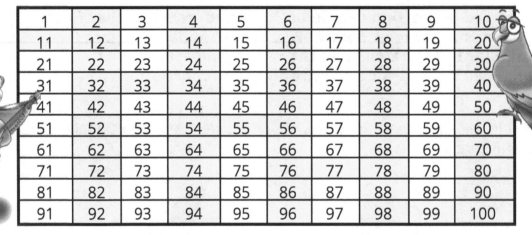

1	2	3	4	5	6	7	8	9	10
11	12	13	14	15	16	17	18	19	20
21	22	23	24	25	26	27	28	29	30
31	32	33	34	35	36	37	38	39	40
41	42	43	44	45	46	47	48	49	50
51	52	53	54	55	56	57	58	59	60
61	62	63	64	65	66	67	68	69	70
71	72	73	74	75	76	77	78	79	80
81	82	83	84	85	86	87	88	89	90
91	92	93	94	95	96	97	98	99	100

Look at the table below that show the decimal equivalents of fractions. Do you see a pattern? Many decimal equivalents and fraction equivalents have interesting patterns.

$\frac{1}{2}$ = 0.50	$\frac{2}{2}$ = 1.00	$\frac{3}{2}$ = 1.50	$\frac{4}{2}$ = 2.00	$\frac{5}{2}$ = 2.50	$\frac{6}{2}$ = 3.0
$\frac{1}{3}$ = 0.33	$\frac{2}{3}$ = .66	$\frac{3}{3}$ = 1.00	$\frac{4}{3}$ = 1.33	$\frac{5}{3}$ = 1.66	$\frac{6}{3}$ = 2.00
$\frac{1}{4}$ = 0.25	$\frac{2}{4}$ = .50	$\frac{3}{4}$ = .75	$\frac{4}{4}$ = 1.00	$\frac{5}{4}$ = 1.25	$\frac{6}{4}$ = 1.50
$\frac{1}{5}$ = 0.20	$\frac{2}{5}$ = .40	$\frac{3}{5}$ = .60	$\frac{4}{5}$ = .80	$\frac{5}{5}$ = 1.00	$\frac{6}{5}$ = 1.20

Look at the multiplication table shown below. Do you see a pattern in the shaded areas? Are there other patterns in the multiplication table that are not shown?

X	**1**	**2**	**3**	**4**	**5**	**6**	**7**	**8**	**9**	**10**
1	1	2	3	4	5	6	7	8	9	10
2	2	4	6	8	10	12	14	16	18	20
3	3	6	9	12	15	18	21	24	27	30
4	4	8	12	16	20	24	28	32	36	40
5	5	10	15	20	25	30	35	40	45	50
6	6	12	18	24	30	36	42	48	54	60
7	7	14	21	28	35	42	49	56	63	70
8	8	16	24	32	40	48	56	64	72	80
9	9	18	27	36	45	54	63	72	81	90
10	10	20	30	40	50	60	70	80	90	100

1 **Complete the chart to find a pattern.** The first one has been done for you.

$\frac{1}{10}$ = 0.1	$\frac{1}{100}$ =	$\frac{1}{1000}$ =	$\frac{1}{10000}$ =
$\frac{2}{10}$ =	$\frac{2}{100}$ =	$\frac{2}{1000}$ =	$\frac{2}{10000}$ =
$\frac{3}{10}$ =	$\frac{3}{100}$ =	$\frac{3}{1000}$ =	$\frac{3}{10000}$ =
$\frac{4}{10}$ =	$\frac{4}{100}$ =	$\frac{4}{1000}$ =	$\frac{4}{10000}$ =

2 **Solve.**

The ratio of mayonnaise to chicken in a salad recipe is 1 cup to 3 cups.
If 3 cups of mayonnaise are used, how many cups of chicken are needed?

The ratio of juice to soda in a punch recipe is 1 gallon to 2 liters.
If only 1 liter of soda is used, how much juice is needed?

To mix a certain shade of pink paint, a paint store mixes 2 parts of white with 3 parts of red. How many parts of red are needed for 8 parts of white?

$\frac{2}{3}$ of the local church participated in a visitation blitz into new neighborhoods.
What percentage of the church participated?

Kelly purchased 100 stamps. 37 of them were Christmas stamps.
What percentage were not Christmas stamps?

3 **Each spinner is spun once.**

blue, 1	blue, 3	blue, 5	____
____	____	____	____
____	____	____	____
____	____	____	____

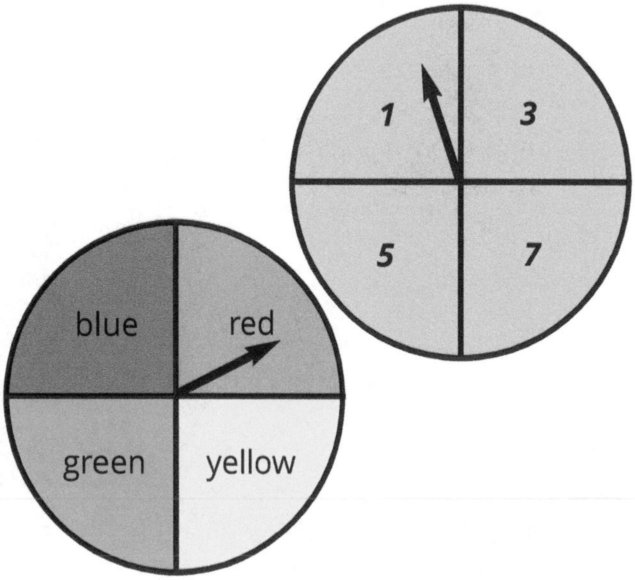

4 **Rename each mixed number.**

$10\frac{4}{3}$ = ____ $256\frac{11}{9}$ = ____ $45\frac{9}{5}$ = ____ $34\frac{12}{12}$ = ____

$2\frac{10}{8}$ = ____ $897\frac{4}{3}$ = ____ $9\frac{8}{7}$ = ____ $3\frac{11}{6}$ = ____

5 **Solve.**

5?,923 – 44,937 = 8,986 80,342 – ?,517 = 70,825 ?7,21? – 18,112 = 49,102

1,061 – ?9? = 865 52.81 – 2?.09 = 30.72 1?9,0?0 – 97,138 = 41,922

6 **Find the missing measurements.**

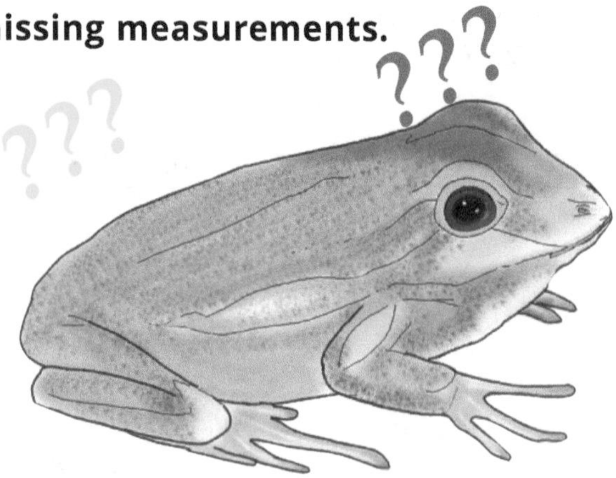

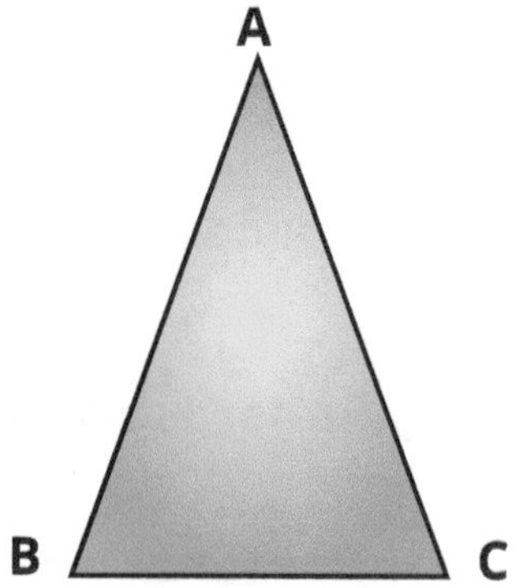

If angle A measures 30° and angles B and C are the same size, what are their measurements?

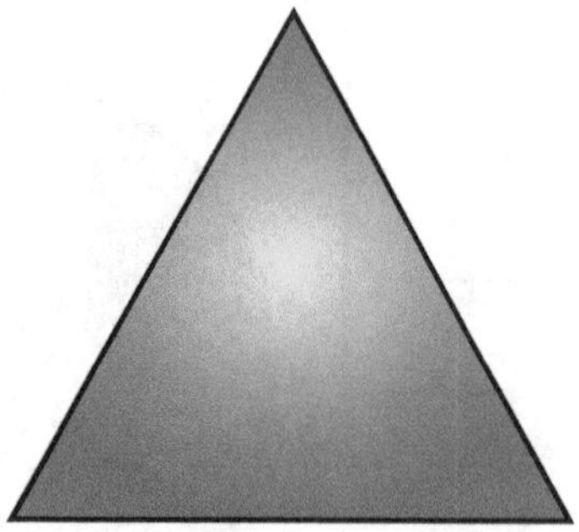

This is an equilateral triangle. What are the measurements of each angle? What do you know about the measurements of each side?

1. **Draw a regular hexagon using a compass and straightedge.** The side of the hexagon is 2 centimeters. 2 pts.

2. **Construct an equilateral triangle using a compass and straightedge.** Use Line UV as one side of the triangle. Label the triangle ΔTUV. 2 pts.

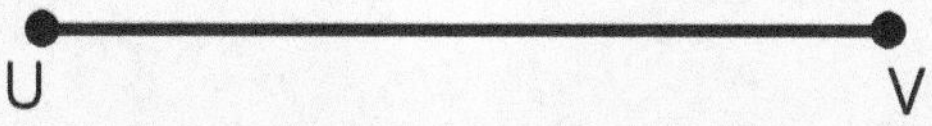

3. **Construct a right triangle using a compass and straightedge.** Use Line CD as one side of the triangle. Label the triangle ΔCDE. 2 pts.

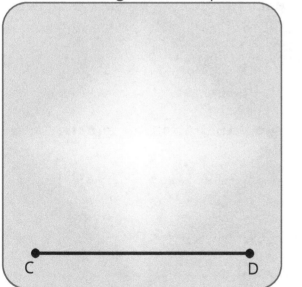

4. **Construct a square using Line JK as one side.** Label the square JKLM. 2 pts.

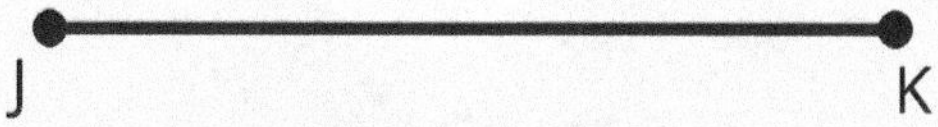

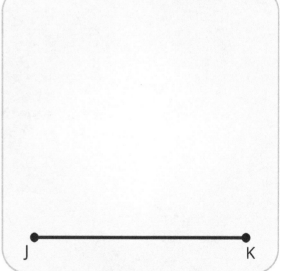

5. **Construct a parallelogram with the length of one side 6 cm and the length of the other side 3 cm.** The measure of the angle is 50°. The length of one side has been drawn for you. Label the parallelogram HIJK. 2 pts.

6 **Adam's dartboard scores are listed below. Write the ratios based on his scores.** 5 pts.

1. Number of Bullseyes to total throws
2. Number of 5s to total throws
3. Number of 5s to 15s
4. Number of 15s to 20s
5. Number of 20s to total throws

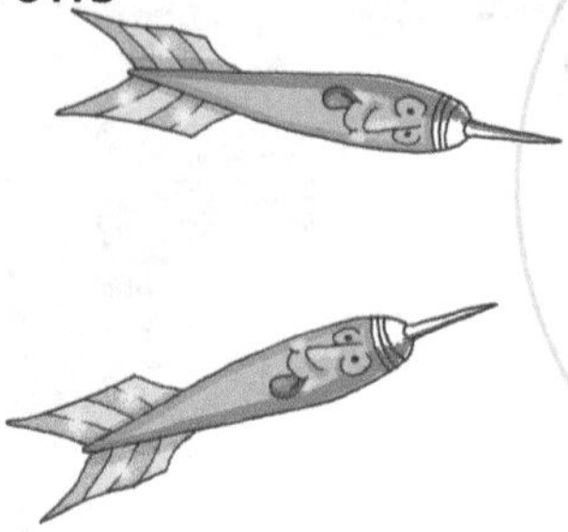

Throw #1	Bullseye
Throw #2	5
Throw #3	15
Throw #4	5
Throw #5	20
Throw #6	Bullseye
Throw #7	15
Throw #8	20

7 **Complete the table.** 4 pts.

Tablespoons of Sugar	6	9		15		
Tablespoons of Cinnamon	2	3	4		6	7

8 **Divide. Write two equal ratios for each.** 8 pts.

$\frac{40}{50} =$ $\frac{90}{450} =$ $\frac{240}{210} =$ $\frac{300}{900} =$

9 **Use the cross-products method to see if the ratios are equal. Circle the ratios that are equal.** 4 pts.

$\frac{7}{15}$	$\frac{28}{60}$	$\frac{6}{13}$	$\frac{12}{23}$	$\frac{18}{45}$	$\frac{55}{135}$	$\frac{8}{59}$	$\frac{32}{236}$

Use cross products to solve each equation. 4 pts.

$\frac{N}{7} = \frac{4}{14}$ $\frac{12}{15} = \frac{N}{20}$ $\frac{2}{9} = \frac{N}{81}$ $\frac{42}{N} = \frac{21}{25}$

Percentages

What is a percent? We have talked about percentages when we discussed ratios. Percentages come from ratios with a denominator of 100. The word percent comes from the Latin word "per centum" which means "for a hundred."
This means "per hundred" or "parts of a hundred." Remember from your previous lessons, that numbers over 100 can be written as both decimals and percents.

Look at the example below:

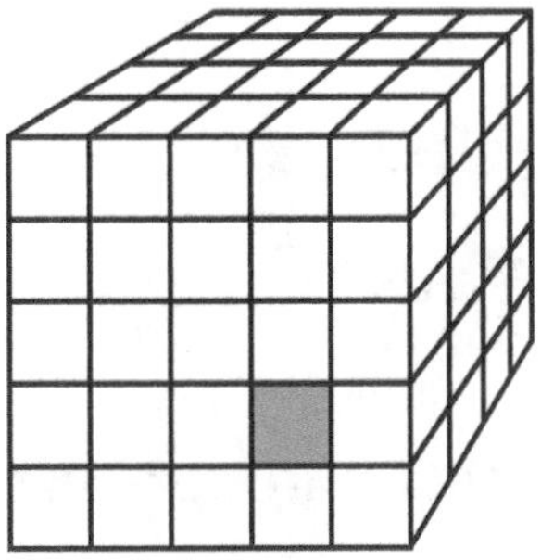

1 out of 100 boxes is shaded.

$\frac{1}{100} = 0.01 = 1\%$

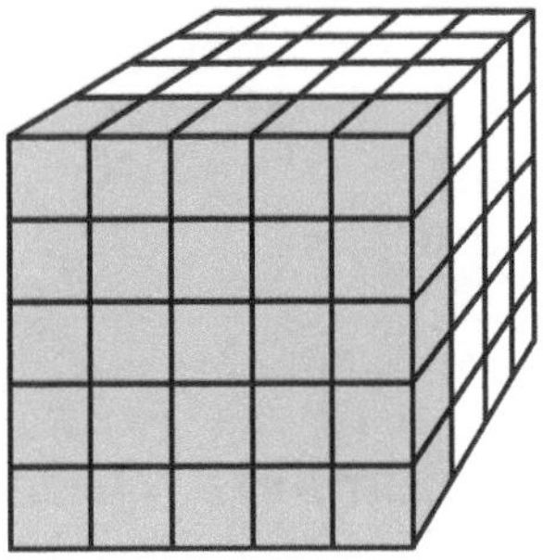

25 out of 100 boxes are shaded.

$\frac{25}{100} = 0.25 = 25\%$

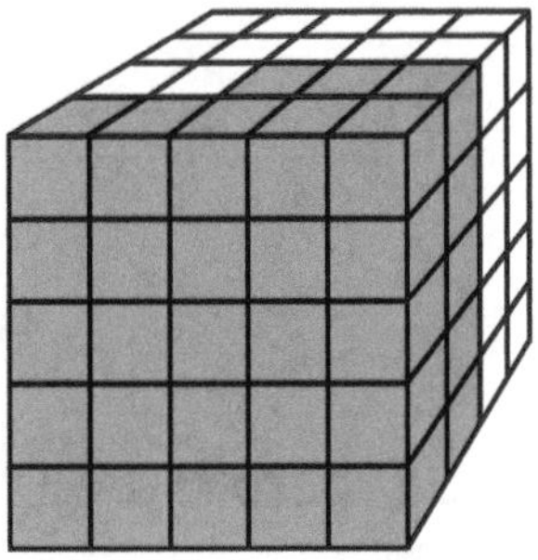

40 out of 100 boxes are shaded.

$\frac{40}{100} = 0.40 = 40\%$

Remember: any number over itself is equal to 1 whole. $\frac{100}{100} = 1$ whole or 100%.

If 100% of the boxes were shaded the whole figure would be shaded.

100% of the box is shaded.

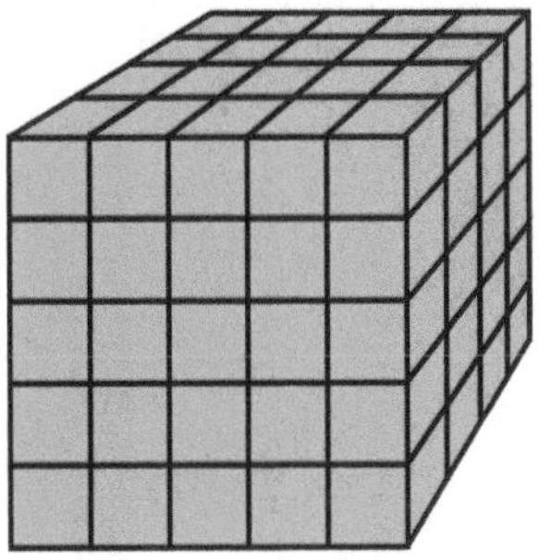

$\frac{1}{2}$ or 50% of the pie is eaten.

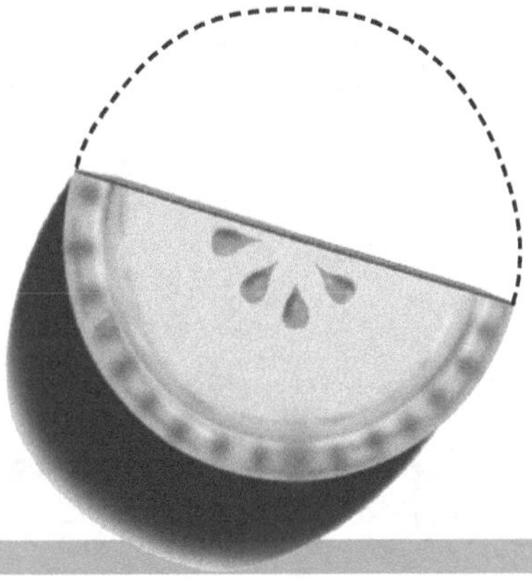

$\frac{1}{2} = \frac{50}{100} = 0.50 = 50\%$

1 **What percentage of the region is shaded?**

$\frac{1}{4} = \frac{N}{100}$

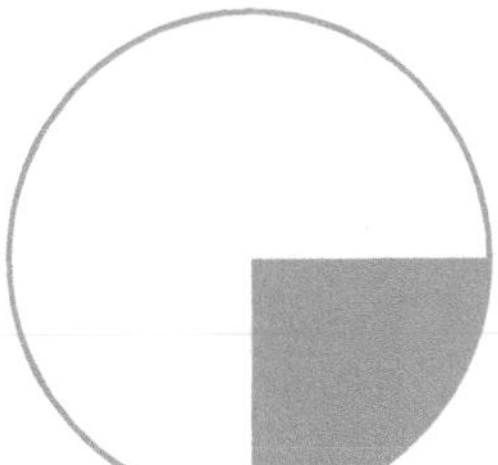

$\frac{2}{4} = \frac{1}{2} = \frac{N}{100}$

$\frac{3}{4} = \frac{N}{100}$

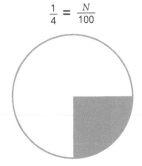

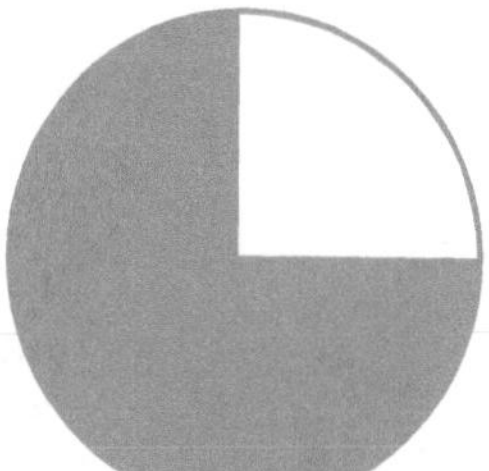

2 **Label the following quadrilaterals.**

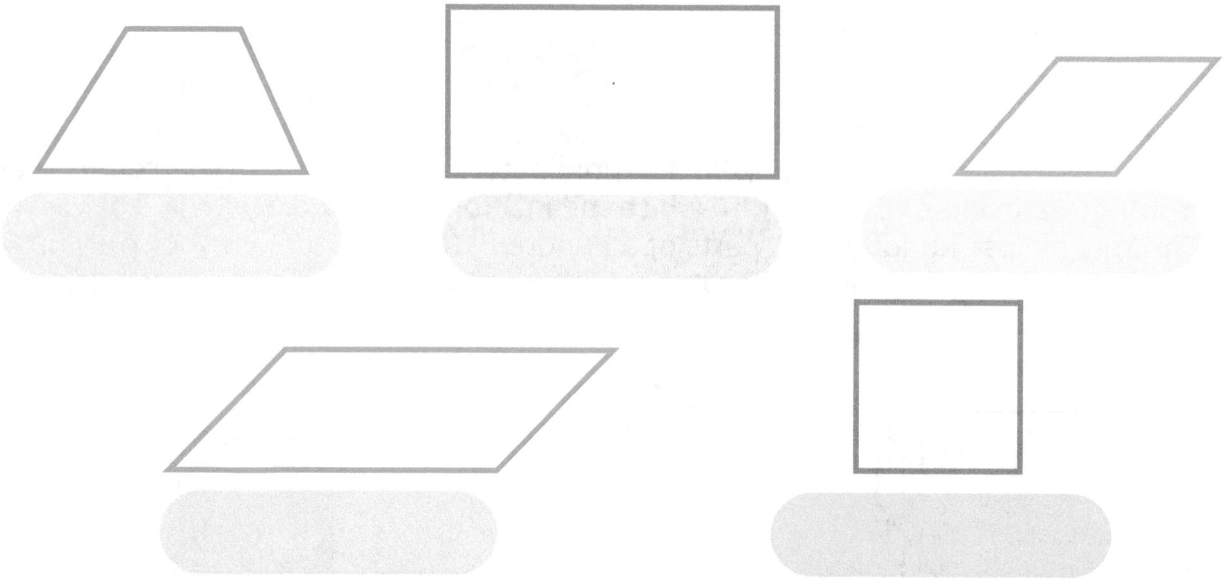

3 **Use a factor tree to find prime numbers. Write the missing numbers in the circles.**

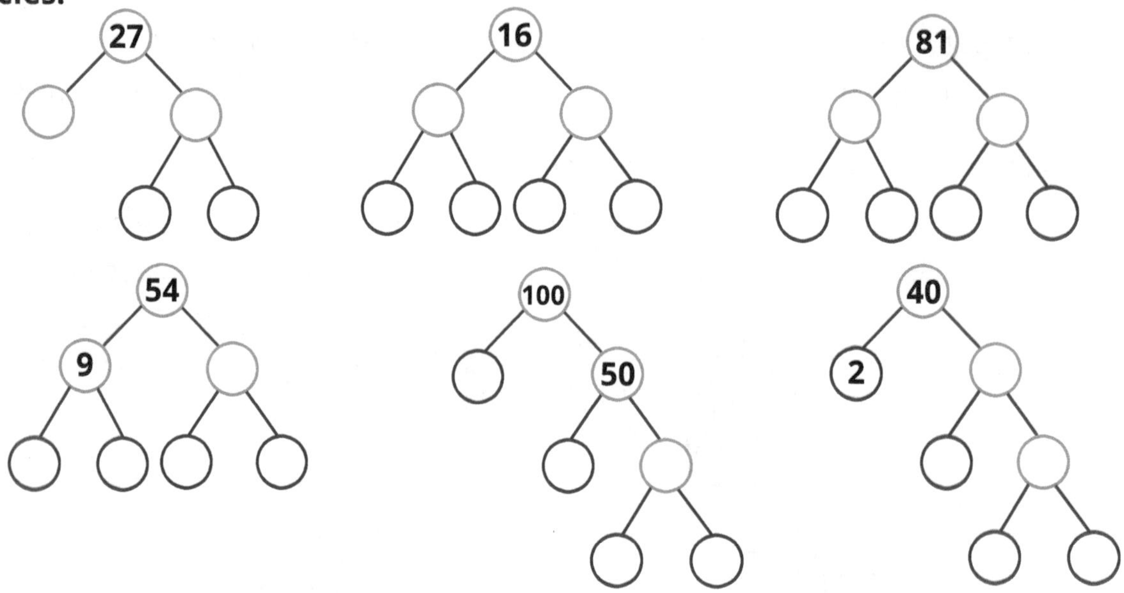

4 **Rewrite each problem vertically and solve.**

$3.7 \times 4 =$ $4.8 \times 8 =$ $11.12 \times 40 =$ $52.10 \times 30 =$

$1.33 \times 25 =$ $14.02 \times 12 =$ $1.27 \times 5 =$ $12.97 \times 6 =$

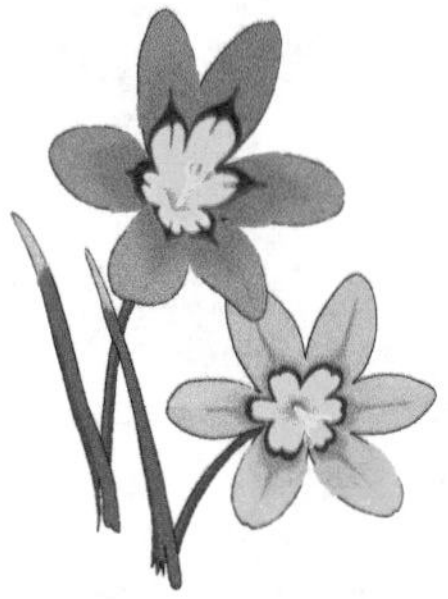

$0.86 \times 7 =$ $0.09 \times 9 =$

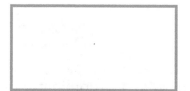

5 Multiply and reduce to lowest terms.

$\frac{1}{2} \times \frac{1}{8} =$	$\frac{2}{3} \times \frac{3}{8} =$	$\frac{12}{15} \times \frac{1}{3} =$	$\frac{1}{7} \times \frac{1}{3} =$
$\frac{2}{3} \times 4 =$	$\frac{7}{8} \times \frac{3}{9} =$	$\frac{1}{4} \times \frac{3}{2} =$	$\frac{2}{7} \times \frac{3}{1} =$

6 Use a compass to draw the specified circle.

Use a separate sheet of paper if necessary.

Diameter of 5 cm

Diameter of 4 inches

Radius of 3 cm

Radius of 1 inch

7 Use your protractor to measure the following angles.

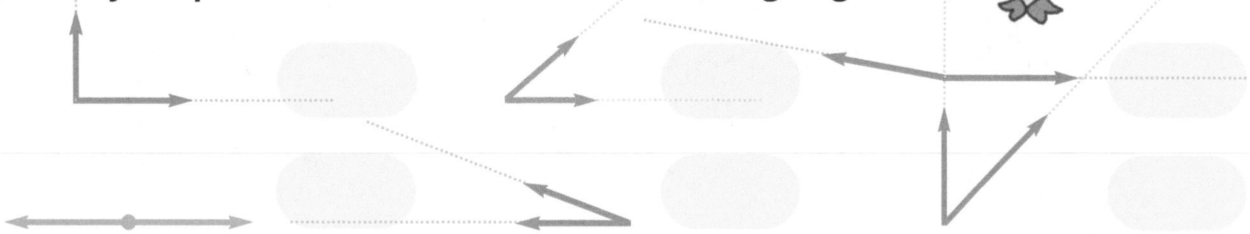

Problems with Percentages

Mr. Moyer's class surveyed 50 students on their favorite type of books. The results are shown below. How many students liked mystery books the best? To find 50% of 50, we convert the percent to a decimal and then multiply.

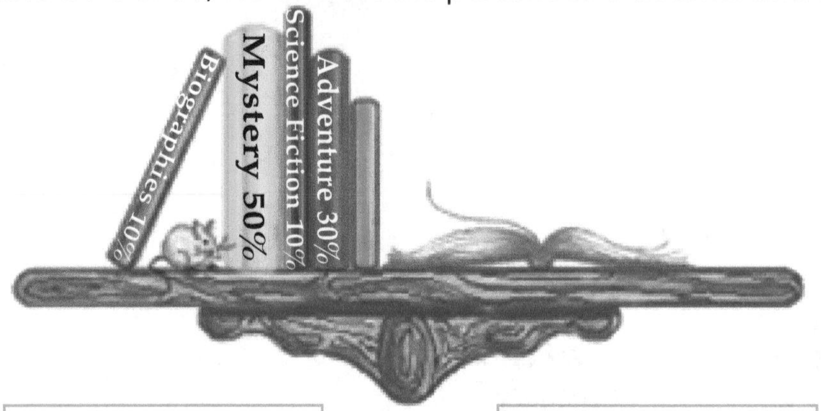

Step 1:
Convert the percent to a decimal.

50% = 0.50

Step 2:
Multiply.

$$\begin{array}{r} 50 \\ \times\ 0.50 \\ \hline 25.00 \end{array}$$

25 students liked mystery stories the best.

Another example: 30% of 50

$$\begin{array}{r} 50 \\ \times\ 0.30 \\ \hline 15.00 \end{array}$$

We find that 15 of the students chose Adventures as their favorite type of book.

How many students chose Science Fiction?

How many students chose Biographies?

The answer is 5 for both categories. 10% of 50 is 5.

(1) **Find the percent of each number.**

20% of 100	25% of 75	12% of 48	66% of 9
75% of 8	50% of 250	10% of 70	60% of 180

2 **Draw the indicated shapes.**

trapezoid rectangle rhombus

parallelogram square

3 **Identify the prime numbers to reveal a message.**

21	11	8	13	25	30	31	7	6	19	9	17	23
A	W	C	O	T	B	R	S	U	H	S	I	P

____ ____ ____ ____ ____ ____ ____

Psalms 95:6

4 **Find the missing number.**

1.09
× ?.7
2.943

?0.21
× 0.31
3.1651

1?.7
× 9.3
136.71

91.20
× 4?.1
3,930.72

5 **Multiply. Write the product in lowest terms.**

$2 \times 11 \frac{3}{7} =$ $10 \frac{1}{8} \times 5 \frac{3}{4} =$ $2 \frac{1}{2} \times 15 \frac{1}{6} =$

$1 \frac{5}{8} \times 1 \frac{1}{2} =$ $2 \frac{3}{4} \times 3 \frac{1}{5} =$ $4 \frac{2}{5} \times 3 \frac{1}{11} =$

6 **Use a protractor to measure each angle.**

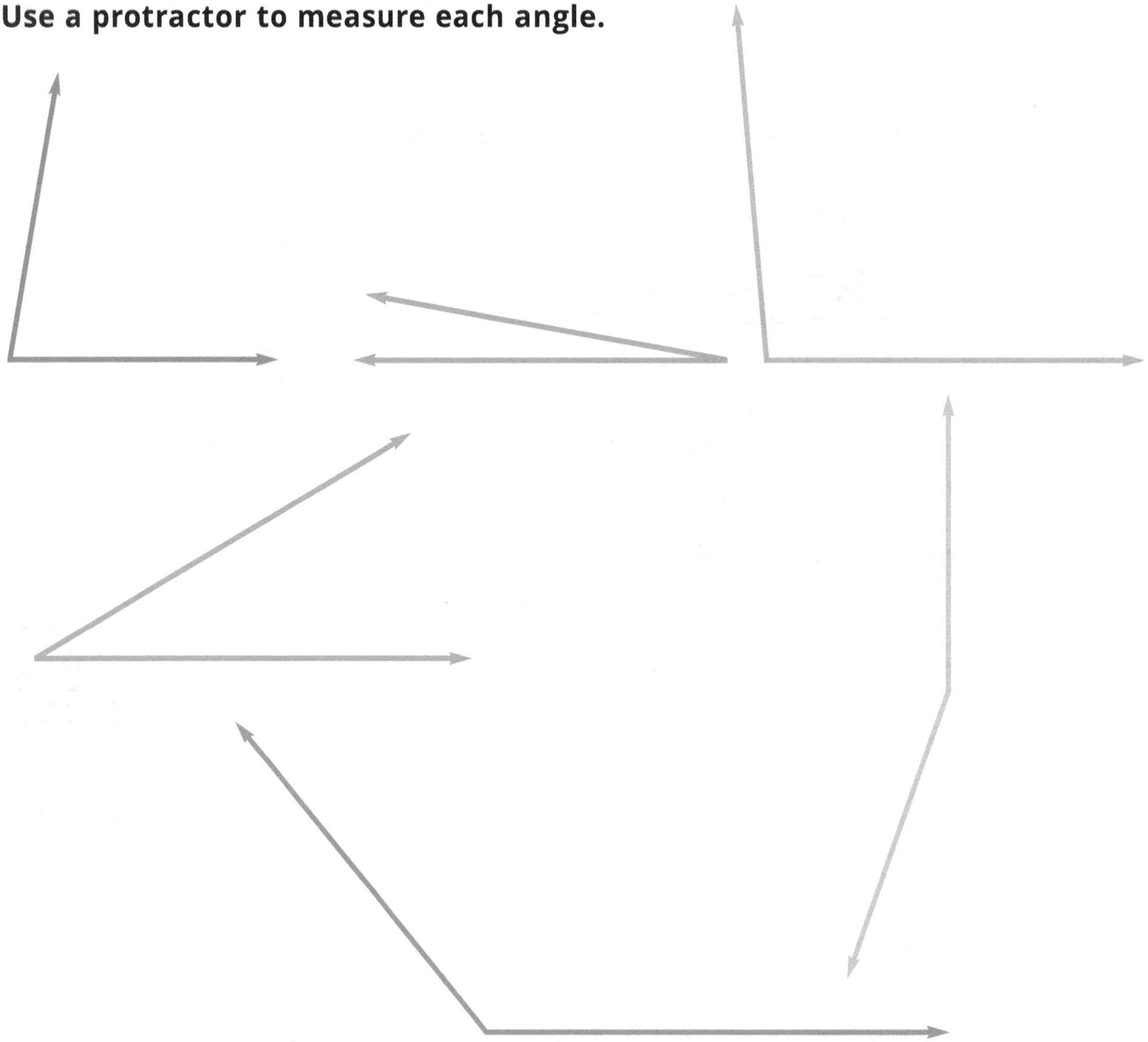

Problems with Percentages

Sarah conducted a survey as part of her Social Studies project. She asked people where they would go on a dream vacation. Below are the results of her survey.

Hawaii	23%
Australia	20%
France	16%
Italy	8%
England	15%
Switzerland	18%

Write each percent as a decimal.

Think of 23 as 23 per one hundred, or $\frac{23}{100}$. $\frac{23}{100}$ = twenty-three hundredths = 0.23

Look at these:

18% = $\frac{18}{100}$ = eighteen hundredths = 0.18

16% = $\frac{16}{100}$ = sixteen hundredths = 0.16

Can you complete the rest of the percentages shown in the box?
Look at the answers below and match the answer with the correct country.

0.20 → Australia
0.15 → England
0.08 → Italy

1 **Complete the table.**

Fraction	Decimal	Percent
$\frac{19}{100}$	0.19	19%
$\frac{75}{100}$		
	0.21	
		2%
$\frac{99}{100}$		
$\frac{9}{100}$	0.09	
$\frac{29}{100}$		
		54%
	1.00	

2 **Match the answer with the correct problem.**

____ $\frac{1}{3}$ of 180	A. 8
____ $\frac{1}{5}$ of 150	B. 6
____ $\frac{3}{4}$ of 360	C. 250
____ $\frac{2}{3}$ of 6	D. 60
____ $\frac{2}{7}$ of 21	E. 500
____ $\frac{1}{2}$ of 500	F. 30
____ $\frac{1}{4}$ of 2,000	G. 4
____ $\frac{1}{6}$ of 48	H. 270

3 **Calculate the measurement of the missing angle.**

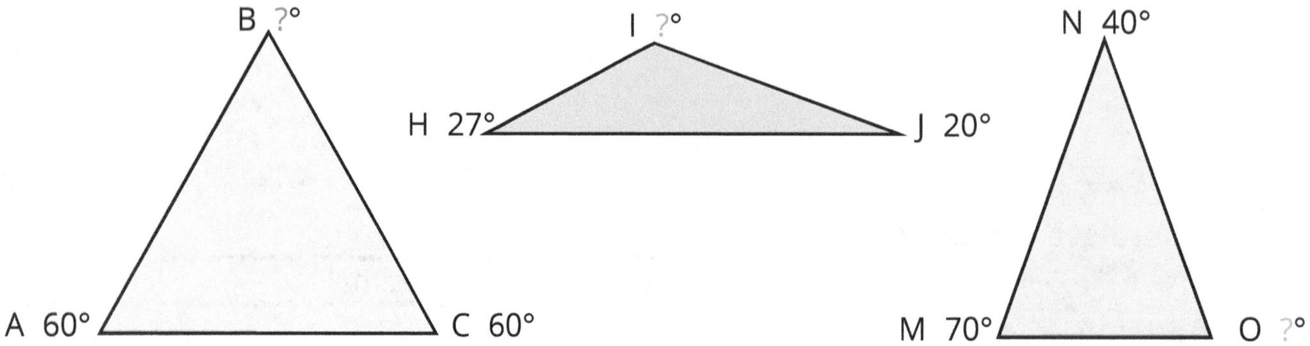

4 **Find the value of each number.**

$2^5 =$

$8^2 =$

$3^9 =$

$7^4 =$

$4^3 =$

$3^3 =$

5 **Find the product.**

$45.3 \times .78 =$

$1.3 \times 0.98 =$

$65.03 \times 3.9 =$

$127.3 \times 2.5 =$

6 **Use cross-simplification to reduce each fraction into lowest terms and multiply.**

$\frac{2}{5} \times \frac{1}{2}$

$\frac{5}{8} \times \frac{2}{3}$

$\frac{3}{4} \times \frac{5}{6}$

$\frac{2}{3} \times \frac{3}{4}$

$\frac{12}{20} \times \frac{2}{4}$

$3 \times \frac{3}{21}$

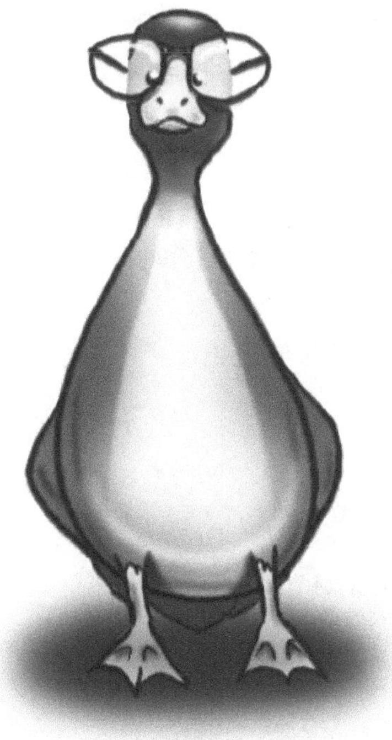

Fraction Equivalents

The students in Mrs. Hawkin's 4th grade class took a pop quiz. The scores of several students are shown below. What percent of the questions did Ellen get correct?

Student	Fraction	Equivalent 100th Fraction	Decimal	Percent
Randy	$\frac{20}{25}$	$\frac{80}{100}$	0.80	80%
Ellen	$\frac{21}{25}$	?	?	?
Tyler	$\frac{18}{25}$	$\frac{72}{100}$	0.72	72%
Sally	$\frac{25}{25}$	$\frac{100}{100}$	1.00	100%

We wrote the scores as fractions. There were 25 questions on the quiz. For this reason, 25 is the denominator. Ellen received 21 correct answers. 21 out of 25 answers were correct = $\frac{21}{25}$.

There are two different ways to convert Ellen's score to a percent. Look at both examples below.

Find an equivalent fraction with a denominator of 100.

$21 \times 4 = 84$

$\frac{21}{25} = \frac{84}{100}$

$25 \times 4 = 100$

$\frac{84}{100} = .84 = 84\%$

Find an equivalent decimal in hundredths.

$\frac{21}{25} = 25\overline{)21.00}$ = 0.84 or 84%

The numbers $\frac{84}{100}$ and 0.84 are both read eighty-four hundredths. Ellen received 84 hundredths. 84% of the answers were correct on her quiz.

Consider this example:

25% of Mrs. Wilson's class said that baseball was their favorite sport. What fraction on the class liked baseball the best?

Can you reverse the previously learned process to convert a percent to a fraction in lowest terms? $25\% = 0.25 = \frac{25}{100} = \frac{1}{4}$

$\frac{1}{4}$ of the class liked baseball the best.

Other examples:

$\frac{1}{10} = \frac{10}{100} = 0.10 = 10\%$ $\frac{1}{25} = \frac{4}{100} = 0.04 = 4\%$

$75\% = 0.75 = \frac{75}{100} = \frac{3}{4}$ $80\% = 0.80 = \frac{80}{100} = \frac{4}{5}$

1 **Write an equivalent fraction in lowest terms for each percent.**

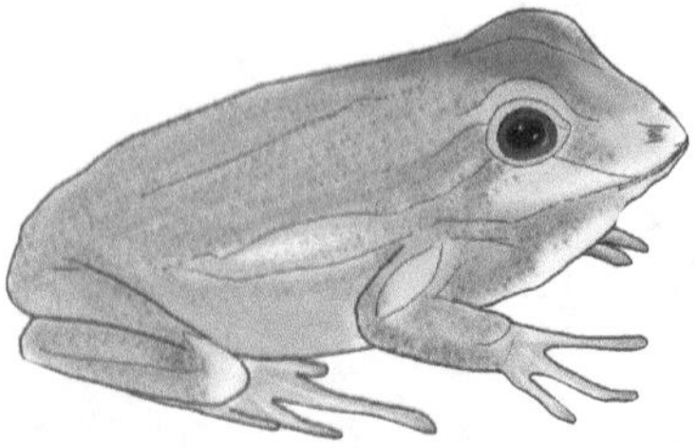

20% ________	70% ________	5% ________
60% ________	33% ________	95% ________
27% ________	45% ________	13% ________

(2) Write each decimal as a percent.

0.70	0.38	0.27	1.00	0.19	0.29
0.3	0.89	0.07	0.01	0.64	0.88

(3) The graph shows how Brett spends his allowance each week. Use the graph to answer the questions.

How much money does Brett tithe and give to charity each week?

How much money does Brett put into savings each week?

How much money does Brett have to spend on miscellaneous items each week?

Over a month's time (4 weeks), how much does Brett tithe?

Brett's Weekly Allowance $20.00

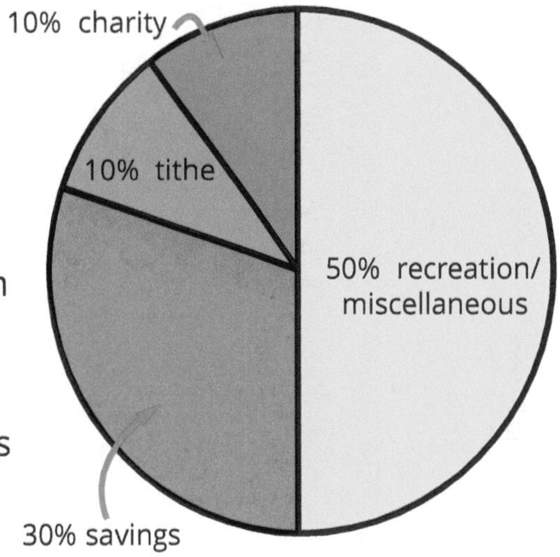

(4) Find the measure of the missing angles.

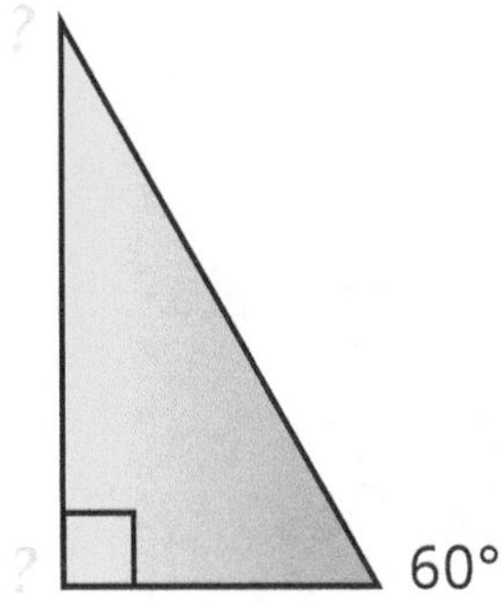

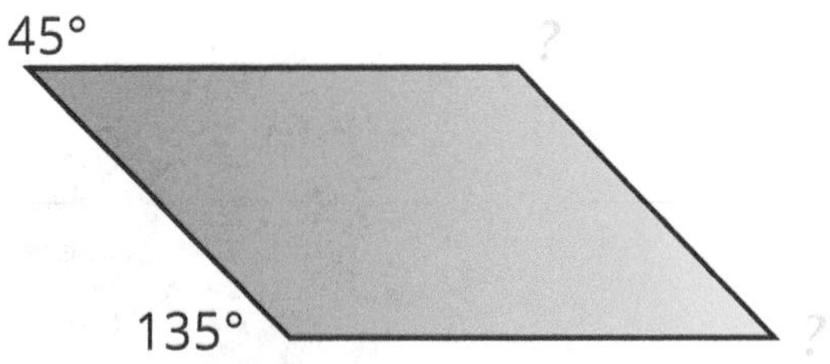

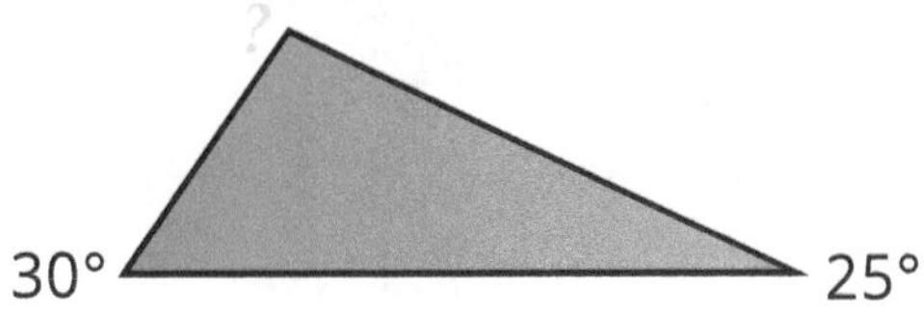

5 **Write each product in exponential form. The first one has been done for you.**

$10 \times 10 = 10^2$

$10 \times 10 \times 10 \times 10 \times 10 \times 10 =$

$7 \times 7 =$

$9 \times 9 \times 9 \times 9 =$

$5 \times 5 \times 5 \times 5 \times 5 =$

$144 =$

6 **Divide.**

$2 \div \frac{1}{3} =$ $7 \div \frac{1}{4} =$ $19 \div \frac{1}{2} =$ $12 \div \frac{1}{6} =$

$4 \div \frac{1}{2} =$ $3 \div \frac{1}{8} =$ $1 \div \frac{1}{4} =$ $4 \div \frac{1}{9} =$

Fractions, Decimals, and Percents

Throughout this book, you have been exposed to the relationship between fractions, decimals, and percents. The chart below shows some of the most commonly used fractional equivalents. Study them carefully and memorize them.

Fraction	Decimal	Percent
$\frac{1}{4}$	0.25	25%
$\frac{1}{2}$	0.50	50%
$\frac{3}{4}$	0.75	75%
$\frac{1}{3}$	0.33	33%
1	1.00	100%

1 **Complete the chart.**

Fraction (in lowest terms)	Decimal	Percent
		42%
$\frac{7}{100}$		
	0.02	
$\frac{59}{100}$		
		62%
		78%
	0.90	
$\frac{1}{20}$		
		4%

2 **Look at each series of numbers. Find the pattern and the next two numbers.**

43% 45% 47% 49% ______ ______

Pattern: ______________________________

0.15 0.19 0.23 0.27 ______ ______

Pattern: ______________________________

0.11 11% 0.22 22% 0.33 33% ______ ______

Pattern: ______________________________

100% $\frac{9}{10}$ 80% $\frac{7}{10}$ 60% ______ ______

Pattern: ______________________________

0 50% $\frac{1}{4}$ 75% $\frac{1}{2}$ 100% ______ ______

Pattern: ______________________________

3 **Fill in the appropriate dollar amount for each section of the graph.**

Christopher's Monthly Budget $2,000

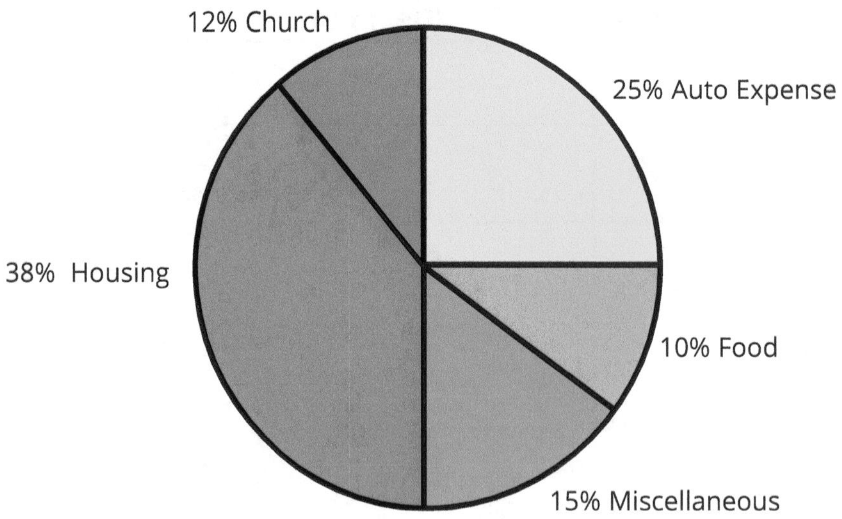

4 **Match the square root to the appropriate number and reveal a message.**

625 8,100 121 144 225 100

____ ____ ____ ____ ____ ____

Proverbs 14:12

Data Bank:

10	12	15	11	25	90
M	D	O	S	W	I

5 **Divide. Then use the quotient as the dividend in the next problem.**
Hint: All will divide evenly to 4 decimal places or less.

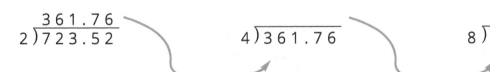

$2\overline{)723.52}$ = 361.76 → $4\overline{)361.76}$ → $8\overline{)}$

$2\overline{)971.796}$ = 485.898 → $6\overline{)485.898}$ → $2\overline{)}$

6 **Solve.**

$\frac{1}{2} \div \frac{1}{4} =$

$\frac{1}{2} \div \frac{1}{8} =$

$\frac{2}{3} \div \frac{1}{3} =$

$3 \div \frac{1}{3} =$

$4 \div \frac{1}{2} =$

$\frac{1}{4} \div \frac{1}{8} =$

$2 \div \frac{1}{4} =$

$\frac{1}{2} \div \frac{1}{6} =$

Calculating Tax

Connie purchased a pair of jeans through a mail order catalog. When filling out her order form she needed to pay a 1% order fee for packing materials.
If her order totaled $35.98, how much will she need to add for this 1% fee?

When calculating a percentage tax, you simply follow the steps listed in **Lesson 132** on finding a percent of a number.

What is 1% of $35.98?

Change the percent to a decimal and then multiply.

0.01 × $35.98 = 0.3598 = $0.36 (round to the nearest hundredth)

$0.36 is 1% of $35.98 so, Connie will need to add $0.36 to her order.

(1) **Find 1%. (Round to the nearest hundredth.)**

$5,687.25	$6,779.00	$342.25	$10,926.00
7,821	45,665	132,450	34

(2) **Complete the chart.**

Fraction (in lowest terms)	Decimal	Percent
		22%
$\frac{7}{10}$		
	0.20	
$\frac{17}{25}$		
$\frac{2}{6}$		
$\frac{51}{100}$		

(3) **Complete the pattern.**

2% .07 $\frac{3}{25}$ 17% ______ ______

Pattern: ____________________________________

$\frac{20}{30}$ $\frac{8}{15}$ $\frac{2}{5}$ ______ ______

Pattern: ____________________________________

25% 10% 15% ______ ______

Pattern: ____________________________________

0.58 70% 0.67 69% 0.81 78% ______ ______

Pattern: ____________________________________

(4) **Write each number in expanded form using exponents.**

6,875 =

7,218,443 =

5,203,456,798,002 =

1,009,247 =

5 **Complete the pattern.**

$2 \times 10^2 = 200$	____ $= 4$	____ $= 9$
$3 \times 10^3 =$ ____	____ $= 16$	____ $= 36$
$4 \times 10^4 =$ ____	____ $= 36$	____ $= 81$
$5 \times 10^5 =$ ____	____ $= 64$	____ $= 144$

6 **Divide.**

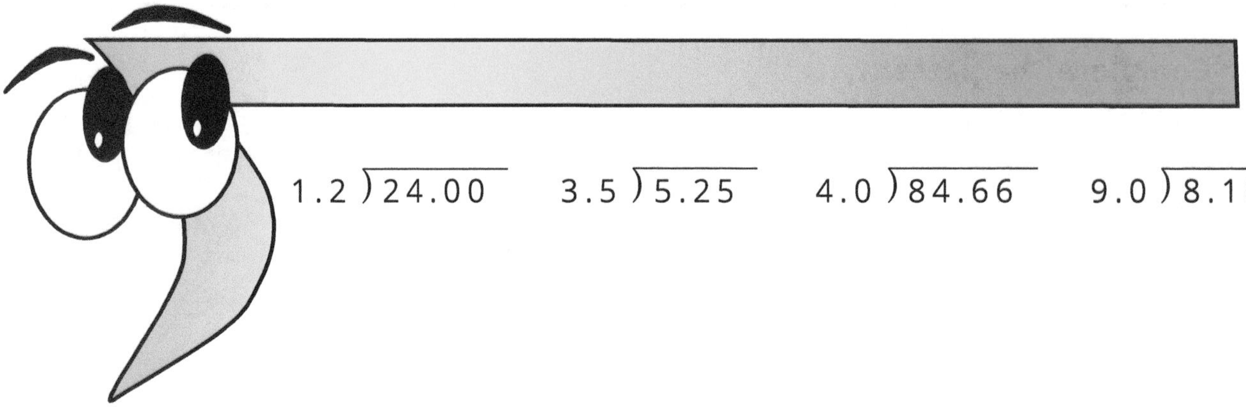

$1.2\overline{)24.00}$ $3.5\overline{)5.25}$ $4.0\overline{)84.66}$ $9.0\overline{)8.100}$

Calculating Percentages

Tom just started a new job and received his very first paycheck.
His gross earnings (earnings before taxes) was $1,947.25.
If Tom chooses to tithe 10%, how much money will he give to the church?

When calculating a percentage, you simply follow the same steps necessary to find a percent of a number.

What is 10% of $1,947.25?

Change the percent to a decimal and then multiply.

$0.10 \times \$1947.25 = 194.725 = \$194.73$ (round to the nearest hundredth)

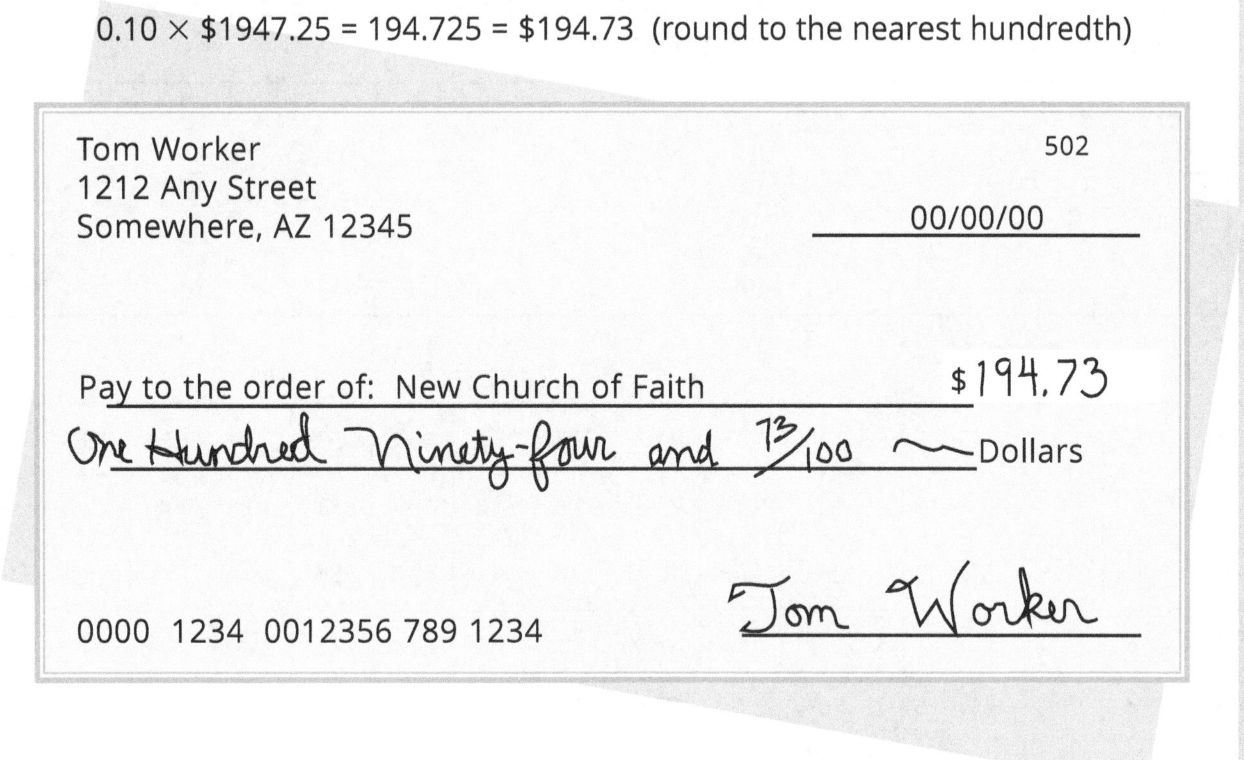
Tom Worker
1212 Any Street
Somewhere, AZ 12345
502
00/00/00
Pay to the order of: New Church of Faith
$194.73
One Hundred Ninety-four and 73/100 Dollars
0000 1234 0012356 789 1234
Tom Worker

$194.73 is 10% of $1947.25 so, Tom's tithe check will be $194.73.

1 **Find 10% of each number.**

100	120	75	160	400	1,298
87,250	613	87	256	8,972	15,207

2 **Match the equivalent numbers.**

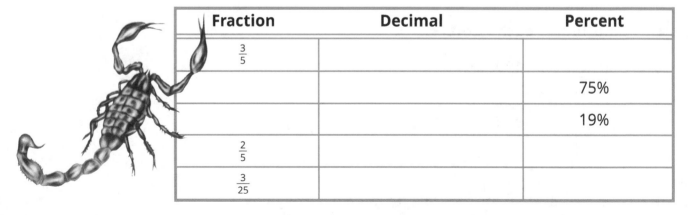

0.03973	3.973×10^{12}
3,973,000,000	3.973×10^{4}
3,973,000,000,000	3.973×10^{-2}
0.003973	3.973×10^{8}
39,730	3.973×10^{-3}
397,300,000	3.973×10^{9}

3 **Shade the percents that are equal to the fractions in the data box. The shaded areas will reveal a message.**

Data Bank:

$\frac{2}{5}$ $\frac{89}{100}$ $\frac{1}{5}$ $\frac{17}{100}$ $\frac{1}{10}$ $\frac{29}{100}$ $\frac{1}{100}$ $\frac{41}{100}$ $\frac{1}{2}$

$\frac{7}{10}$ $\frac{19}{50}$ $\frac{16}{25}$ $\frac{99}{100}$ $\frac{1}{4}$ $\frac{6}{100}$ $\frac{1}{20}$ $\frac{3}{100}$ $\frac{19}{100}$

70%	38%	2%	98%	64%	11%	13%	99%	62%	25%	6%	5%	2%	3%	13%	19%
40%	33%	62%	20%	34%	10%	27%	70%	51%	23%	10%	88%	16%	40%	23%	29%
1%	89%	77%	5%	17%	25%	47%	40%	49%	44%	38%	55%	15%	10%	25%	89%
29%	27%	13%	3%	23%	6%	52%	1%	77%	9%	20%	11%	98%	29%	39%	3%
10%	2%	11%	41%	55%	50%	33%	17%	2%	73%	64%	33%	76%	1%	9%	5%

4 **Fill in the chart.**

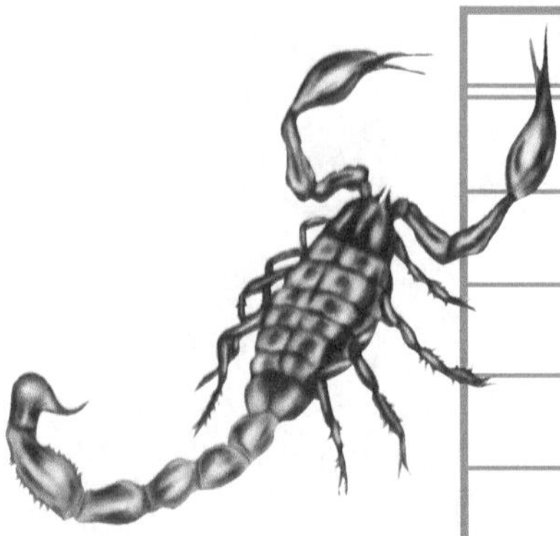

Fraction	Decimal	Percent
$\frac{3}{5}$		
		75%
		19%
$\frac{2}{5}$		
$\frac{3}{25}$		

(5) **Find 1% of the number shown.**

45,893	987,123,450	14,978	23,780
______	______	______	______
37,100	457	891	74,206
______	______	______	______

(6) **Write each of the following Roman Numerals as a standard number.**

XXVI **VIII** **DLV** **MCMXLVI** **XXXI**

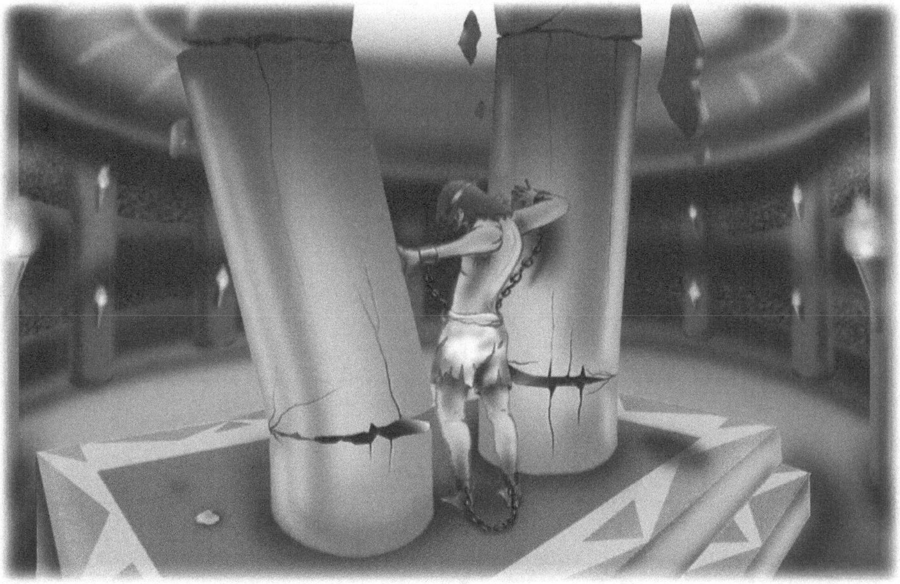

Calculating Sales Tax

Chet purchased a new pick up truck. The sale price of the truck was $21,998.00. Chet also had to pay 6% for sales tax. How much was the total truck price, including tax?

Each time something is purchased, you must pay sales tax. This tax will always be a percentage of your total sale.

When calculating sales tax, you simply follow the same steps necessary to find a percent of a number.

What is 6% of $21,998.00?

Change the percent to a decimal and then multiply.

$0.06 \times \$21,998.00 = \$1,319.88$

Sales tax on Chet's new truck will be $1,319.88.

$\$21,998.00 + \$1,319.88 = \$23,317.88$,

so, the total price of Chet's new truck will be $23,317.88.

1 **Calculate the sales tax and shipping on each order.**
Use the shipping chart to calculate the appropriate charge.

Shipping/Handling Charges:

Amount of Purchase	S/H	Amount of Purchase	S/H
$ 0 - $25	$2.95	$151 - $300	$5.95
$26 - $75	$3.95	$301 - $500	$6.95
$76 - $150	$4.95	$500 - $1,000	$8.95

Order #1

Item	Quantity	Price each
Jeans	1	$45.00 ea
Sweater	1	$50.00 ea
Blouse	1	$25.00 ea
Total		
6% sales tax		
Shipping		
Grand Total		

Order #2

Item	Quantity	Price each
Comforter Set	1	$295.00 ea
Sheet set	1	$40.00 ea
Pillows	4	$20.00 ea
Total		
12% sales tax		
Shipping		
Grand Total		

Order #3

Item	Quantity	Price each
Stationary	3 boxes	$7.50 ea
Pens	2 boxes	$12.50 ea
Stapler	1	$5.75 ea
File Folders	5 boxes	$9.75 ea
Total		
11% sales tax		
Shipping		
Grand Total		

Order #4

Item	Quantity	Price each
T-shirts	4	$15.00 ea
Total		
5% sales tax		
Shipping		
Grand Total		

2 **Find the correct percentage calculation.**
Circle the correct answer to reveal a message.

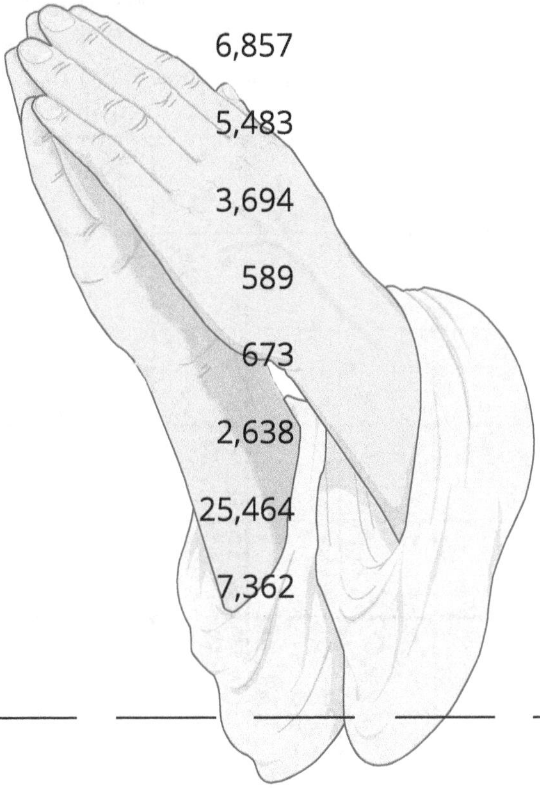

10%		Number		1%
6.857	M	6,857	F	68.57
548.30	O	5,483	E	5.483
369.40	U	3,694	R	3.694
589.00	A	589	N	5.89
67.3	T	673	M	0.673
2.638	S	2,638	A	26.38
25.464	L	25,464	I	254.64
736.20	N	7,362	Y	7.362

_____ _____ _____ _____ _____ _____ _____ _____

John 4:14

3 **Write each decimal as a fraction (in lowest terms) and a percent.**

Decimal	Percent	Reduced Fraction
0.5		
0.75		
0.99		
0.7		
0.63		
0.34		
0.01		
0.04		
0.6		
0.12		
0.85		

4 **Complete the crossword puzzle by writing the names of the number shown. There is a separate box for the decimal point.**

Across

1. Five and one thousandth
3. Four thousandths
5. Five and nine hundred twenty-two thousandths

Down

2. Two and three hundredths
4. Twenty-five and four tenths
6. Seven hundred twenty-one and eight tenths

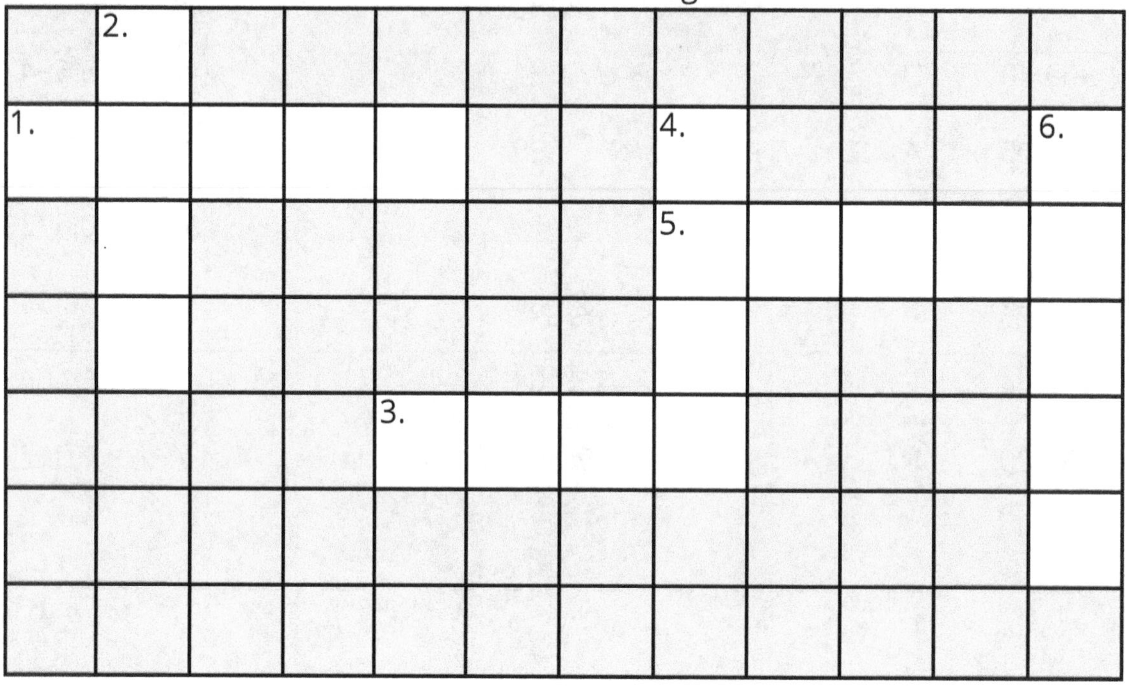

5 **Complete the table.**

Standard Form	Scientific Notation
	10×10^4
	6.88×10^{12}
33,000,000	
	7.1×10^{-7}
	10×10^3
236,000,000	
	6.521×10^{12}
0.000093	

6 **Write each fraction as a decimal. (Round to the nearest tenth.)**

$\frac{16}{25}$ ______ ______

$\frac{7}{16}$ ______ ______

$\frac{2}{10}$ ______ ______

$\frac{31}{100}$ ______ ______

$\frac{5}{8}$ ______ ______

$\frac{9}{20}$ ______ ______

Calculating Percentage Discounts

Mrs. Smith went to the pre-Thanksgiving sale at Sargent's Department Store. Everything in the kitchen department was marked 30% off. Mrs. Smith decided to purchase a bread machine. The regular price was $398.99. How much did Mrs. Smith save with the 30% discount? How much will the bread machine cost her?

When calculating a percentage discount, you simply follow the same steps necessary for finding a percent of a number.

What is 30% of $398.99?

Change the percent to a decimal and then multiply.

$$0.30 \times \$398.99 = 119.697 = \$119.70$$

$119.70 is 30% of $398.99 so, Mrs. Smith will save $119.70 on the bread machine.

$398.99 – $119.70 = $279.29 so, Mrs. Smith will spend $279.29 on the bread machine.

(1) Find the indicated percentage discount.

Item	Regular Price	Percentage Discount	Discounted Dollar Amount	New Sale Price
Car	$25,986.00	20%		
Washing Machine	$469.95	15%		
Computer	$1,239.50	5%		
Book	$20.00	50%		
Lawn Mower	$595.00	10%		
Jacket	$197.35	30%		

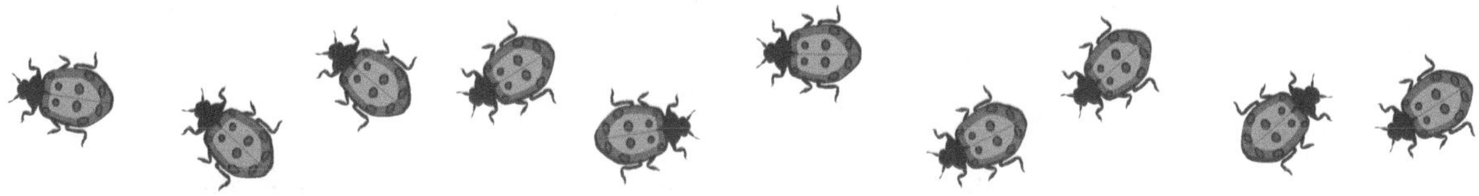

2 **Calculate the 7% tax on each order. (Round to the nearest penny.)**

$567.98	$12.50	$41.32	$101.90	$76.75	$23.00
________	________	________	________	________	________

3 **Fill in the chart by finding 10% and 1% of each number.**

Number	10%	1%
7,400		
1,930		
850		
14,510		
12,600		
121		
352		

4 **Complete the Binary Place Value Chart.**

Binary Place Value Chart								**Base 10 Equivalent**
(64) **2^6**	(32) **2^5**	(16) **2^4**	(8) **2^3**	(4) **2^2**	(2) **2^1**	(1) **2^0**		
		1	1	0	0	0	=	
							=	11
	1	0	0	1	1	1	=	
							=	7
1	1	1	1	1	1	1	=	
							=	47

5 **Divide and simplify.**

$\frac{3}{7} \div 3 =$	$\frac{1}{4} \div 5 =$	$\frac{2}{5} \div 7 =$	$\frac{1}{8} \div 6 =$
$\frac{4}{6} \div 2 =$	$\frac{9}{5} \div 3 =$	$\frac{10}{5} \div 4 =$	$\frac{5}{2} \div 2 =$

6 **Order these numbers from the smallest to the largest.**

76,564 O	76,465 W	78,564 H	79,456 I
78,465 S	79,546 P	76,654 R	

_______ _______ _______ _______ _______ _______ _______

_______ _______ _______ _______ _______ _______ _______

Problem Solving using an Organized List

The local yogurt store offers three flavors of yogurt each day. Today's flavors are chocolate mint, vanilla, and strawberry cheesecake. They have three different toppings you can get on your yogurt: M & M's, trail mix, or chocolate shavings. How many different one scoop yogurt cups can be made?

A helpful strategy to solve this problem is called **making an organized list**. Write all the possible answers for a chocolate mint cup. Then, write all the combinations with a vanilla cup. Finally, write all the possibilities with a strawberry cheesecake cup.

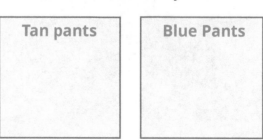

Chocolate Mint - M&M's
Chocolate Mint - Trail Mix
Chocolate Mint - Chocolate Shavings

Vanilla - M&M's
Vanilla - Trail Mix
Vanilla - Chocolate Shavings

Strawberry Cheesecake - M&M's
Strawberry Cheesecake - Trail Mix
Strawberry Cheesecake - Chocolate Shavings

There are 9 possible flavor-topping combinations.

(1) **Solve.**

Carson Home Builders builds four basic houses: a ranch, a cape cod, a traditional two-story, and a split foyer. All four houses may be either brick, vinyl sided, cedar, or stucco. What are the different house combinations which can be built?

Ranch	Cape Cod	Traditional Two-story	Split Foyer

Brett must wear school uniforms to school. He can wear tan or blue pants and either yellow, white, or blue shirts. How many different clothing combinations can he make?

Tan pants	Blue Pants

2 **Write these base 10 numerals in base 2.** Use the place value chart, if needed.

10 = ____________

18 = ____________

12 = ____________

15 = ____________

23 = ____________

3 **Complete the addition block by adding the rows and columns to find the sums.**

23,451	2,110	
5,803	34,512	

4 **Divide. Write each answer in lowest terms.**

$2\frac{2}{5} \div 1\frac{3}{4} =$ $2\frac{3}{4} \div 4\frac{1}{2} =$ $3\frac{1}{9} \div 2\frac{1}{3} =$ $3\frac{3}{4} \div 4\frac{2}{7} =$

$4\frac{1}{2} \div \frac{3}{8} =$ $8\frac{3}{4} \div \frac{1}{3} =$ $3\frac{5}{6} \div 2\frac{2}{3} =$ $5\frac{1}{2} \div 3\frac{1}{8} =$

5 **Find the discount and sales tax on each order.**

Customer Name: *John*

Book bag	$16.00
Picture frame	$25.00
Bag of Pretzels	$1.25
Sub-total	
15% discount	
Total	
6% sales tax	
Grand Total	

Customer Name: *Jack*

Cereal	$3.29
Milk	$2.59
Cheese	$3.78
Sub-total	
25% discount	
Total	
10% sales tax	
Grand Total	

Customer Name: *Monica*

Book	$25.00
Chair	$225.00
Desk	$698.00
Computer	$1,300.00
Sub-total	
10% discount	
Total	
8% Sales tax	
Grand Total	

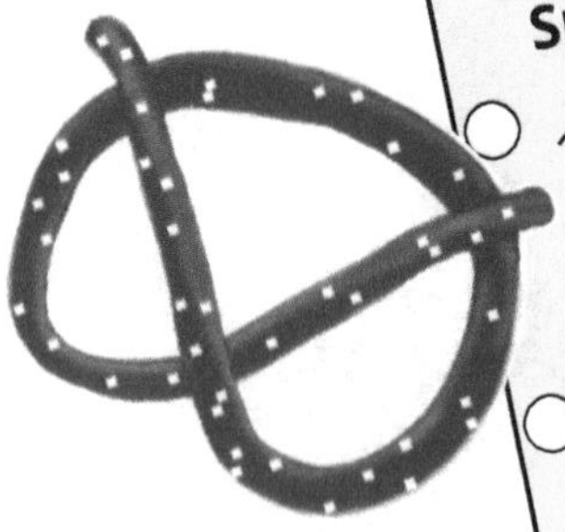

6 **Find 10% of each number shown.**

327,902	6,493	4,372	19,101	6,791	2,222
______	______	______	______	______	______

1 **Write each ratio as a percent.** 4 pts.

$\frac{6}{10}$ = ________% $\frac{19}{20}$ = ________% $\frac{4}{25}$ = ________% $\frac{4}{5}$ = ________%

2 **Figure the probability of the draws.** 6 pts.

Amy has ten cards. They are pictured below. If she shuffles the cards and puts them face down, what is the probability she will draw:

1. a star ________   2. a blue card ________   3. a red card ________

4. a flower ________   5. a red key ________   6. a cross ________

3 **Solve.** 2 pts.

A factory packs 12 golf balls in every box. If they have 1,020 golf balls, how many boxes will they need?

The Italian restaurant bought 57 bags of mozzarella cheese for $276.45. How much cheese could be purchased for $708.10?

4 **Complete the pattern.** 10 pts.

Fraction	Decimal	Scientific Notation
$\frac{1}{10}$	0.1	1×10^{-1}
$\frac{1}{100}$		
	0.001	
$\frac{1}{10{,}000}$		
		1×10^{-5}
	0.000001	

5 **Write each fraction as a percent.** 6 pts.

$\frac{1}{10}$ ________

$\frac{4}{20}$ ________

$\frac{1}{3}$ ________

$\frac{1}{4}$ ________

$\frac{8}{100}$ ________

$\frac{4}{10}$ ________

6 **Find the percent of each number.** 4 pts.

80% of 100 ________ 25% of 200 ________ 5% of 140 ________ 10% of 250 ________

7 **Complete the table.** 11 pts.

Fraction	Decimal	Percent
$\frac{88}{100}$	0.88	88%
$\frac{55}{100}$		
	0.07	
		29%
$\frac{89}{100}$		
$\frac{33}{100}$	0.33	
$\frac{79}{100}$		

8 **Write an equivalent fraction in lowest terms for each percent.** 6 pts.

50% ________ 90% ________ 4% ________

20% ________ 16% ________ 98% ________

9 **Complete the chart.** 18 pts.

Fraction (in lowest terms)	Decimal	Percent
		12%
$\frac{2}{25}$		
	0.06	
$\frac{89}{100}$		
		5%
		88%
	0.2	
$\frac{8}{10}$		
		24%

Integers

An integer is a positive whole number, negative whole number, or zero.

Integers can be shown as points on a number line.

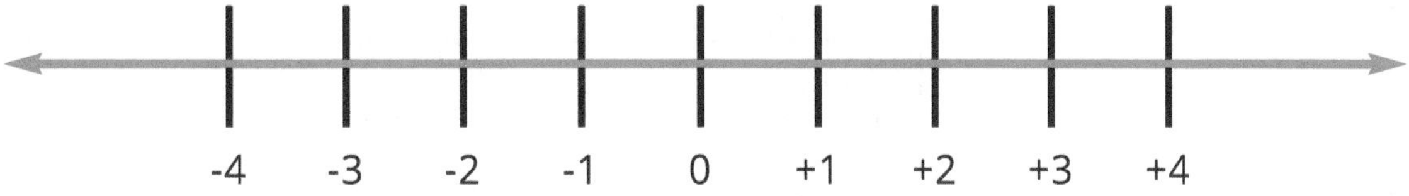

The integers less than 0, -4, -3, -2, and -1, are negative integers.

The integers greater than 0, +4, +3, +2, and +1, are positive integers.

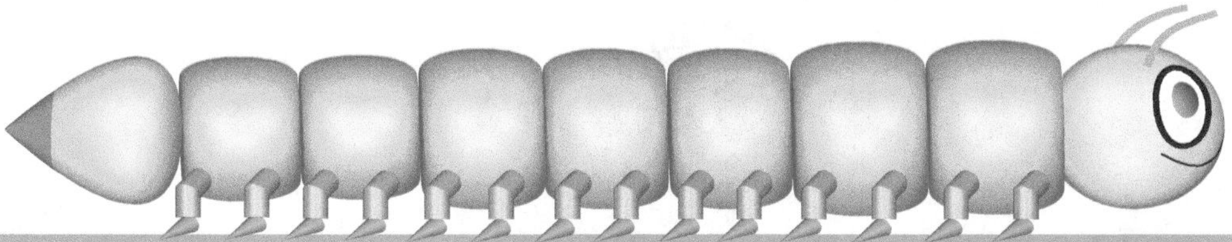

1 **Write positive or negative for each example.** The first one has been done for you.

1. 20 degrees below zero ________ -20° ________
2. stock up 9 points ____________________
3. 30 feet below sea level ____________________
4. 25 degrees above zero ____________________
5. 4 yard gain ____________________
6. 6 yard loss ____________________
7. gained 15 pounds ____________________
8. lost 8 pounds ____________________

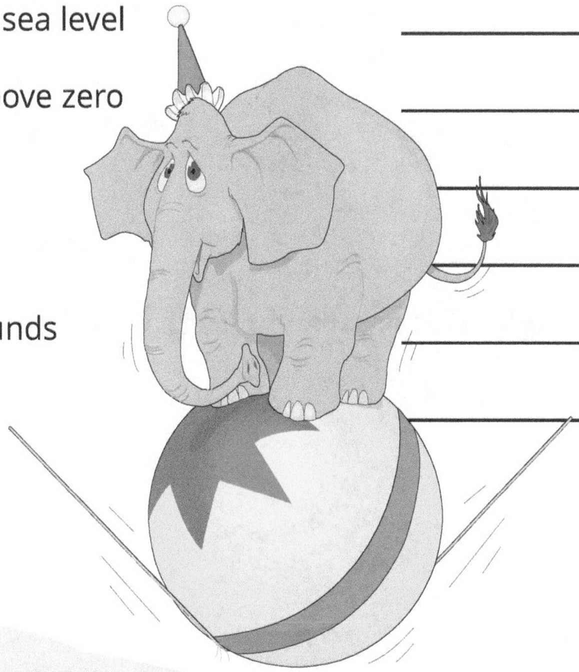

2 **Complete the table.** The first one has been done for you.

Fraction	Decimal	Percent
$\frac{75}{100}$	0.75	75%
$\frac{99}{100}$		
	0.05	
		30%
		50%
	0.16	
$\frac{88}{100}$		
		25%

3 **Place parentheses in the problem to make each statement true.**

2 × 2.39 + 9.09 − 1.88 = 11.99

14.9 + 2.7 + 3.1 × 8.2 = 43.02

56.2 ÷ 2 + 9 = 37.1

3 × 8 + 13 − 33 = 30

4 **Draw a rectangle with a perimeter of 20 cm and an area of 24 cm².**

Draw another rectangle with an area of 24 cm² with different dimensions.

5 **Use a protractor to measure the angles in the circle.**

∠BXE + ∠EXC + ∠CXD + ∠DXA + ∠AXB = 360°

_____ + _____ + _____ + _____ + _____ = 360°

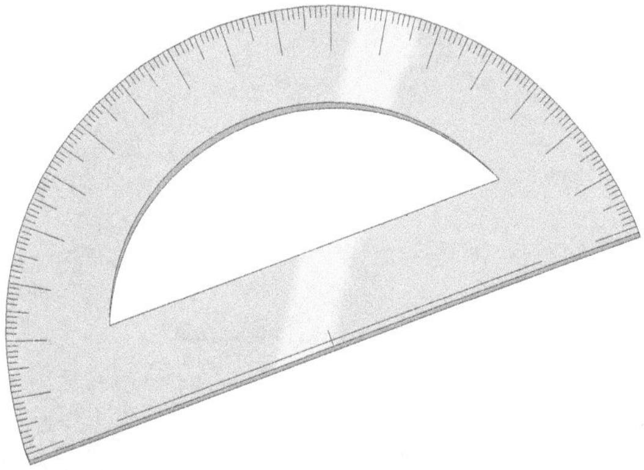

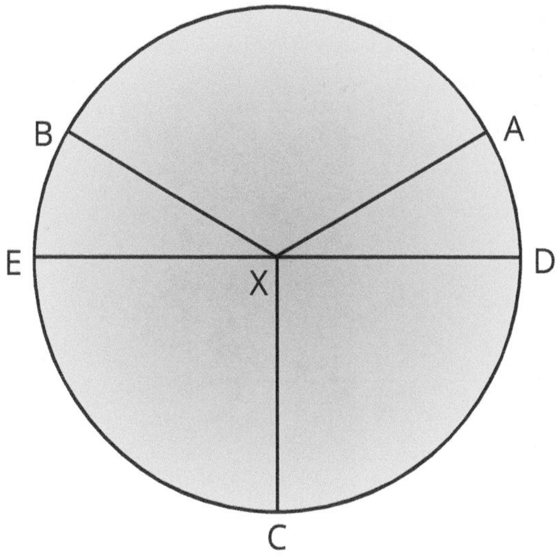

6 **Write the missing number.**

$\frac{1}{6} = \frac{7}{\square}$ $\frac{3}{4} = \frac{15}{\square}$ $\frac{11}{12} = \frac{44}{\square}$ $\frac{4}{7} = \frac{12}{\square}$

$\frac{2}{3} = \frac{\square}{12}$ $\frac{3}{4} = \frac{\square}{28}$ $\frac{9}{10} = \frac{\square}{40}$ $\frac{5}{9} = \frac{\square}{63}$

7 **Plot the points on the coordinate graph. Connect the points in the order given.**

(4, 5)	(4, 11)
(3, 4)	(4, 5)
(2, 3)	(4, 3)
(3, 2)	(5, 3)
(4, 1)	(6, 3)
(5, 1)	(6, 5)
(6, 1)	(6, 11)
(7, 2)	(4, 11)
(8, 3)	**STOP**
(7, 4)	
(6, 5)	
STOP	

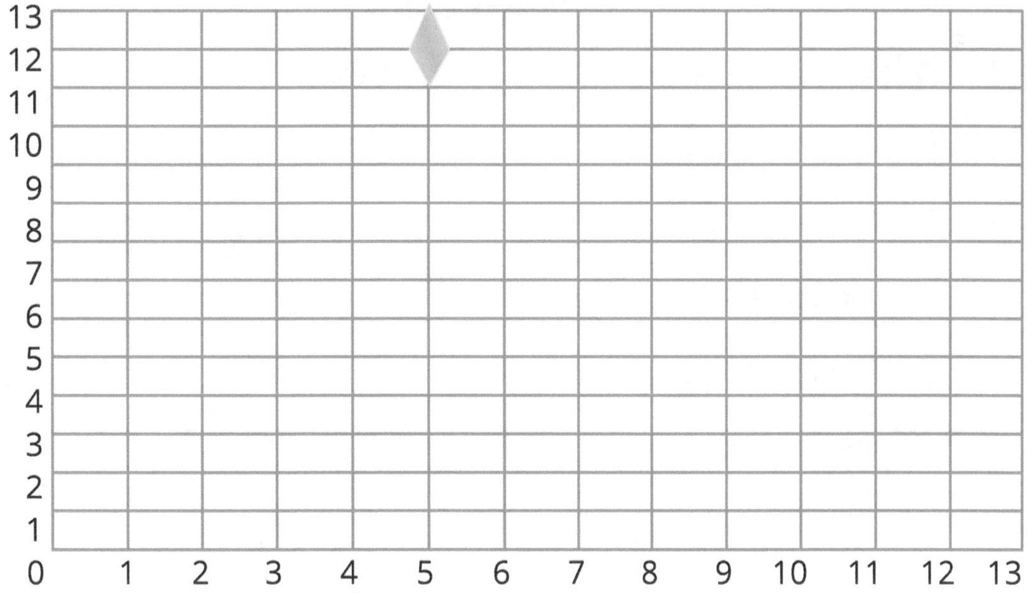

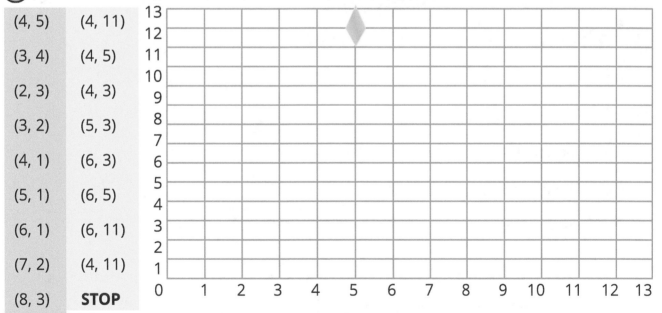

"You are the light of the world." Matthew 5:14a

Opposites

Integers are opposites if they are the same distance from zero in opposite directions.

For instance:

-2 and +2 are opposites,
-9 and +9 are opposites,
-37 and +37 are opposites,
Zero is its own opposite.

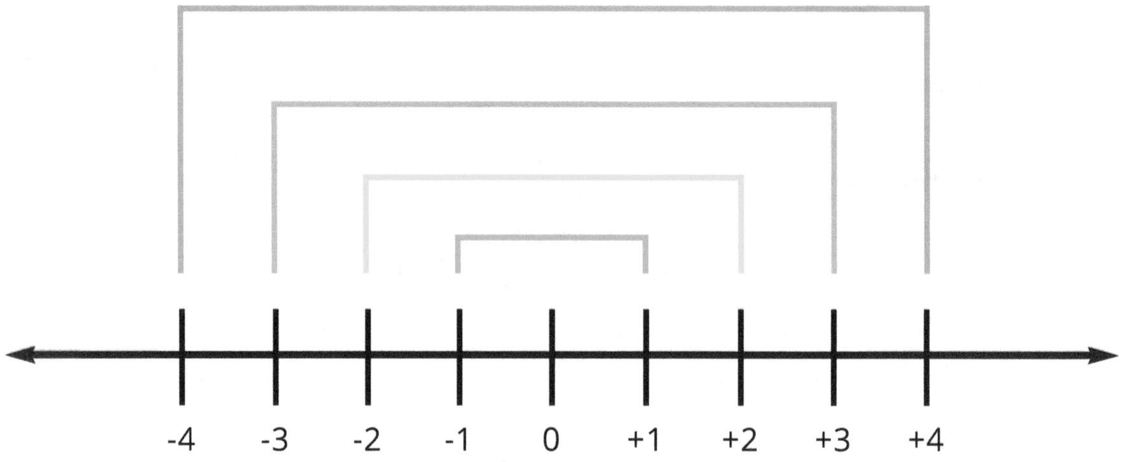

We can connect pairs of opposites on a number line.

① Write the opposite of each integer or situation.

1. -7 __________
2. +19 __________
3. 8 kilometers below sea level __________
4. 25 degrees above zero __________
5. -346 __________
6. 0 __________
7. 17 degrees below zero __________
8. +99 __________

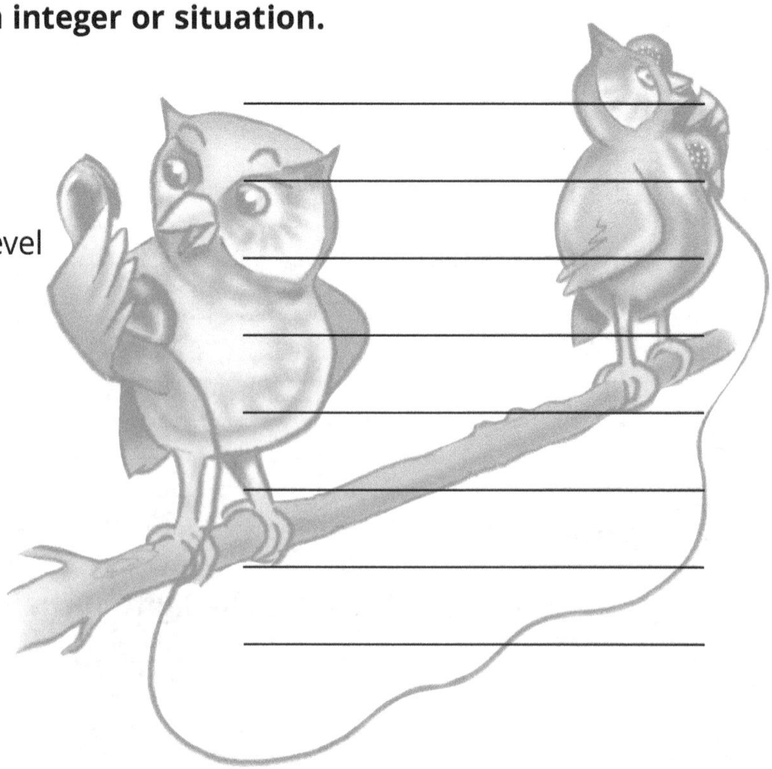

2 **Replace the letters with the correct numbers.**

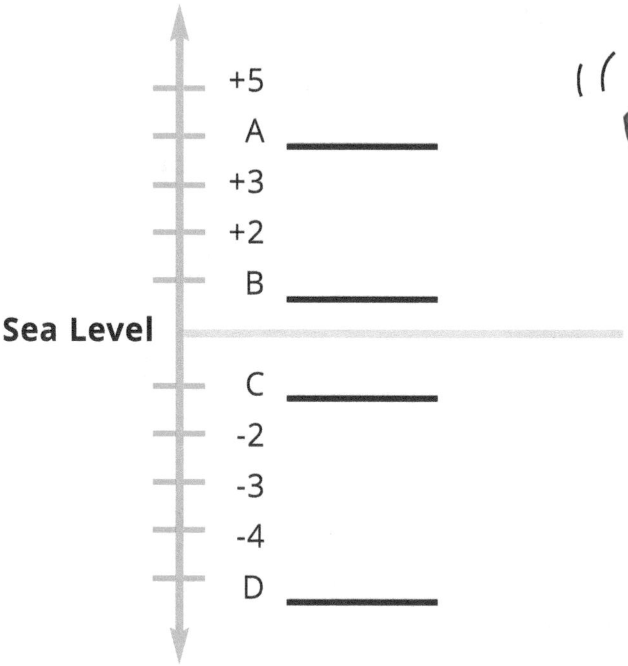

A ______

B ______

C ______

D ______

3 **Find the area and perimeter of the figure below.**

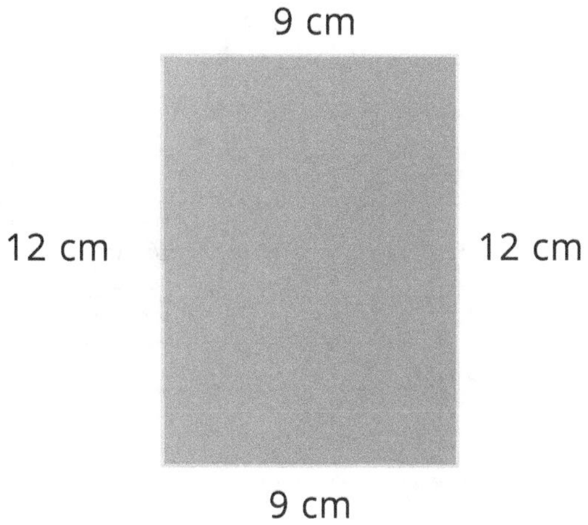

Area = ______

Perimeter = ______

4 **Use your calculator to help solve these problems.** Write the missing number.

$\frac{9}{17} = \frac{81}{\quad}$ $\frac{6}{19} = \frac{108}{\quad}$ $\frac{7}{15} = \frac{49}{\quad}$ $\frac{9}{19} = \frac{63}{\quad}$

$\frac{22}{45} = \frac{\quad}{90}$ $\frac{23}{34} = \frac{\quad}{204}$ $\frac{53}{110} = \frac{\quad}{440}$ $\frac{45}{59} = \frac{\quad}{472}$

5 **Write each percent as a fraction in simplest form.**

25 %	4 %	5 %
35 %	20 %	10 %
70 %	8 %	95 %

Write each fraction as a percent.

$\frac{1}{2}$	$\frac{1}{10}$	$\frac{16}{40}$
$\frac{21}{70}$	$\frac{48}{80}$	$\frac{3}{4}$
$\frac{1}{5}$	$\frac{1}{25}$	$\frac{2}{5}$

6 **Plot the points on the coordinate graph.** Connect the points in the order given. You will see the solution to the riddle: **What star goes to jail?**

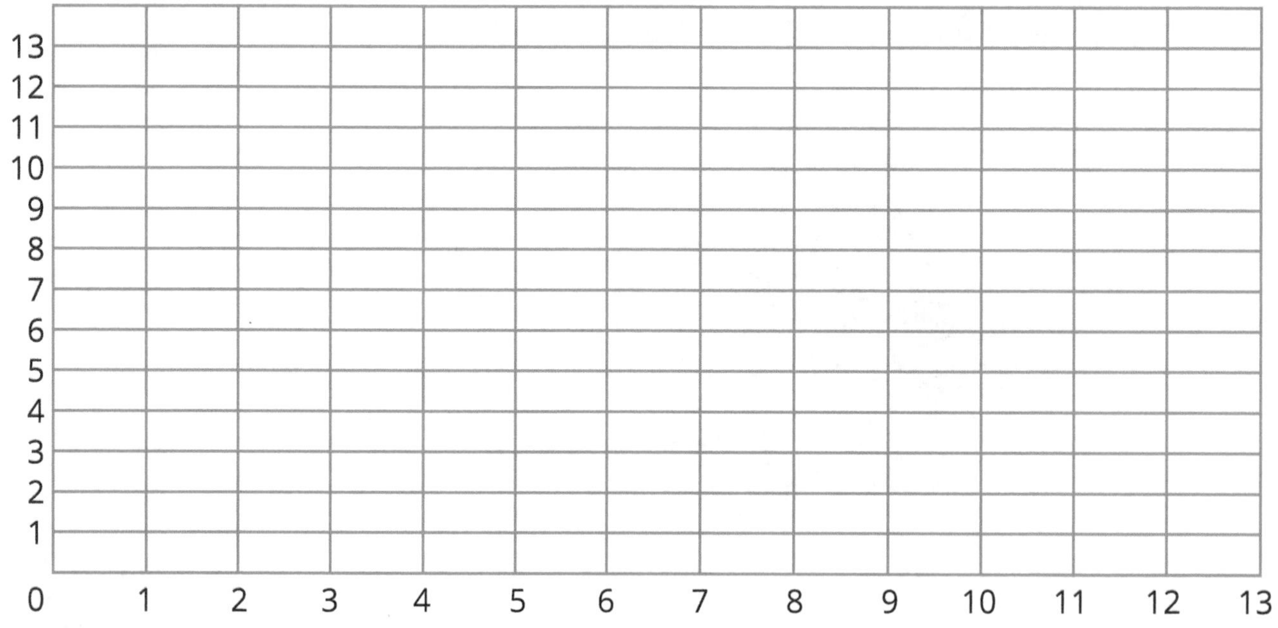

(6, 12)	(1, 2)	(11, 2)	(8, 7)	(4, 7)
(8, 2)	(4, 6)	(8, 6)	(11, 12)	(1, 12)
(4, 9)	**STOP**	**STOP**	**STOP**	**STOP**
(8, 9)				
(4, 2)				
(6, 12)				
STOP				

Answer: A shooting star.

Compare Integers

We can compare two numbers on the number line and easily see which number is larger.

The number to the right on the number line is greater than the number to the left.

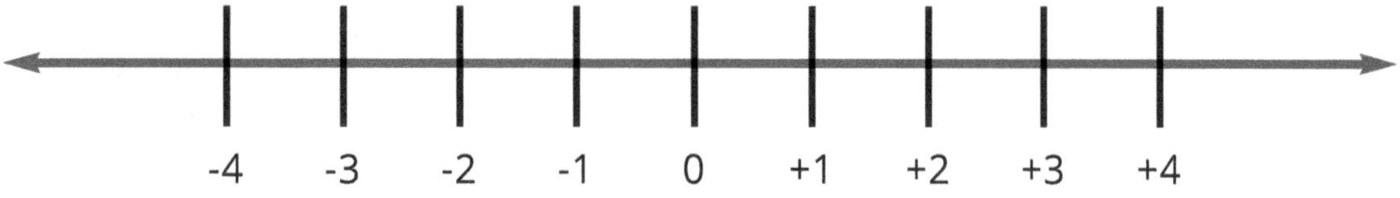

Which number is greater: -4 or -3? -3 is greater; -3 is to the right of -4.

Which number is greater: 0 or +2? +2 is greater; +2 is to the right of 0.

1 **Use <, >, or = to compare the integers.**

-6 ⬡ +2	-8 ⬡ -12	+2 ⬡ +7
-1 ⬡ -2	-4 ⬡ 0	+1 ⬡ +10
-9 ⬡ -4	-2 ⬡ -12	+8 ⬡ +14
+22 ⬡ +24	-10 ⬡ -18	+56 ⬡ +50

2 **Write the opposite of each integers or situation.**

1. -1 ______________________
2 +32 ______________________
3. 0 ______________________
4. -12 ______________________
5. -346 ______________________
6. 14 feet below sea level ______________________
7. 32 degrees below zero ______________________
8. +41 ______________________

3 **Use the grid below to draw three different rectangles with a perimeter of 24 cm.**

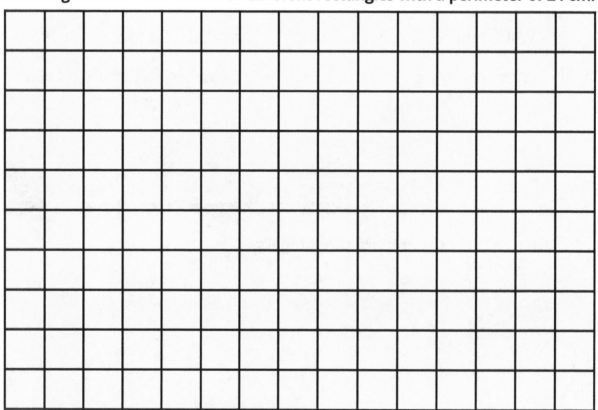

4 **Multiply. Use a calculator. Since the answers for these are large, an online or computer calculator may be needed.**

$$\begin{array}{r} 23{,}945 \\ \times\, 10{,}933 \\ \hline \end{array} \qquad \begin{array}{r} 12{,}055 \\ \times\, 9{,}812 \\ \hline \end{array} \qquad \begin{array}{r} 45{,}011 \\ \times\, 3{,}277 \\ \hline \end{array} \qquad \begin{array}{r} 39{,}822 \\ \times\, 12{,}056 \\ \hline \end{array}$$

5 **Find the area of the parallelograms.**

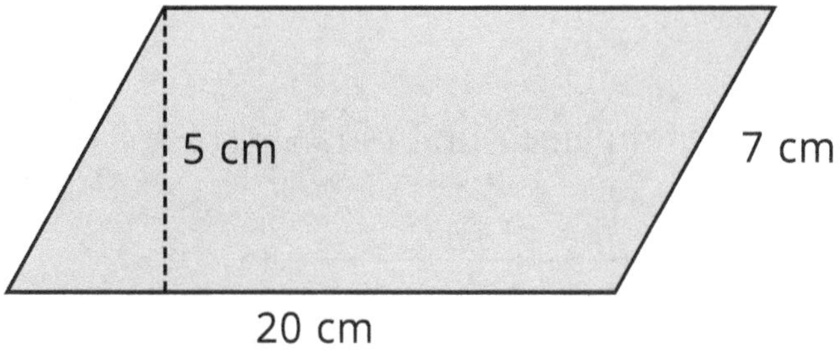

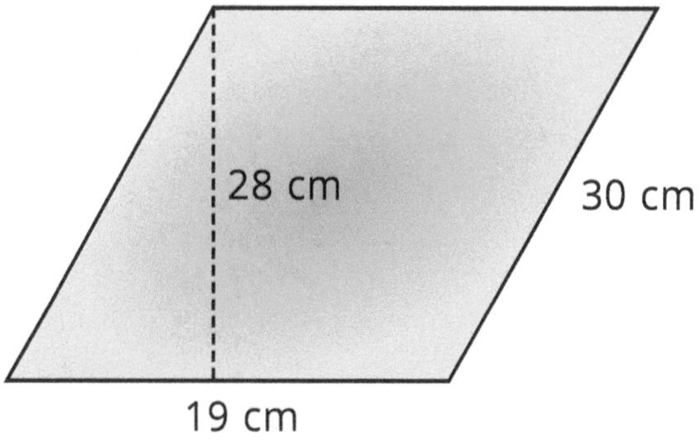

Area = _______________ cm^2

Area = _______________ cm^2

6 **Construct a square using Line CD as one side. Label the square ABCD.**

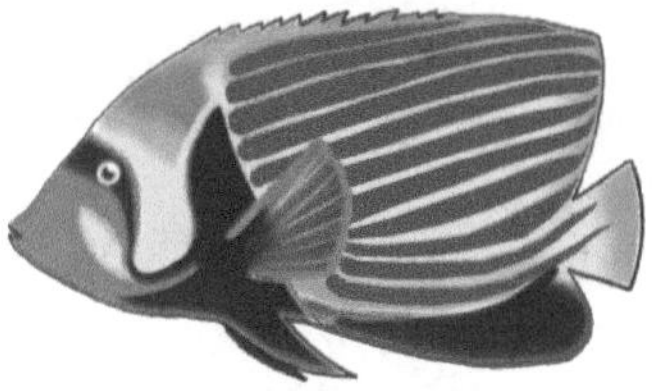

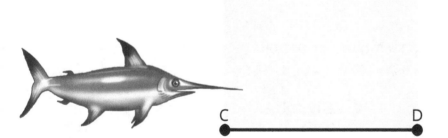

7 **Find the sum.**

24.9 + 13.9 + 128 =

345.9 + 22 + 206.7 =

2.8 + 452 + 1.55 =

199.4 + 8.8 + 2.12 =

Adding Integers with Like Signs.

Add (+1) + (+5).

We can use arrows to show each number of units. +1 unit plus +5 units = +6

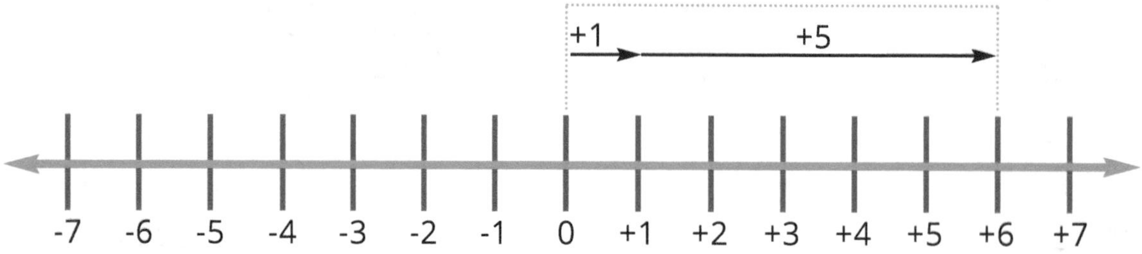

Add (-1) + (-1).

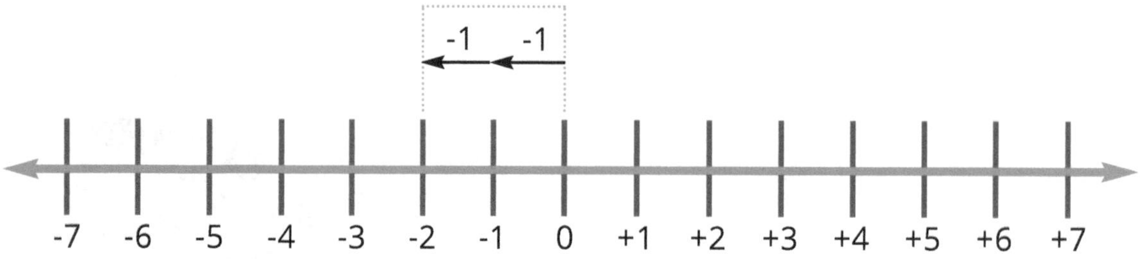

We can use arrows to show each number of units. -1 unit plus -1 unit = -2

1 **Use the number line to help you visually solve the problems.**

(-1) + (-3) __________ (+1) + (+1) __________ (-1) + (-2) __________

(-6) + (-1) __________ (+4) + (+3) __________ (-4) + (-2) __________

0 + (-1) __________ (+2) + (+2) __________ (+3) + (+3) __________

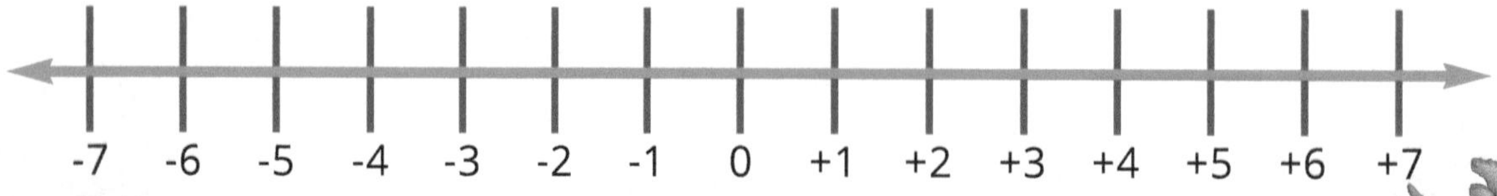

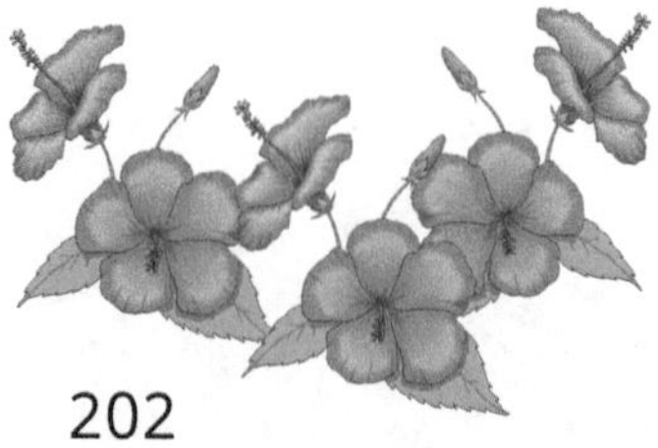

2 **After each example, write true or false.**

$(-17) < (+2)$ ______ $(-9) > (-22)$ ______

$(-23) < (-24)$ ______ $(+12) < (+19)$ ______

$(-6) < (+6)$ ______ $(+33) > (+32)$ ______

$(-15) < (-16)$ ______ $(-21) > (-12)$ ______

3 **Write the opposite of each integers or situation.**

1. -37 ______
2. +42 ______
3. 24 kilometers above sea level ______
4. 83 degrees above zero ______

Write three of your own opposites on the lines below.

______

______

______

4 **Arrange the integers into two groups—positive integers and negative integers. Order the integers in each group from the largest integer to the smallest.**
The corresponding letters will spell the solution to this riddle:
What runs, leaps, and jumps around all day, then lays on the floor all night with its tongue hanging out?

-45 E	-5 S	+49 O	+16 R
+20 U	-29 H	+56 Y	-44 O

Positive Integers		Negative Integers	
1. ______	___	______	___
2. ______	___	______	___
3. ______	___	______	___
4. ______	___	______	___

5 **Find the perimeter and area of the parallelograms.**

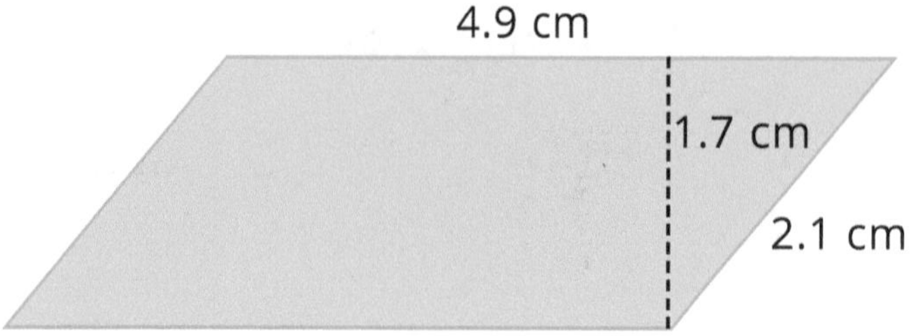

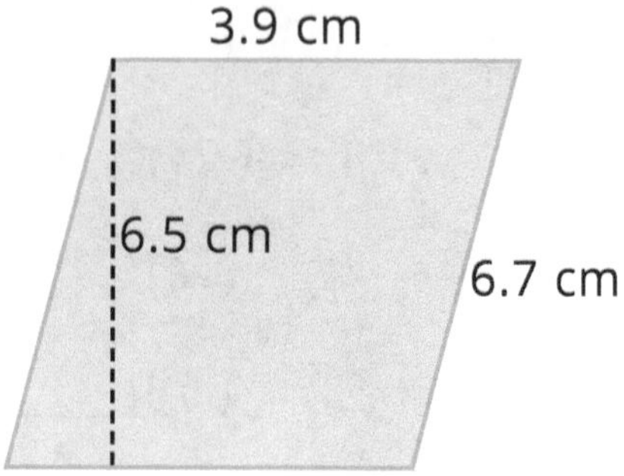

Perimeter = ____________ cm

Area = ____________ cm^2

Perimeter = ____________ cm

Area = ____________ cm^2

6 **Draw a regular hexagon using a compass and straightedge. The side of the hexagon is 2 centimeters.**

Addition of Integers with Unlike Signs

Add (+7) + (-4).

We can use arrows to show addition of integers with unlike signs.

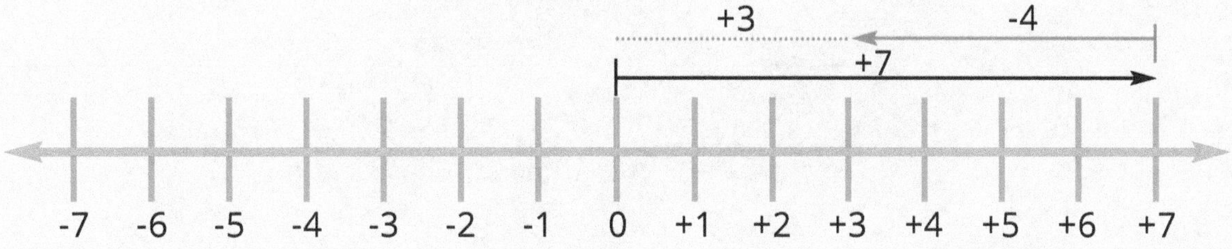

We can see that (+7) + (-4) = (+3)

Look at the number lines below. Write the addition problems shown by each picture. Check your answers at the bottom of the explanation section.

Example One

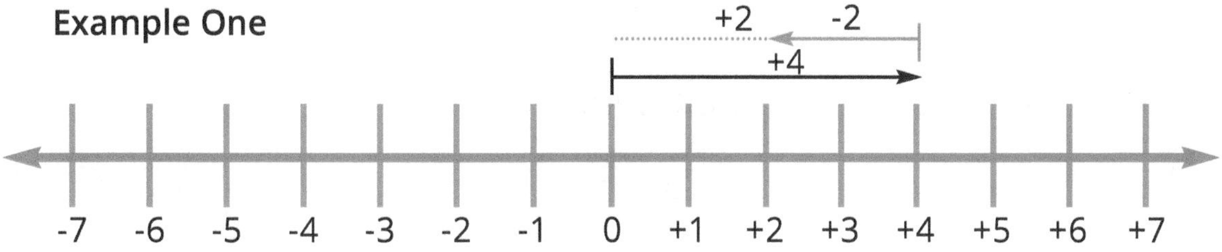

Write the number sentence here. ____________________

Example Two

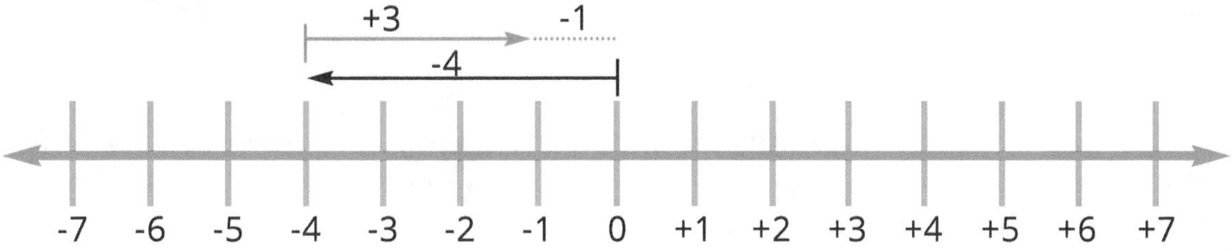

Write the number sentence here. ____________________

Example Three

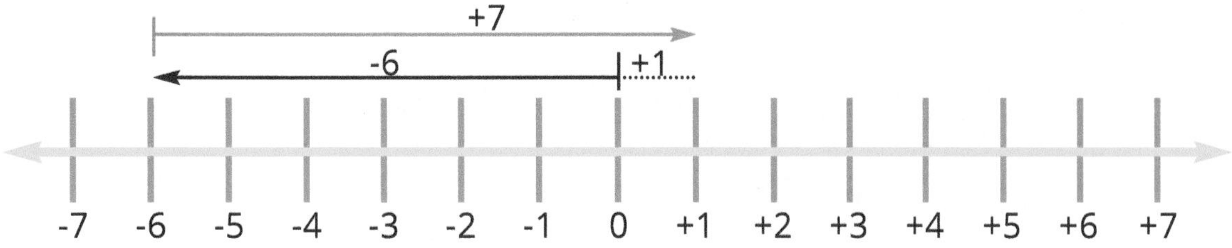

Write the number sentence here. ____________________

Example One: (+4) + (-2) = (+2)
Example Two: (-4) + (+3) = (-1)
Example Three: (-6) + (+7) = (+1)

1 **Add.**

(+7) + (-6) = ______________

(-4) + (-4) = ______________

(+11) + (-5) = ______________

(+3) + (-6) + (-6) = ______________

(+12) + (-2) + (+8) = ______________

(+6) + (-7) = ______________

(-14) + (+7) = ______________

(+5) + (-12) = ______________

(+1) + (-5) + (+7) = ______________

(+4) + (-6) + (+13) = ______________

2 **Add.**

(-15) + (-13) = __________ (+10) + (+14) = __________ (-11) + (-24) = __________

(-9) + (-4) = __________ (+9) + (+9) = __________ (-42) + (-11) = __________

0 + (-19) = __________ (+8) + (+23) = __________ (+26) + (+31) = __________

3 **Use <, >, or = to compare the integers.**

-21	◯	-20	-8	◯	-9	-10	◯	+1
-19	◯	-25	-1	◯	0	+25	◯	+40
-5	◯	-2	+3	◯	-3	+12	◯	+13

4 **Divide each fraction and rename in lowest terms. Circle the greatest answer.** Write the letter of the greater answer in the matching numbered box on the next page to find the solution to the riddle:

What man is strong enough to hold up a Mack® truck with one hand?

1. K $\frac{1}{9} \div \frac{3}{7}$ = ___ 2. P $\frac{3}{8} \div \frac{1}{2}$ = ___ 3. J $\frac{1}{10} \div \frac{2}{3}$ = ___ 4. L $\frac{2}{3} \div \frac{3}{2}$ = ___ 5. I $\frac{1}{9} \div \frac{2}{7}$ = ___

A $\frac{5}{9} \div \frac{3}{5}$ = ___ T $\frac{1}{2} \div \frac{2}{2}$ = ___ O $\frac{1}{4} \div \frac{5}{13}$ = ___ H $\frac{1}{9} \div \frac{1}{2}$ = ___ C $\frac{5}{6} \div \frac{3}{1}$ = ___

6. C $\frac{1}{4} \div \frac{3}{11}$ = ___ 7. E $\frac{1}{5} \div \frac{3}{13}$ = ___ 8. M $\frac{1}{5} \div \frac{2}{7}$ = ___ 9. A $\frac{1}{9} \div \frac{2}{11}$ = ___ 10. N $\frac{1}{2} \div \frac{5}{9}$ = ___

K $\frac{1}{6} \div \frac{2}{5}$ = ___ F $\frac{2}{5} \div \frac{6}{7}$ = ___ U $\frac{3}{6} \div \frac{5}{5}$ = ___ N $\frac{1}{6} \div \frac{3}{7}$ = ___ V $\frac{1}{5} \div \frac{2}{4}$ = ___

1	2	3	4	5	6	7	8	9	10

5 **Find the quotient. Check your answers by multiplying.**

$1{,}808\,\overline{)5424}$ $\quad$ $2{,}001\,\overline{)38{,}021}$ $\quad$ $3{,}103\,\overline{)46{,}546}$ $\quad$ $3{,}261\,\overline{)84{,}786}$

6 **Find the area of each triangle.** Write the answer on the line provided.

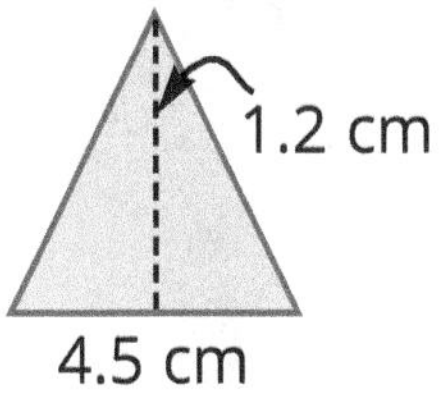

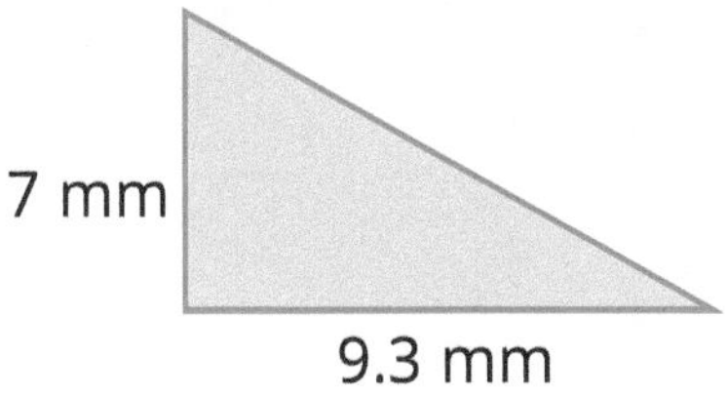

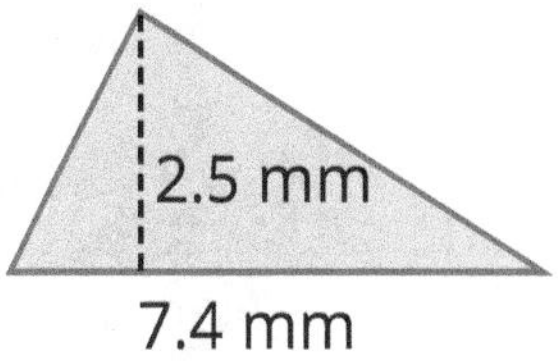

__________ __________ __________

Given the following data, find the area of each triangle.

base = 10 cm
height = 18 cm

Area = __________ cm^2

base = 5.7 mm
height = 11.4 mm

Area = __________ mm^2

base = 19.5 cm
height = 4.2 cm

Area = __________ cm^2

7 **Construct a square using Line JK as one side. Label the square JKLM.**

Subtracting Integers on a Number Line

Subtraction is finding the distance between two points on the number line.

Find 2 – (-7).

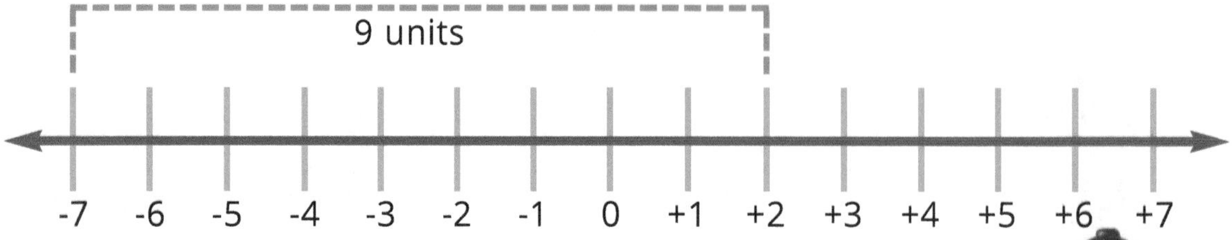

The distance between -7 and +2 on the number line is 9.
Starting from the subtrahend the move is 9 to the right,
therefore 2 – (-7) = 9.

Find (-6) – (-2).

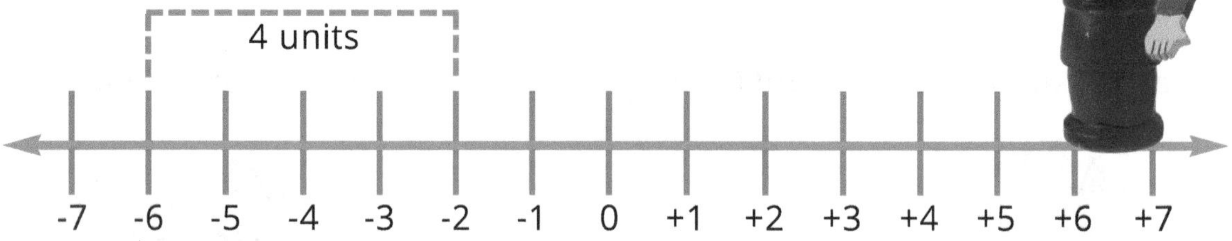

The distance between -6 and -2 is 4.
Starting from the subtrahend the move is 4 to the left,
therefore (-6) – (-2) = (-4)

1 **Use a number line to find each answer.**

(-7) – (-3) = ____________ 6 – (-2) = ____________

(-4) – (-2) = ____________ 5 – (-4) = ____________

0 – 3 = ____________ 0 – (-3) = ____________

6 – (-3) = ____________ (-7) – (-2) = ____________

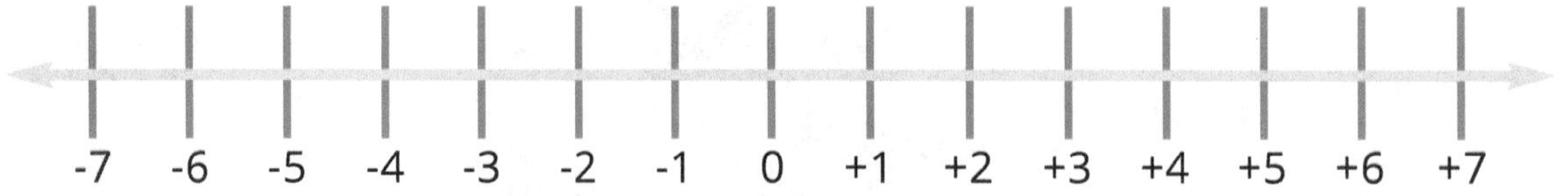

2 **Solve.**

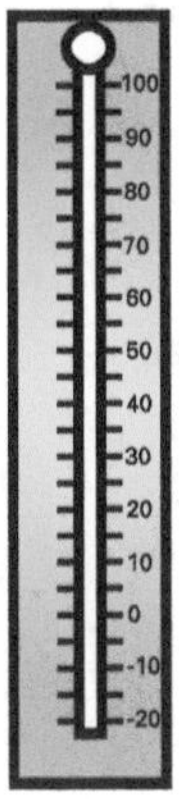

Shane looked at the thermometer in the cabin; it was 2 degrees below zero Celsius. He started a fire in the fireplace and the temperature increased by 12 degrees. What is the temperature now?

During the day the temperature in the mountains reached 45 degrees Celsius. In the evening, the temperature dipped to 17 degrees below zero. How much did the temperature drop from daytime to evening?

3 **Add. Shade the correct answer and circle the corresponding letters.** The letters spell the answer to the riddle: **Knights only eat one kind of fish**. Name it.

(+9) + (-12) =	-3 S	+1 B
(-6) + (-4) =	+2 A	-10 W
(+22) + (-9) =	+13 O	-13 S
(+8) + (-5) + (-12) =	-9 R	-8 S
(+17) + (-3) + (+14) + (+19) =	+50 F	+47 D
(+4) + (-12) + (+15) =	-7 I	+7 F
(+2) + (-19) + (+7) =	-11 S	-10 I
(+51) + (-32) =	-19 H	+19 S
(-56) + (+14) =	-42 H	-40 T

____ ____ ____ ____ ____ ____ ____ ____ ____

4 **After each example, write true or false.**

$(-22) < (-21)$ __________

$(-33) < (-34)$ __________

$(-9) < 0$ __________

$(-65) < (-16)$ __________

$(-98) > (-97)$ __________

$(+22) > (+21)$ __________

$(+17) < (+16)$ __________

$(-21) > (-52)$ __________

5 **Find the area of the triangles. Round the answers to the nearest tenth.**

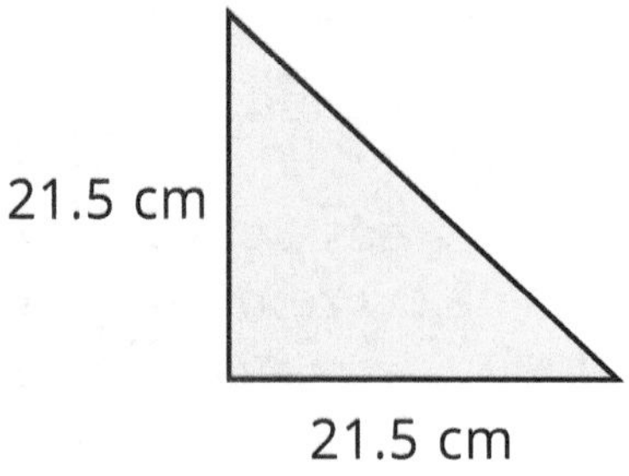

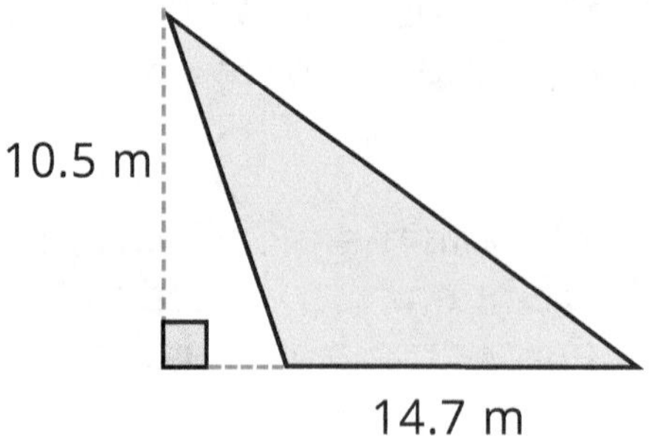

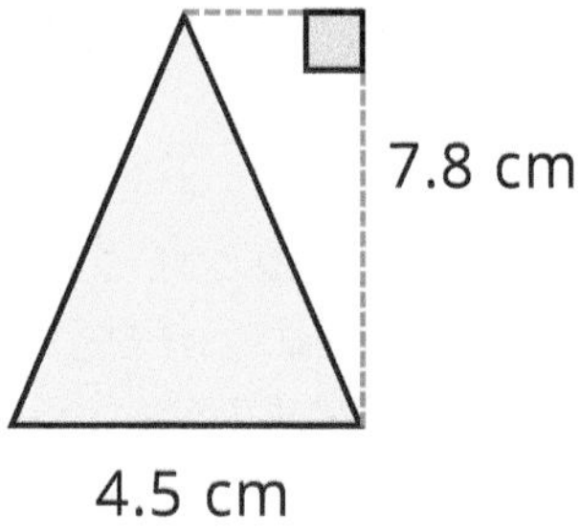

Area = ___________ Area = __________ Area = ___________

6 **Construct a square using Line FG as one side. Label the square FGHI.**

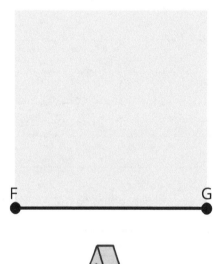

Subtract Integers by Adding the Opposite

Let's look at the previous lesson.

We learned that when subtracting integers, we are finding the distance between two points on the number line.

Find 2 – (-7).

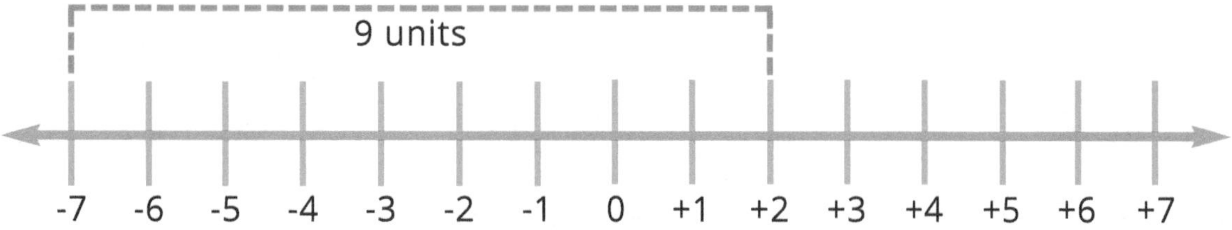

We learned that the distance between –7 and +2 on the number line is 9, therefore 2 – (-7) = 9.

To see how to subtract without a number line, we can always subtract by adding the opposite. For example, the opposite of - 3 is 3; the opposite of 5 is -5. The opposite of -7 is 7, so we change 2 – (-7) to 2 + (+7). We know that 2 + 7 = 9.

In the previous lesson, we learned how to find the solution to (-6) – (-2) on a number line.

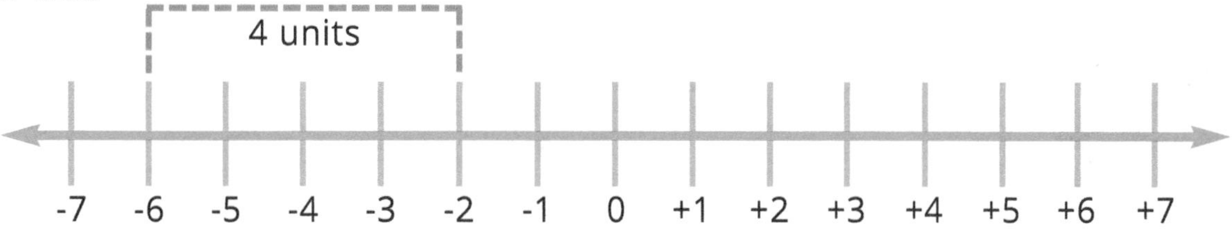

The distance between -6 and -2 is 4, therefore (-6) – (-2) = -4

To see how to subtract without a number line, we can always subtract by adding the opposite.
In other words, change -6 – (-2) to (-6) + (+2) We know that (-6) + 2 = -4.

It is easy to subtract integers with or without a number line.

1 **Give the opposite of each number.**

6 ____ -12 ____ 7 ____ 25 ____ -34 ____ -1 ____

Do these additions and subtractions and compare.

5 – 2 = __________ 5 + (-2) = __________

8 – (-2) = __________ 8 + 2 = __________

(-2) – 3 = ___________ (-2) + (-3) = ___________

(-4) – (-2) = ___________ (-4) + 2 = ___________

② **Solve.**

7 − 3 = ________ (-15) − 3 = ________ (-6) − (-6) = ________

4 − 10 = ________ (-7) − (-12) = ________ 9 − (-3) = ________

13 − (-7) = ________ (-15) − 8 = ________ 12 − (-4) = ________

③ **Add.**

(+71) + (-61) = ____________ (+45) + (-56) = ____________

(-42) + (-16) = ____________ (-44) + (+6) = ____________

(+61) + (-18) = ____________ (+55) + (-72) = ____________

(+22) + (-9) + (-26) = ____________ (+43) + (-33) + (+8) = ____________

(+32) + (-9) + (+15) = ____________ (+11) + (-12) + (+45) = ____________

④ **Place the numbers in order from least to greatest. If the numbers are in the correct order they will spell a message.**

+41 D -11 S -41 U +1 N +12 G

0 I -61 T +32 O -1 T -55 R

1. __________ ___
2. __________ ___
3. __________ ___
4. __________ ___
5. __________ ___

6. __________ ___
7. __________ ___
8. __________ ___
9. __________ ___
10. __________ ___

Message ______________________________

5 **Fill in the blanks under each circle. Round the answer to the nearest tenth.**

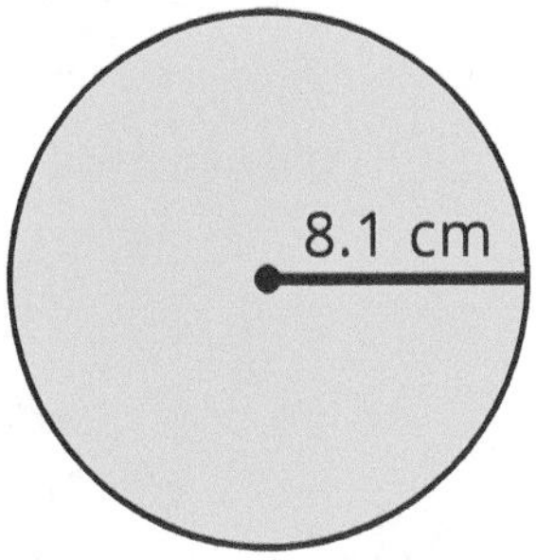

$A = \pi r^2$

$= 3.14$ (______ cm × ______ cm)

$= 3.14$ (______ cm^2)

= ______ cm^2

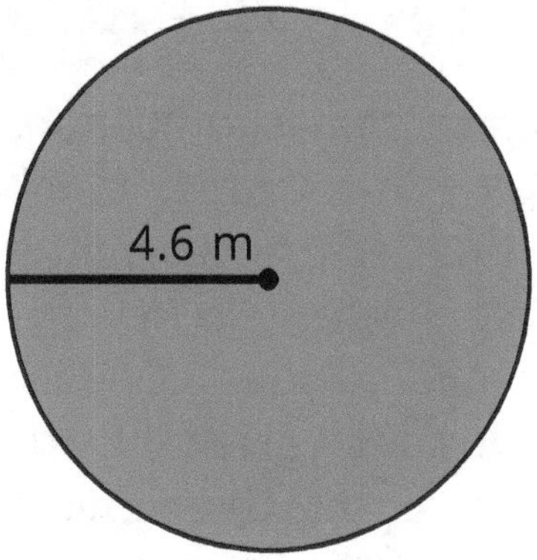

$A = \pi r^2$

$= 3.14$ (______ cm × ______ cm)

$= 3.14$ (______ cm^2)

= ______ cm^2

6 **Find the difference.**

$$\begin{array}{r} 18.655 \\ -\ \ 7.981 \\ \hline \end{array} \qquad \begin{array}{r} 91.332 \\ -\ \ 7.981 \\ \hline \end{array} \qquad \begin{array}{r} 792.56 \\ -133.91 \\ \hline \end{array}$$

$$\begin{array}{r} 356.326 \\ -\ \ 35.909 \\ \hline \end{array} \qquad \begin{array}{r} 32.001 \\ -\ \ 3.917 \\ \hline \end{array} \qquad \begin{array}{r} 63.26 \\ -28.17 \\ \hline \end{array}$$

24.56 – 6.09 = __________

355.15 – 35.8 = __________

Graphing Ordered Pairs

The horizontal number line is called the **x-axis**. The vertical number line is called the **y-axis**. The pairs of numbers on the grid below are called **ordered pairs.**

An ordered pair is a pair of numbers that refer to a specific point on a grid. The first number tells how many units to move right or left on the x-axis. The second number tells how many units to move up or down on the y-axis.

For instance, given the ordered pair (2, 3), one would move two units to the right on the x-axis and three units up on the y-axis. Given the ordered pair (2, -1), one would move two units to the right on the x-axis and one unit down on the y-axis.

Can you tell what ordered pair describes the other two points pictured?

The ordered pair for point A is (-2, 4).

The ordered pair for point B is (-4, -3).

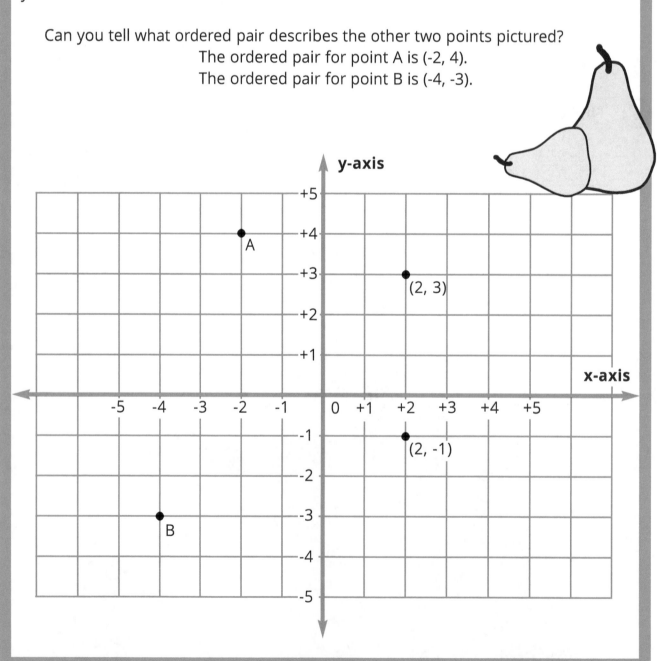

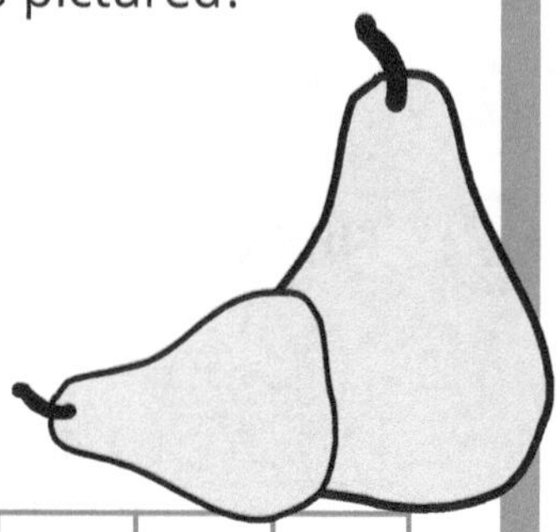

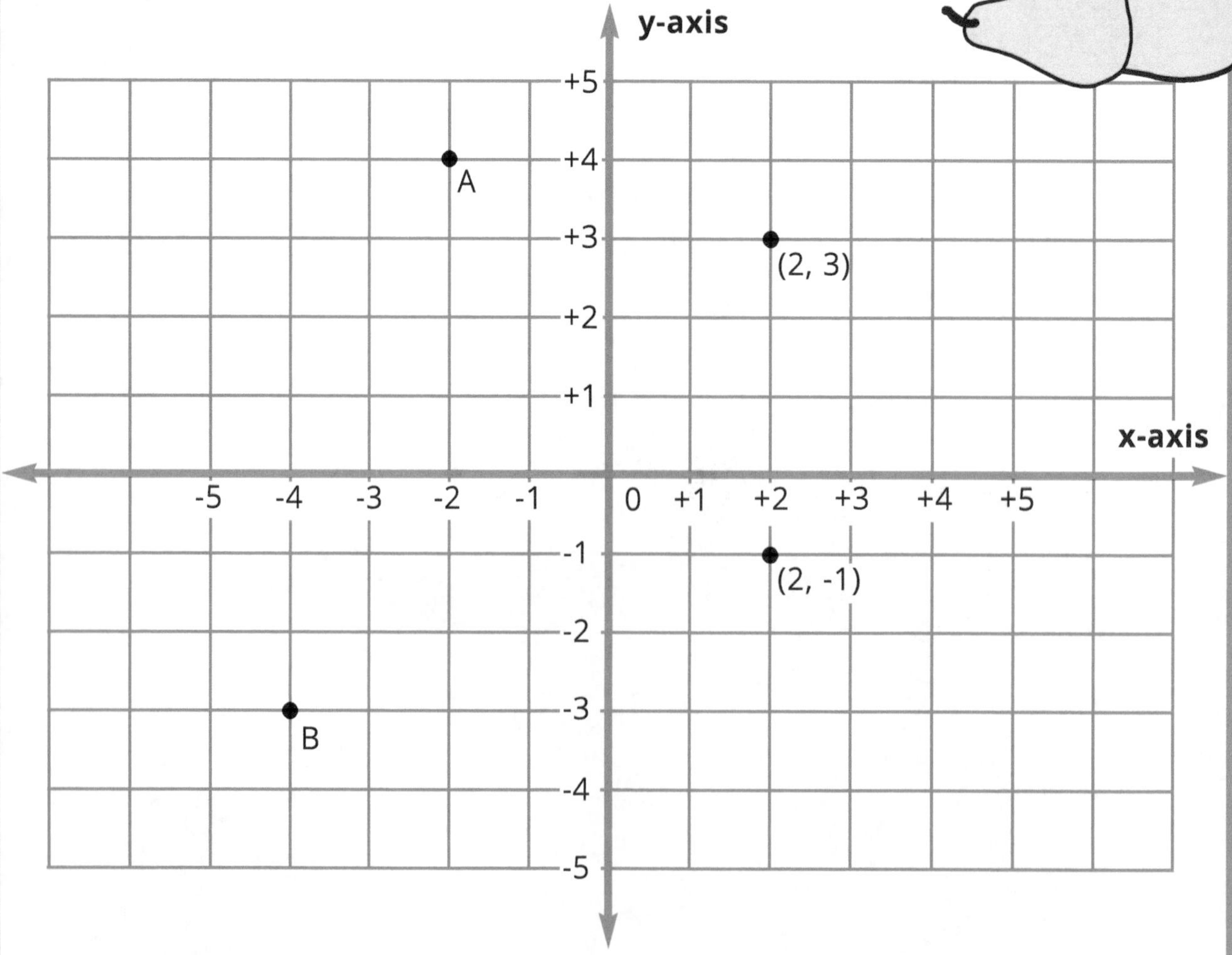

1 **Find these points on the grid below and connect them in the order given.**

(0, 2)	(2, -2)	(-4, 2)
(1, 3)	(1, -3)	(-3, 4)
(2, 4)	(0, -4)	(-2, 4)
(3, 4)	(-1, -3)	(-1, 3)
(4, 2)	(-2, -2)	(0, 2)
(3, -1)	(-3, -1)	**STOP**

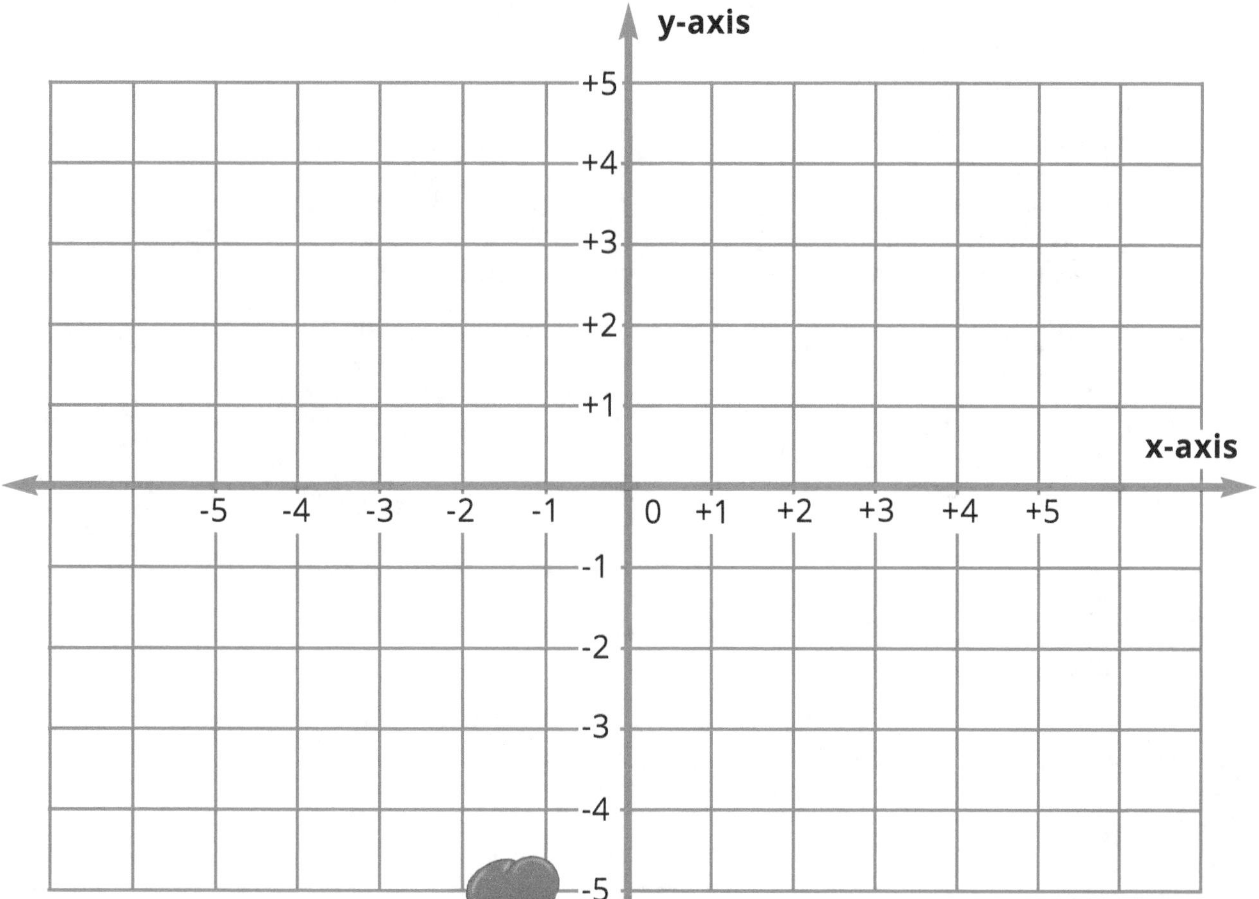

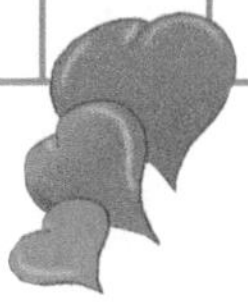

The crucible for silver and the furnace for gold. But the Lord tests the heart.
Proverbs 17:3

2 **Solve.**

23 – 3 = ________	(-11) – 12 = ________	(-14) – (-14) = ________
25 – 30 = ________	(-11) – (-12) = ________	4 – (-9) = ________
92 – (-8) = ________	11 – 12 = ________	34 – (-11) = ________

3 **Add.**

(+25) + (-14) = ______________

(-17) + (-17) = ______________

(+19) + (-15) = ______________

(+12) + (-12) + (-21) = ______________

(+73) + (-13) + (+11) = ______________

(+24) + (-25) = ______________

(-64) + (+29) = ______________

(+45) + (-19) = ______________

(+33) + (-17) + (+12) = ______________

(+12) + (-15) + (+3) = ______________

4 **Find the area of the gray part of the circle.** Round the answer to the nearest tenth.

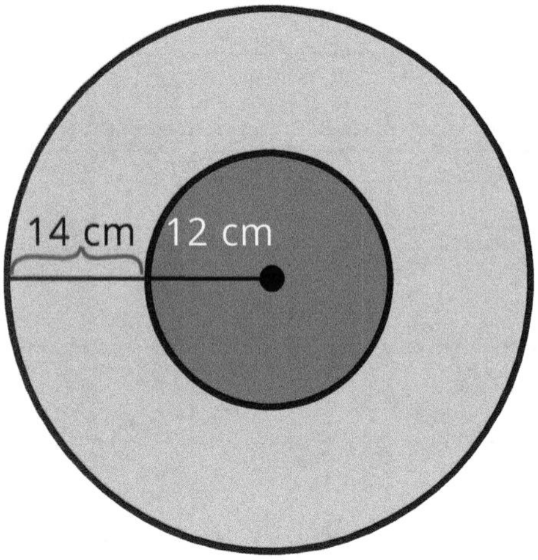

5 **Count the change. Use the fewest coins and bills possible. Write the total amount due.**

Price	Paid	Change Due
Example: $1.75	$2.00	1 quarter = $0.25
$5.94	$6.00	
$18.29	$20.00	
$21.50	$30.00	
$48.15	$50.00	
$2.19	$20.00	

Multiplying Integers

When multiplying integers there are three basic rules to remember.

1. The product of two positive integers is always positive.

   7 × 3 = 21

2. The product of two negative integers is positive.

   (-7) × (-3) = (+21)

3. The product of a positive and a negative integer is negative.

   (-7) × (+3) = (-21)

   (+7) × (-3) = (-21)

1 **Find the product.**

(+6) × (-3) = ____________

(-7) × (-7) = ____________

9 × 5 = ____________

(+12) × (-2) = ____________

(+8) × (-9) = ____________

(+11) × (-7) = ____________

(+4) × (-5) = ____________

(-4) × (+9) = ____________

(-5) × (-3) = ____________

3 × 2 = ____________

(+6) × (-9) = ____________

8 × 5 = ____________

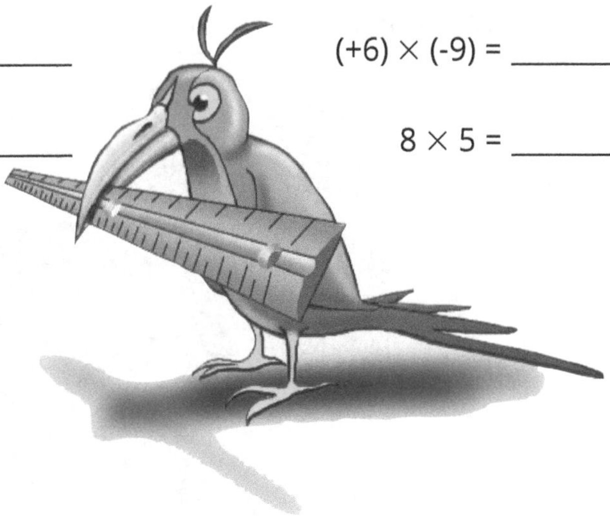

2 **Solve.**

3 – (-3) = ____________

(-3) – (-3) = ____________

3 – 3 = ____________

(-3) – 3 = ____________

15 – (-3) = ____________

(-15) – (-3) = ____________

(-15) – 3 = ____________

15 – 3 = ____________

3 **Find the volume of each cylinder. Round the answer to the tenths.**

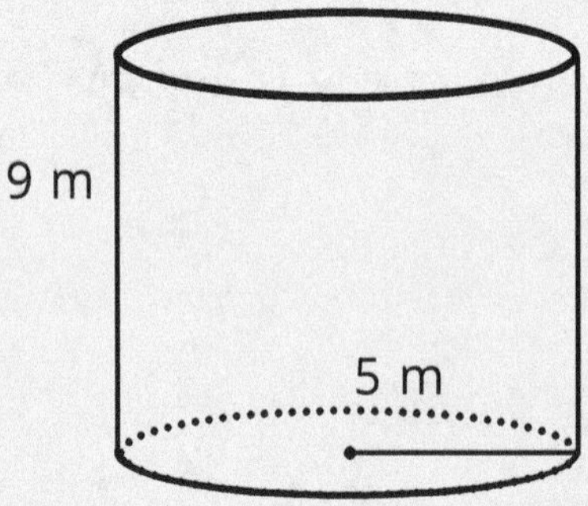

Volume = ____________ m^3

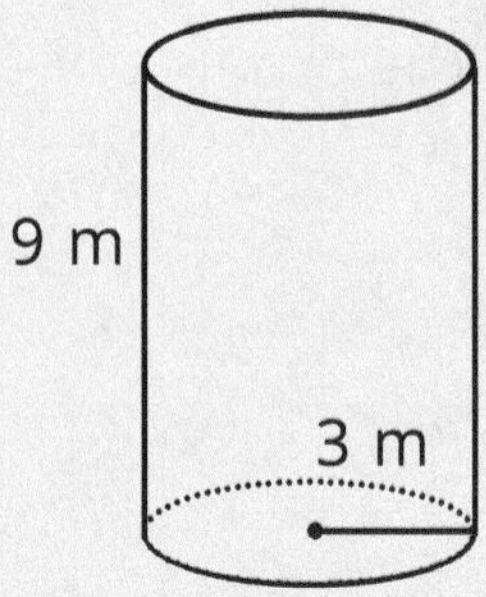

Volume = ____________ m^3

radius: 6.2 m
height: 3 m

Volume = ____________ m^3

radius: 3.4 m
height: 7 m

Volume = ____________ m^3

4 **Give the coordinates of the points on the grid that is on the next page. Can you connect the points and form a cube?**

A ________

B ________

C ________

D ________

E ________

F ________

G ________

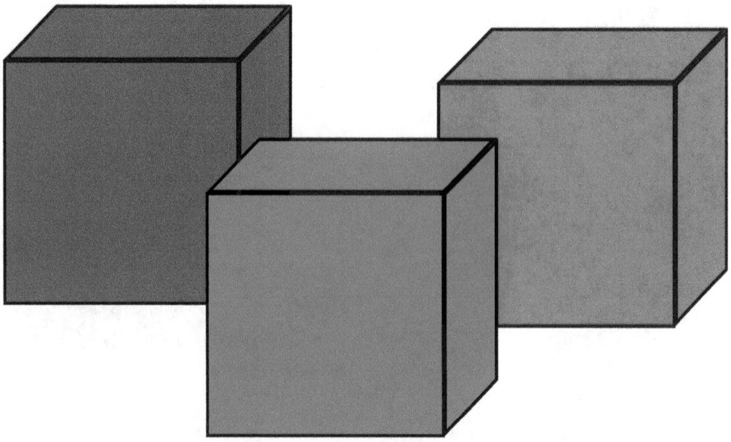

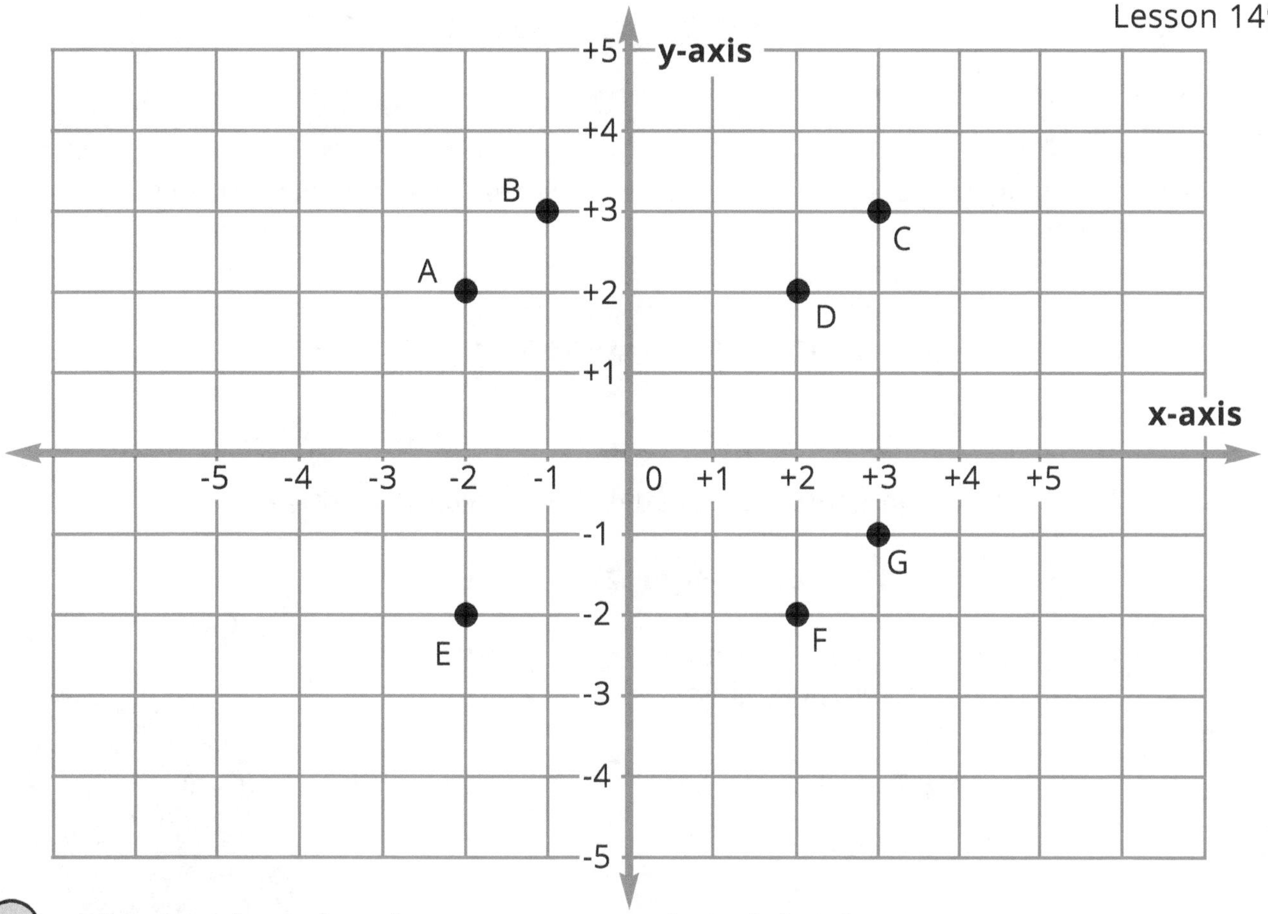

5 **Bisect each angle using a compass and straightedge.**

1.

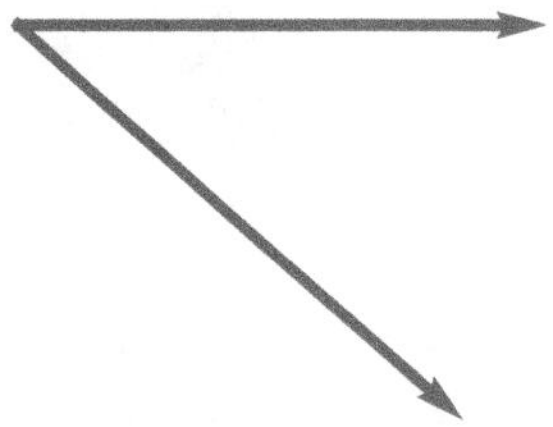

2.

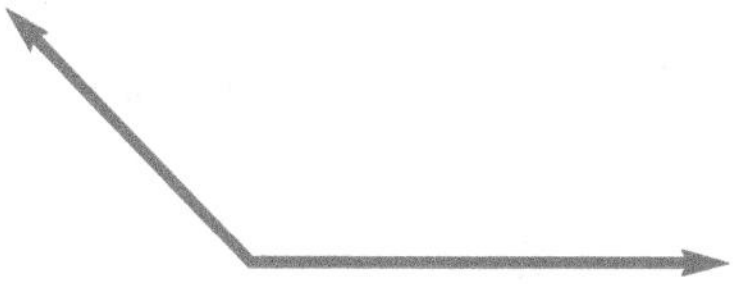

6 **Use a compass and straightedge to construct perpendicular bisectors to line CD.** Label it line LM.

Dividing Integers

When dividing integers, you apply the same three basic rules you used for multiplication.

1. If both integers are positive, the answer is positive.

   6 ÷ 3 = 2

2. If both integers are negative, the answer is positive.

   (-6) ÷ (-3) = (+2)

3. If one integer is positive and the other integer is negative, the answer is negative.

   (-6) ÷ (+3) = (-2)   or   (+6) ÷ (-3) = (-2)

(1) Find the quotient.

(-6) ÷ (-2) = ____________

(-7) ÷ (+7) = ____________

15 ÷ 5 = ____________

(+12) ÷ (-2) = ____________

(+18) ÷ (-9) = ____________

(+21) ÷ (-7) = ____________

(+45) ÷ (-5) = ____________

(-36) ÷ (+9) = ____________

(-15) ÷ (-3) = ____________

12 ÷ 2 = ____________

(-81) ÷ (-9) = ____________

20 ÷ 5 = ____________

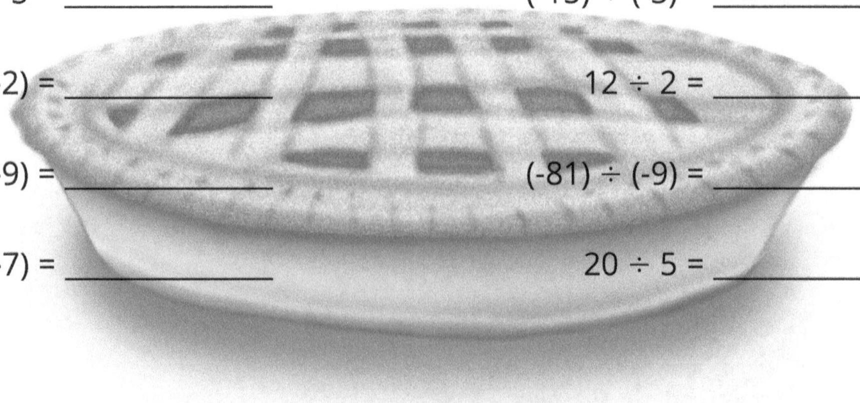

② Multiplication.

Write three different multiplication problems with integers that come out positive.

____

____

____

Write three different multiplication problems with integers that come out negative.

____

____

____

③ Simplify and multiply.

$\frac{6}{11} \cdot \frac{2}{3}$ $\frac{7}{18} \cdot \frac{2}{21}$ $\frac{7}{16} \cdot \frac{2}{1}$ $\frac{20}{21} \cdot \frac{3}{15}$ $\frac{10}{9} \cdot \frac{3}{25}$

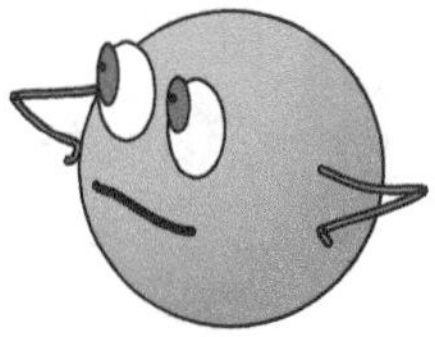

④ Plot the points on the graph below. Connect the points in the order given.

(2, 4)
(4, 2)
(4, -2)
(2, -4)
(-2, -4)
(-4, -2)
(-4, 2)
(-2, 4)
(2, 4)
STOP

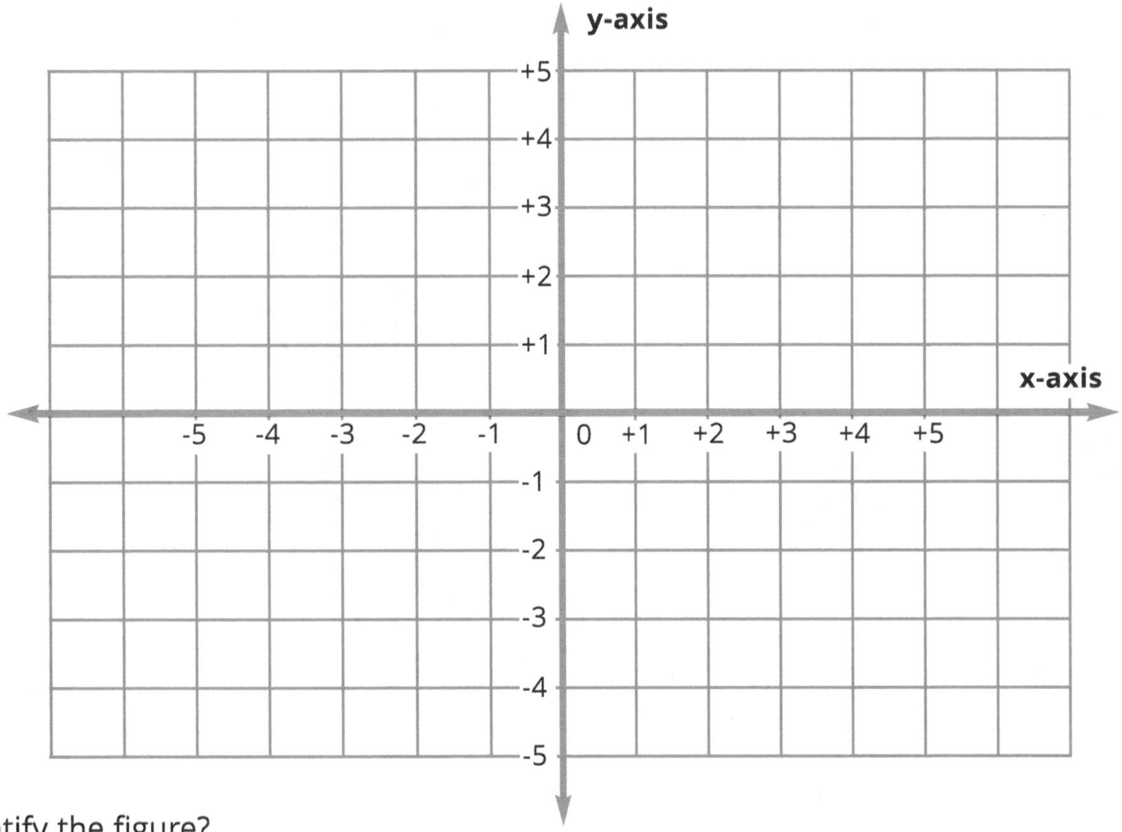

Can you identify the figure? ______________

5 **Find the volume of each cylinder. Round the answer to the tenths.**

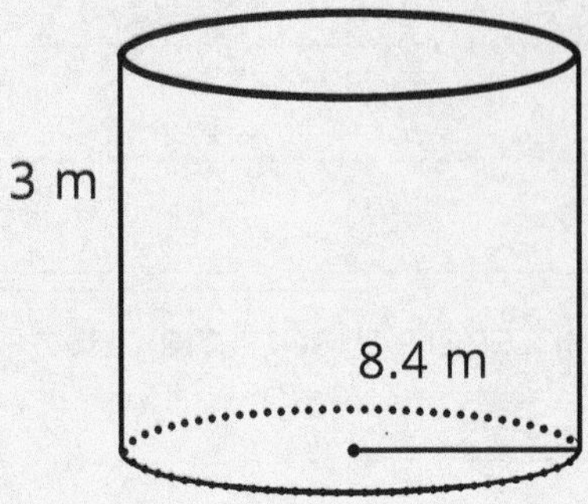

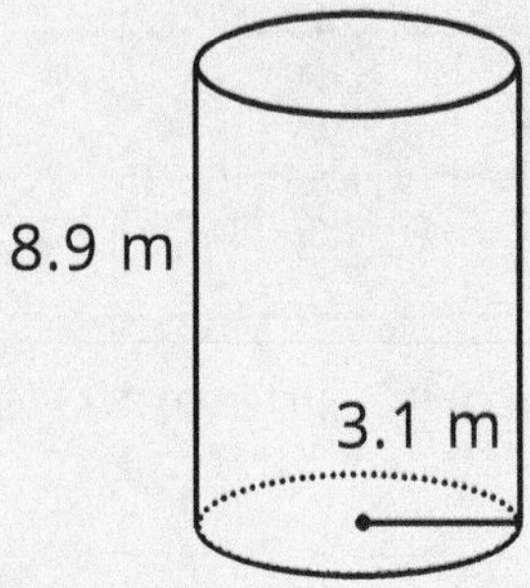

Volume = ________________ m^3 Volume = ________________ m^3

6 **Divide. Rename each fraction as a mixed number in lowest terms.**

$\frac{6}{9} \div \frac{1}{3}$ $\frac{2}{5} \div \frac{4}{7}$ $\frac{7}{12} \div \frac{2}{1}$ $\frac{2}{3} \div \frac{3}{8}$ $\frac{1}{9} \div \frac{3}{5}$

$\frac{5}{6} \div \frac{2}{7}$ $\frac{7}{13} \div \frac{2}{5}$ $\frac{7}{11} \div \frac{2}{9}$ $\frac{2}{15} \div \frac{2}{15}$ $\frac{1}{9} \div \frac{7}{7}$

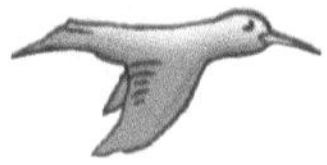

1. **Find 1%. (Round to the nearest hundredth)** 8 pts.

$207.05	$3,081.00	$90,300.75	$6.77
9,331	665	9	15

2. **Find 10% of each number.** 5 pts.

25	590	917	9,008	11,208

3. **Complete the order form to determine how much the bookstore owes its supplier.** 6 pts.

Order #1			
Item	**Quantity**	**Price each**	**Total**
Bible Covers	7	$15.99 ea	
Read and Sing Bible Stories	20	$5.99 ea	
Memory Verse Pkg	15	$3.50 ea	
		Total	
		6% sales tax	
		Shipping	$10.00
		Grand Total	

4. **Each book at Nautical Tales is discounted. Determine the amount of the discount by rounding each decimal number to the nearest hundred. Then find the new sale price for each book.** 10 pts.

Item	Regular Price	Percentage Discount	Discounted Dollar Amount	New Sale Price
The Capable Cruiser	$32.00	20%		
Storm Tactics	$19.95	10%		
Celestial Navigation	$14.95	5%		
Cruising the South Pacific	$39.95	15%		
Sailing Around the World	$25.00	10%		

5. **Determine how many sandwich combinations are possible using organized lists. List all of the combinations on the next page in space provided.** 28 pts.

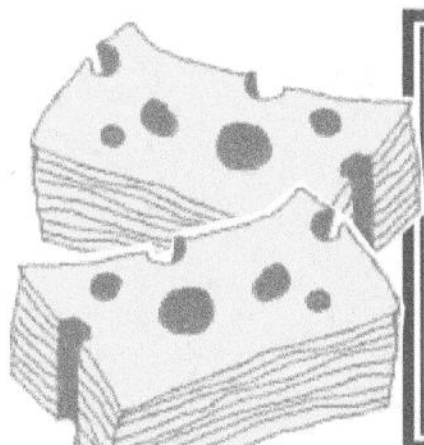

Sanguini's Deli

Meats	Bread	Cheese
ham	rye	Provolone
turkey	white	Swiss
salami	whole wheat	American

How many different combinations of sandwiches can Sanguini's Deli make? ____

List all of the combinations below.

(6) Write positive or negative for each example. 6 pts.

1. 10 degrees below zero ______
2. 9 points gain ______
3. 10 yard loss ______
4. grew 6 inches ______
5. gained 10 pounds ______
6. lost 10 pounds ______

(7) Write the opposite of each integer or situation. 6 pts.

1. 15 degrees below zero ______
2. +11 ______
3. 10 kilometers above sea level ______
4. 0 ______
5. -39 ______
6. 10 yard gain ______

(8) Use <, > or = to compare the integers. 8 pts.

-2 ⬡ +2	-6 ⬡ -2	0 ⬡ +15	+17 ⬡ +11
-10 ⬡ -33	-7 ⬡ -4	+1 ⬡ -1	-3 ⬡ -13

(9) Solve. 9 pts.

(0) + (-8) ______	(+1) + (+7) ______	(-25) + (-4) ______
(-8) + (-14) ______	(-14) + (-10) ______	(-56) + (-13) ______
(-8) + (-40) ______	(+67) + (+23) ______	(+31) + (+45) ______

(10) Add. 8 pts.

(+12) + (-11) = ______	(+6) + (-17) = ______	(+36) + (-4) = ______
(-44) + (+27) = ______	(+13) + (-16) + (-6) = ______	(+11) + (-9) + (-5) = ______
(+32) + (-12) + (+45) = ______	(-22) + (-34) + (+53) = ______	

Budgeting

Callie began a new job. She earns $33,500 per year as a school teacher. To be sure that she is living within her income, Callie needs to make a budget. A **budget** is a plan for meeting expenses. The Bible talks about money and money management many times. All of our possessions are not really ours; they belong to God. Being responsible with money is a principal God found important. (*Matthew 24:45*)

When creating a budget, you must recognize the divisions of income.
Below is a listing of all the major categories that need to be included in a budget.

God	The first part of all earnings belongs to God. 10% needs to be given to Him. *Genesis 28:22, Deuteronomy 14:22, Malachi 3:8*
Government	The government will collect its share through taxes: federal, state, and local. *Matthew 22:15-21*
Family	Family needs such as food, housing, and insurance must come next. *1 Timothy 5:8*
Debts	Debts are bills owed such as an automobile loan, credit card, a student loan, etc. *Proverbs 3: 27–28, Romans 13:8, Psalm 37:21*
Savings	Saving should be a part of every budget. There needs to be a surplus of money once expenses are paid so that money can be placed into savings. *Proverbs 6:6-8*

If Callie makes $33,500.00 per year, then her **gross monthly income** will be $2,791.66. **Gross monthly income** is the amount Callie makes before the tithe and taxes ($33,500 ÷ 12). Below is a sample monthly budget. Look closely at all the categories. Each amount has been rounded to the nearest dollar*.

*The income figure was rounded to the nearest dollar.

MONTHLY INCOME	
Salary	2,792.00
Extra income	______
Total Monthly Income	$2,792.00
MONTHLY EXPENSES	
Tithe (10%)	279.00
Taxes (20%)	558.00
Housing	
Rent/Mortgage	400.00
Electricity	50.00
Gas	20.00
Water	10.00
Telephone	35.00
Total Housing	$515.00
Food	$85.00
Automobile	
Payments	350.00
Gas & Oil	90.00

Insurance	70.00
Taxes	15.00
Maintenance/Repair	20.00
Total Automobile	$545.00
Insurance	
Life	10.00
Medical	30.00
Other	
Total Insurance	$40.00
Debts	
Credit Cards	50.00
Loans	75.00
Other	
Total Debts	$125.00
Entertainment & Recreation	
Eating out	30.00
Trips	
Vacation	50.00
Other	
Total Entertainment/Rec	$80.00
Clothing	$40.00
Medical Expenses	
Doctor	30.00
Dentist	30.00
Prescriptions	
Other	
Total Medical	$60.00
Miscellaneous	
Cleaning	10.00
Beauty	10.00
Lunches	60.00
Gifts (including Christmas)	60.00
Laundry	10.00
Spending money	40.00
Other	
Total Miscellaneous	$190.00
TOTAL MONTHLY EXPENSE	**$2,517.00**
INCOME VS. EXPENSE	
Spendable Income:	**$2,792.00**
Less Expense	**$2,517.00**
SURPLUS	**$274.00***

*** Surplus needs to be placed into savings.**

When making a budget, if your income is smaller than your expenses, or the income barely equals the expenses, then you need to reevaluate your spending habits.

You always need to make more money than you are spending!!!

1 **On a separate sheet of paper, use the information provided to fill in Tom's monthly budget sheet. Calculate whether or not Tom's income is enough to cover his expenses.**

Tom's yearly salary:	$45,900.00
house payment	$950.00 per mo.
groceries	$250.00 per mo.
gasoline	$350.00 per mo.
car payments (including taxes & insurance)	$1,025.00 per mo.
phone bill	$45.00 per mo.
cell phone bill	$75.00 per mo.
salary from part-time job	$12,900.00 per year
life insurance	$110.00 per mo.
water bill	$27.00 per mo.
children's school tuition	$435.00 per mo.
school loan	$75.00 per mo.
credit card bills	$300.00
doctor bills	$50.00 per mo.
entertainment & eating out	$100.00 per mo.
church tithe (you calculate this)	
dry cleaning/laundry	$30.00
electric bill	$150.00 per mo.
kid's allowance	$25.00 per mo.
lunch money (for whole family)	$225.00
taxes (calculate at 25%)	
spending money	$200.00
clothing	$40.00 per mo.

2 **Find the difference.**

12,567	354,894	783,254	890,006	56,470	10,009
- 5,889	- 115,703	- 694,228	- 9,842	- 45,701	- 354

3 **Connect the prime numbers to reveal a picture.**

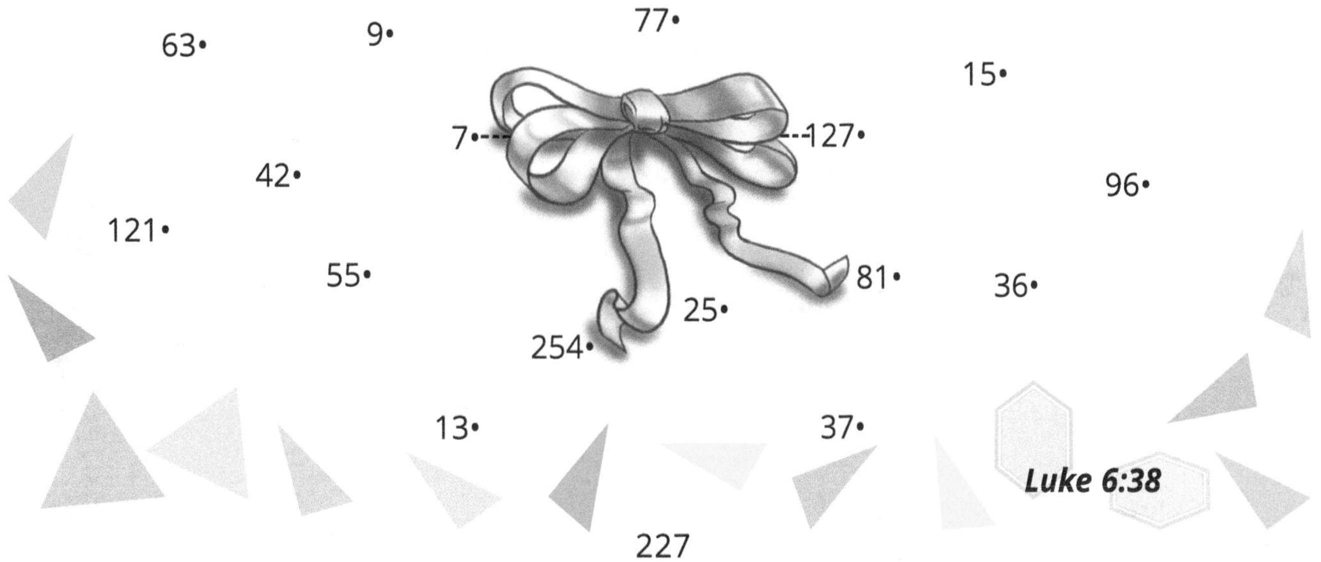

4 **Find the product.**

$1.5 \times 2.3 =$	$.23 \times .78 =$	$56.9 \times 4.1 =$	$45.63 \times 12.1 =$
$.03 \times 0.004 =$	$1.1 \times 3.3 =$	$123.02 \times 56.1 =$	$10.09 \times 14.3 =$

5 **Multiply the fractions. Rename in lowest terms.**

$\frac{7}{8} \times \frac{1}{8} =$	$\frac{3}{5} \times \frac{1}{7} =$	$\frac{1}{8} \times \frac{4}{5} =$	$\frac{8}{9} \times \frac{1}{5} =$
$\frac{4}{7} \times \frac{4}{9} =$	$\frac{2}{3} \times \frac{4}{9} =$	$\frac{7}{12} \times \frac{5}{11} =$	$\frac{5}{7} \times \frac{1}{12} =$

6 **Find the area of each shape.**

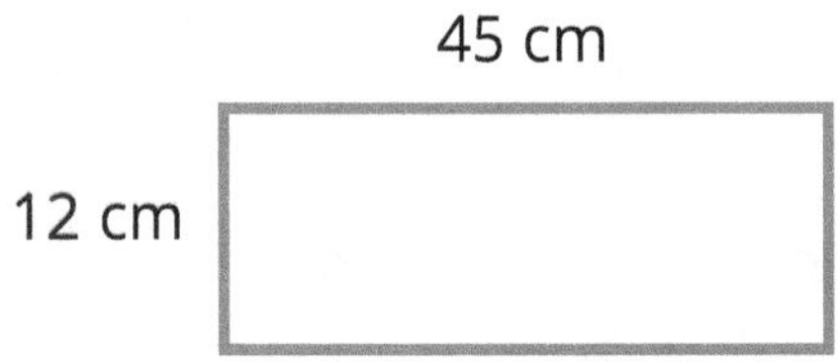

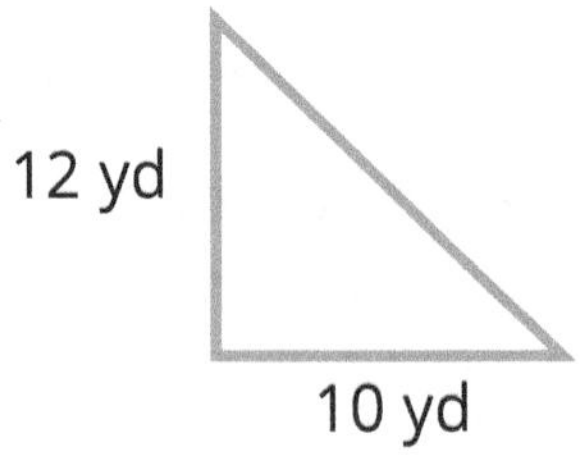

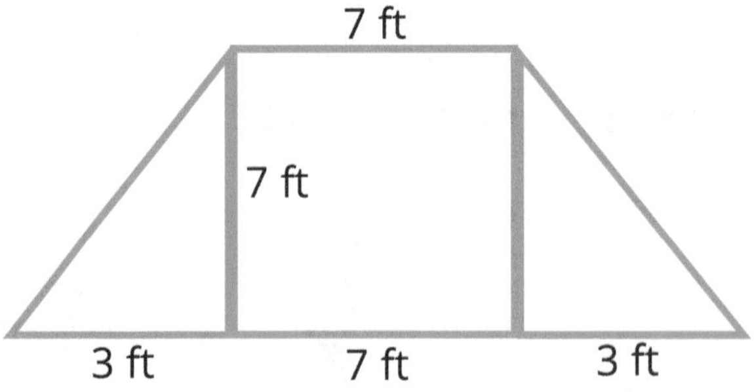

7 **Divide each ratio to find an equal ratio.**

$\frac{7}{21}$ $\frac{18}{21}$ $\frac{9}{12}$ $\frac{100}{200}$ $\frac{12}{48}$ $\frac{6}{18}$

Checking Accounts

The banking industry has many different facets and products to offer. One banking product used is a **checking account**. Having a checking account is an important responsibility. You must understand the purpose of a checking account and you must understand how a checking account functions.

The main purpose of a checking account is to allow an individual to pay cash for items without having to physically carry "green money" in his/her pocket. A checking account is a type of "I Owe You" or promissory note. When a check is given to someone as payment for a product or service, that individual may present the check to your banking institution and receive "green money" in exchange for the promissory note. As the owner of the checking account, you make deposits of money into the account and the bank "holds" this money for you until you need it. Look at the check below. Notice the labeled check parts. You should be familiar with this information from your previous math studies.

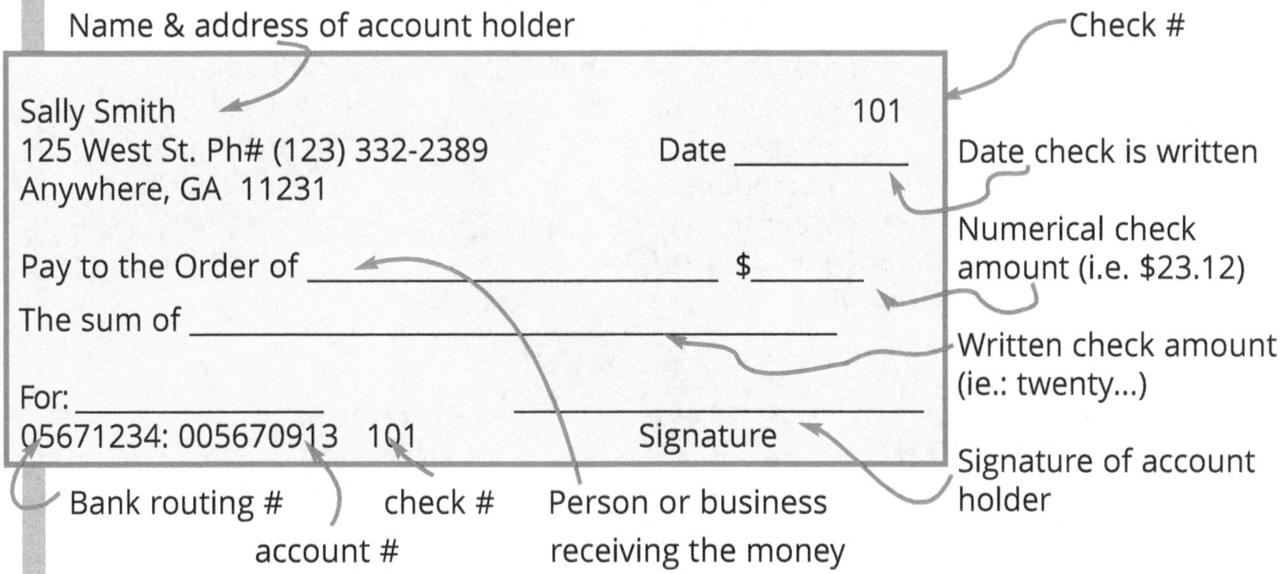

Every person with a checking account also keeps a check register to "register" or show who each check was written to. This log also records deposits which are made to the account. Look at the portion of a check register shown below:

Date	Ck #	To	Credit	Debit	Balance
1/9/18	101	Walker Grocery Store		$123.00	$978.23
1/9/18	102	Ellis Car Repair		$55.00	$923.23
1/10/18	103	Bell Telephone		$35.20	$888.03
1/15/18	-----	Deposit	$986.78		$1,874.81
1/15/18	-----	Service Charges		$4.75	$1,870.06

Credits are the deposits made to an account. **Debits** are the withdrawals, such as a check, made from an account. Notice the last entry marked **Service Charges**.

Service Charges are the fees that the Bank charges the customer for having a checking account. Most individuals can avoid paying these charges by keeping a required balance in the checking account at all times.

Every person with a checking account must keep an accurate register in order to know how much money he/she has in the bank. Once a month, the bank will send a checking account **statement**. This statement shows all transactions made for that month. As the account holder, you are to balance, or **reconcile,** your checkbook. To reconcile means to make sure that your register balance matches the balance shown on the bank statement. Look at the sample statement below.

James E. Ingle
3031 South Street
North City, Alabama 55594

Account # 123456789
From: 09/01/18 To: 10/08/18

Statement Summary
Interest Checking

Previous statement balance on 09/01/18	$710.33
4 deposits & other credits	$798.83
18 withdrawals & other debits	–$1,264.37
average collected balance	$391.00
minimum collected balance	$52.00
Annual percentage yield earned	1.66%
Interest year to date	$13.76
Balance as of 10/8/18	**$244.79**

Statement Activity
Interest Checking
Deposits/Credits

Amount	**Date**	**Description**
+43.17	09/15	Cash deposit
+711.95	09/25	Deposit
+43.18	09/30	Deposit
+0.53	10/08	Interest

Withdrawals/Debits

Amount	Date	Description
–50.00	09/18	Auto transfer

Check Register

Number	Amount	Date	Number	Amount	Date
3167	15.00	09/22	3191	3.50	10/02
3174*	16.00	09/22	3192	30.00	09/29
3183*	60.00	09/15	3193	20.00	09/28
3184	30.00	09/14	3194	79.01	10/01
3185	337.30	09/14	3195	25.00	10/02
3186	88.00	09/18	3196	15.78	10/01
3188*	42.47	09/14	3197	36.30	10/01
3189	62.00	09/15	3198	294.01	10/02
3190	60.00	09/30			

1 **Sally needs to pay her bills. Write a check for each entry shown on the register below.**

Date	Check Number	To	Credit	Debit	Balance
11/2	Deposit	Deposit (pay check)	$950.00		$1,593.98
11/3	1203	Dr. Mann		$52.00	$1,541.98
11/4	1204	ABC Electric Company		$154.25	$1,387.73
11/4	1205	Walker Mortgage Company		$897.38	$490.35
11/4	1206	Walton Water Company		$25.50	$464.85

Sally Smith 1203
125 West St. Ph# (123) 332-2389 Date ___________
Anywhere, GA 11231

Pay to the Order of ___________________________ $_______

The sum of ____

For: ________________ ___________________________
05671234: 005670913 101 Signature

Sally Smith 1204
125 West St. Ph# (123) 332-2389 Date ___________
Anywhere, GA 11231

Pay to the Order of ___________________________ $ _________

The sum of ____

For: ________________ ___________________________
05671234: 005670913 101 Signature

Sally Smith 1205
125 West St. Ph# (123) 332-2389 Date ___________
Anywhere, GA 11231

Pay to the Order of ___________________________ $ _________

The sum of ____

For: ________________ ___________________________
05671234: 005670913 101 Signature

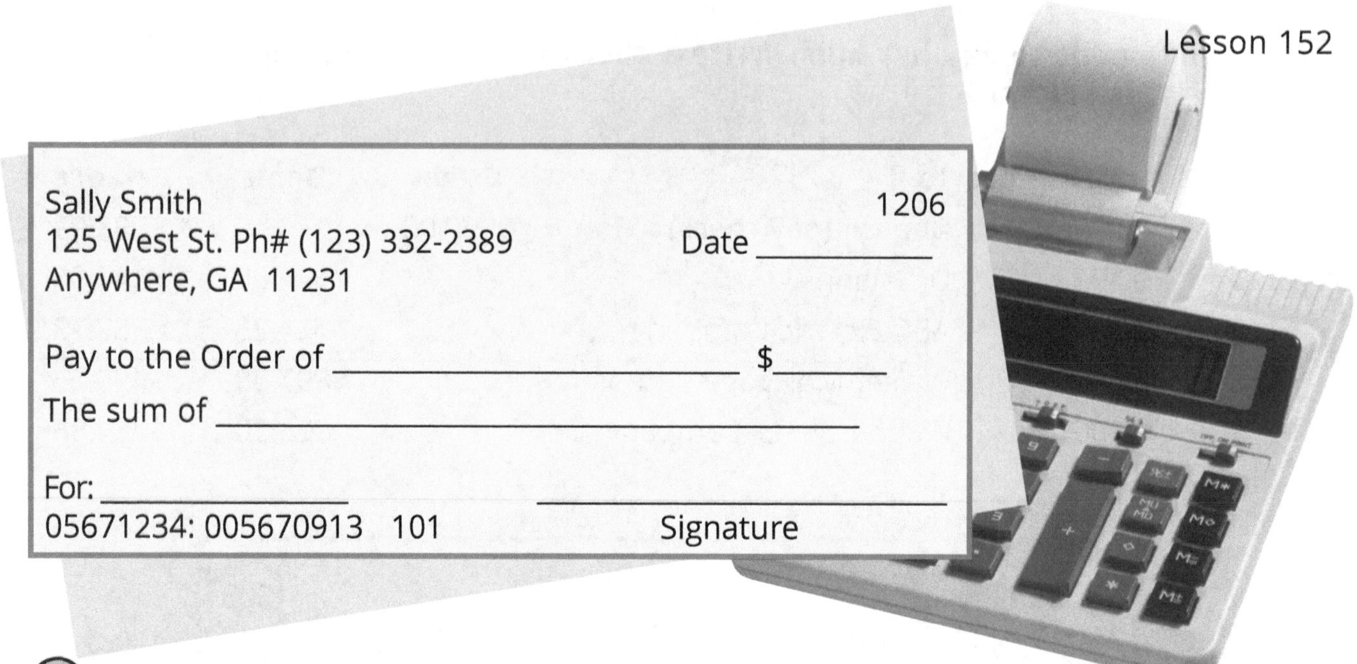

Sally Smith 1206
125 West St. Ph# (123) 332-2389 Date ____________
Anywhere, GA 11231

Pay to the Order of ____________________________ $_______

The sum of ____

For: _________________ ____________________________
05671234: 005670913 101 Signature

2 **Look at the condensed yearly budget shown below. Complete the chart and answer the questions.**

Yearly Income: $________

Category	Yearly Budget	Monthly Budget
1. Tithe	$________	$300
2. Taxes	$3,900	$________
Net Spendable Income (Salary–Taxes & Tithe)	**$**________	**$**________
3. Housing	$________	$625
4. Food	$________	$175
5. Automobile	$2,880	$________
6. Insurance	$1,200	$________
7. Debts	$1,500	$________
8. Enter. & Recreation	$________	$115
9. Clothing	$________	$50
10. Savings	$900	$75
11. Medical	$1,020	$________
12. Miscellaneous	$________	$110
Totals (items 3 – 12)	$________	$________

Is this person living within their means? How do you know?
What should be done with any excess money?

3 **Solve.**

219,654 - 135,892	238,965 - 25,980	452,790 - 389,004
450,678 - 423,889	621,750 - 600,456	564,761 - 144,902

4 **Match the problem with the correct answer.**

$45.96 \div 1.3 =$	4.54
$4.596 \div .013 =$	3.54
$459.6 \div 130.0 =$	35.35
$45.96 \div 10.13 =$	353.54

5 **Find the products. Use the answers to decode the message.**

A	C	R
$1\frac{2}{5} \times 1\frac{1}{2} =$	$2\frac{1}{4} \times 11\frac{5}{6} =$	$3\frac{2}{3} \times 10\frac{1}{2} =$
H	**T**	**E**
$6 \times 3\frac{3}{8} =$	$2\frac{1}{3} \times 1\frac{1}{4} =$	$2\frac{1}{2} \times 1\frac{7}{10} =$

___	___	___	___	___	___	___	___	___
$26\frac{5}{8}$	$20\frac{1}{4}$	$2\frac{1}{10}$	$38\frac{1}{2}$	$2\frac{1}{10}$	$26\frac{5}{8}$	$2\frac{11}{12}$	$4\frac{1}{4}$	$38\frac{1}{2}$

6 **Find the surface area of each shape.**

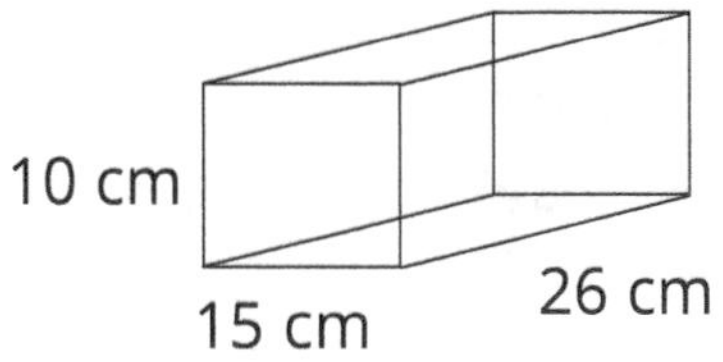

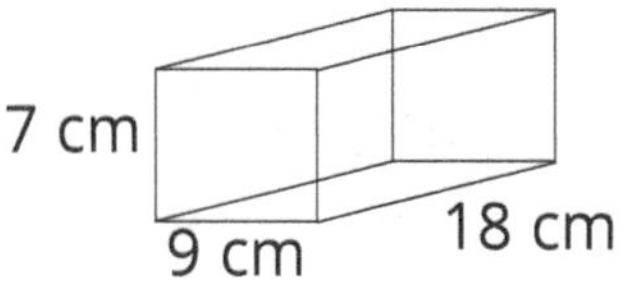

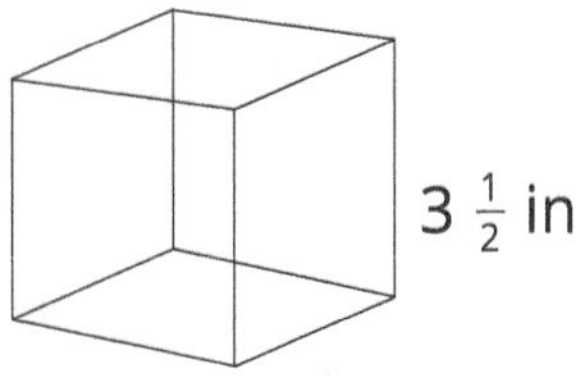

7 **Write a proportion and solve. Round to the nearest hundredth.**

2 for $10.00
8 for ___________

18 for $2.00
36 for ___________

32 for $20.00
96 for ___________

5 for $1.05
25 for ___________

25 for $15.75
100 for ___________

60 for $2.18
90 for ___________

6 for $12.00
15 for ___________

11 for $23.00
15 for ___________

Savings Accounts

Ashley is saving her money to buy a new sound system for her room. She is saving her money in a **savings account** at her bank. A savings account allows you to save your money and earn interest (extra money paid by the savings institution) too. When you deposit money into a savings account, the bank will pay **interest** on that money. Savings account interest is usually paid **quarterly**, or every three months. Unlike a checking account, you may not write payments to other individuals from a savings account. Only account holders, individuals owning the account, may make deposits and withdrawals from a savings account. Most banks will allow the account owner to make unlimited deposits or withdrawals from a regular savings account. The statement below is a sample savings account statement.

James E. Ingle — Account # 123456789
3031 South Street
North City, Alabama 55594 — From: 09/01/18 To: 10/08/18

Statement Summary

Previous statement balance on 01/01/18	7,566.86
4 Deposits and other credits	+366.48
3 Withdrawals or other debits	–1010.00
Interest Earned	+21.48
Avg. collected balance	7,283.38
Annual percentage yield earned	2.53%
43 Days in the period	
Balance as of 2/12/98	**6,923.34**

Date	Transaction	Amount	Balance
01/02	Cash deposit	+20.00	7,586.86
01/02	Check deposit	+275.00	7,861.86
01/05	Transfer debit	–100.00	7,761.86
01/15	Transfer debit	–700.00	7,061.86
01/20	Cash deposit	+50.00	7,111.86
02/05	Cash withdrawal	–210.00	6,901.86
02/12	Interest credit	+21.48	6,923.34

Ashley also has access to several other savings account options. Other services offered by most banks include Certificates of Deposit (CD's), Individual Retirement Accounts (IRAs), and investment services.

Certificates of Deposit: When opening a CD, the account holder agrees to leave a specified amount of money in the bank for a certain amount of time. In exchange for this deposit, the account holder receives a certificate, thus the name Certificate of Deposit. During this time period, the CD account earns interest, but no deposits or withdrawals may be made to or from the account. If a withdrawal is made before the CD term is up, the customer will incur a penalty. When the CD matures (time limit is up), the account holder may do as he/she chooses with the money.

Individual Retirement Account: An IRA is much like a CD but IRAs have certain government restrictions concerning when money may be withdrawn, in most

cases not until the age of 59. When opening an IRA, an individual needs to evaluate if he/she will need the money before retirement. If so, opening an IRA may not be the best option. IRAs are specifically designed for retirement savings. This would not have been an option for Ashley, considering her present needs.
Investment services are often offered at banks. Brokers will direct you on investing through a variety of options such as stocks, bonds or mutual funds. Usually, a person can earn a better interest rate and return on their money through these options.

1. **Circle the answer to the questions.**

Karen is thinking about buying a lake house when she finishes her teaching career. In order to purchase this home she needs to make a financial plan. Which type of account would be her best option when considering her goal?

a checking account   a savings account   CD's   IRAs   Investment Services

Cindy is saving for Christmas gifts. Each month she is saving $50.00 towards her presents. What type of account would be best for her savings need?

a checking account   a savings account   CD's   IRAs   Investment Services

George is extremely busy and needs to be able to pay bills through the mail. What type of account would best suit his needs?

a checking account   a savings account   CD's   IRAs   Investment Services

Sam just changed jobs. His old company gave him a large check for the balance of his company retirement account. Sam must invest this money and does not wish to spend any of it until he retires in 3 years. What type of account would be his best option?

a checking account   a savings account   CD's   IRAs   Investment Services

2. **Label.**

Sally Smith 101
125 West St. Ph# (123) 332-2389 Date __________
Anywhere, GA 11231

Pay to the Order of ______________________ $ ________

The sum of ______________________________________

For: ______________ ______________________
05671234: 005670913 101 Signature

3. **List and explain the 5 divisions of income you need to recognize when making a budget.**

I. ________________

II. ________________

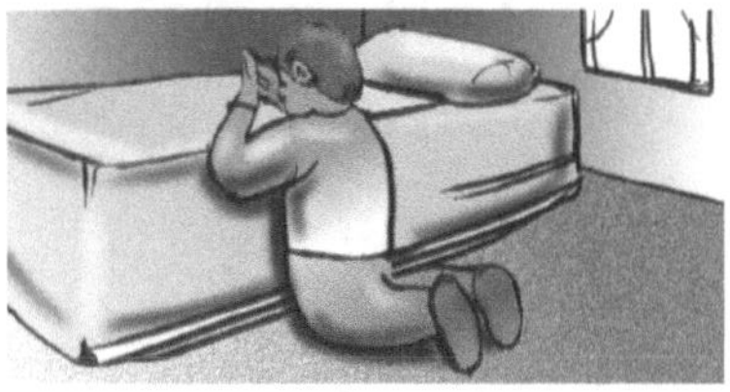

III. ____________________

IV. ____________________

V. ____________________

4 **Solve.**

$4^5 =$ $\quad$ $9^3 =$ $\quad$ $2^6 =$ $\quad$ $5^2 =$

$10{,}000{,}000 = 10^?$ $\quad$ $100 = 10^?$ $\quad$ $144 =$ $\quad$ $225 =$

5 **Find the sum or difference and write all answers in lowest terms. Find the answers in the puzzle. Shade the sums blue and the differences yellow.**

$\frac{24}{100} + \frac{19}{100} =$ $\quad$ $\frac{98}{1{,}001} - \frac{73}{1{,}001} =$ $\quad$ $\frac{78}{100} + \frac{45}{100} =$

$\frac{543}{988} + \frac{127}{988} =$ $\quad$ $\frac{159}{467} + \frac{207}{467} =$ $\quad$ $\frac{298}{100} - \frac{115}{100} =$

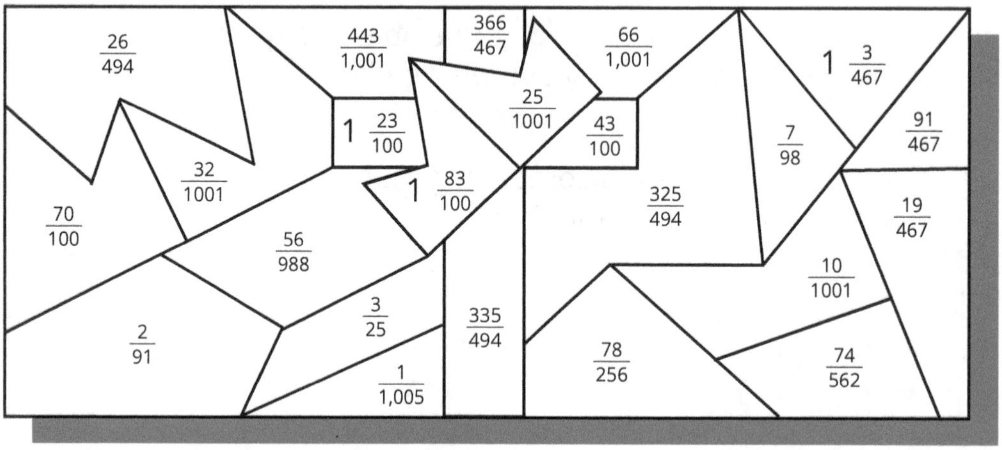

6 **Convert each fraction to its decimal equivalent. Order the answers from smallest to largest to reveal a message.**

A $\frac{9}{100} =$ $\quad$ R $\frac{3}{10} =$ $\quad$ E $\frac{31}{50} =$ $\quad$ A $\frac{4}{10} =$

R $\frac{3}{4} =$ $\quad$ C $\frac{73}{1000} =$ $\quad$ T $\frac{3}{5} =$ $\quad$ C $\frac{427}{1000} =$ $\quad$ H $\frac{89}{1000} =$

7 **Solve.**

$150 \div \frac{1}{3} =$ $\quad$ $25 \div \frac{1}{5} =$ $\quad$ $100 \div \frac{1}{20} =$ $\quad$ $10{,}550 \div \frac{1}{2} =$

$23 \div \frac{1}{7} =$ $\quad$ $989 \div \frac{1}{3} =$ $\quad$ $2{,}500 \div \frac{1}{2} =$ $\quad$ $8 \div \frac{1}{4} =$

What is Interest?

Interest paid is a charge for a loan. It is usually a percentage of the dollar amount borrowed.

Any time money is borrowed for a purchase, the bank, or lender, charges the customer a fee (interest) for borrowing the money. Interest may be calculated different ways, depending on what type of loan you have. **Simple Interest** is interest which is charged only on the **principal**, the amount of money borrowed. Look at the example below. Jim Wilson borrowed $2000.00 from a local community bank for 1 year at an interest rate of 12%.

Simple Interest Calculation:

Step 1: Multiply the principal by the interest rate. This gives you the interest charge.

$$\begin{array}{r} \$2{,}000 \\ \times\ .12 \\ \hline 4000 \\ 20000 \\ \hline \$240.00 \end{array}$$

Step 2: Add the principal amount to the interest charge. This tells the total amount of money due.

$$\begin{array}{r} \$2{,}000.00 \\ +\ 240.00 \\ \hline \$2{,}240.00 \end{array}$$

Interest earned is when you are paid money for loaning money to another party. Savings accounts, IRAs, CD's, and other accounts earn interest for you because you are allowing the bank to use your money. Unfortunately, interest rates offered by banks on these type of accounts are not as much as you are charged through loans or credit cards. Currently, most banks are paying 3% - 5% interest on a savings accounts verses car loan rates of 11% - 14% and fixed credit card rates of 9% - 21%.

(1) **Find the simple interest charge and total loan amount for the following loans.**

$600 at 10% Interest: Total:	$1,285 at 12% Interest: Total:	$1,500 at 7% Interest: Total:	$10,700 at 11% Interest: Total:
$7,750 at $12\frac{3}{4}$ % Interest: Total:	$8,800 at 18% Interest: Total:	$1,250 at $7\frac{1}{2}$ % Interest: Total:	$325 at 13% Interest: Total:

(2) **Complete the savings account deposit slip using your own name and today's date. Make up your own 6 digit account number. Include a cash deposit of $12.19, and two check deposits of $21.16 and $13.88. Be sure to write the total amount of your deposit.**

Savings Account Deposit Slip Wooden Nickel Savings and Loan Pine Cove Branch		Dollars	Cents
	Cash		
	Checks (1)		
	(2)		
Account no. ____________ Date ________	(3)		
	(4)		
	(5)		
Deposit to the account of ________________________________	Total		

(3) **Use the check template below to write a check to your favorite store for $554.99.**

514

Date ___________

Pay to the Order of ____________________________ $________

The sum of ____

Wooden Nickel Savings and Loan
Pine Grove Branch
For: ________________ ______________________________
05671234: 005670913 101 Signature

(4) **Enter the check you wrote in the checkbook record. Also list a deposit made the same day for $ 612.19. Find your new balance after both transactions.**

Date	Check #	Transaction	Amount of Check	Deposit	Balance
					$2,500.89
				Total	

5 Complete.

1. Sandra makes $590.00 a week. If she saves 10% of her salary every week, how much money will she have at the end of the year? (52 weeks)
2. If Sandra makes $590.00 a week, what is her yearly income?
3. If Sandra spends 25% of her income in housing, how much should she put aside each week for rent?
4. If Sandra gets a 5% raise, what will her total income be?

6 Find the sum or difference. Make sure the answer is in simplest form.

$\frac{5}{9} + \frac{3}{9} =$ ______ $\frac{1}{12} + \frac{1}{12} =$ ______ $\frac{7}{9} + \frac{2}{9} =$ ______

$\frac{18}{20} - \frac{7}{20} =$ ______ $\frac{25}{27} - \frac{4}{27} =$ ______ $\frac{6}{15} - \frac{1}{15} =$ ______

7 Divide these fractions. Add zeros in the dividend until the quotient is zero.

$\frac{1}{2} =$ ______ $\frac{5}{8} =$ ______ $\frac{9}{10} =$ ______

Divide these fractions. Write the answers as repeating decimals.

$\frac{2}{3} =$ ______ $\frac{9}{11} =$ ______ $\frac{7}{9} =$ ______

8 Cities determine their own sales tax. Sometimes, you can save a lot of money if you buy an expensive item in a city that charges a lower sales tax. Compute the sales tax for each city. Write the amount of difference between the two cities.

Cost of Item	City One (6% tax)	City Two (8% tax)	Difference
$500.00			
$2,500.00			
$25,465.00			
$189,000.00			

Principal

Interest can be calculated a number of different ways. Most banking institutions calculate interest on a monthly rate or a yearly rate rather than using a simple interest calculation.

Credit cards charge an interest rate when they are not paid off each month.
Look at the example below:
Paul purchased \$225.00 worth of goods & services on his credit card for the month of November. \$225.00 is considered the **Principal**, or the original amount of money on which interest is paid. When the bill came, he paid \$50.00 towards this debt. The credit card company then charged Paul 16.5% interest on the remaining money due. This is the fee the credit card company is charging Paul for borrowing that money. This interest will be charged each month until Paul pays off not only the original \$225.00 but any interest charges as well.

$$\$225.00 - \$50.00 \text{ payment} = \$175.00 \text{ balance on account}$$

The company then divides the 16.5% rate by 365 days so that they know how much to charge you for each day you have a balance on the account.

$$16.5\% \div 365 = 0.0452\% \text{ fee per day}$$
$$\$175.00 \times 0.0452\% = \$0.079 = \$0.08 \text{ per day}$$

If Paul keeps this balance for one month (31 days) he will pay \$2.48 in interest.
That doesn't seem like much money. Let's look at a larger credit card balance.
If Paul has a balance of \$6,873.00 at an interest rate of 13.99%, he pays \$2.63 per day.

$$\$2.63 \text{ per day} \times 31 \text{ days} = \$81.53 \text{ per month in interest!}$$

This is a type of **Compound Interest**. **Compound Interest** is interest computed on the accumulated unpaid interest as well as the original principal.

When calculating interest, we will consider a month as 30 days and a year as 360 days. One formula for calculating interest is as follows:

$$\text{Interest (I)} = \text{principal (p)} \times \text{rate (r)} \times \text{time (t)}$$

Look at this example:
Finding Interest in terms of years:

Step 1: Plug all of the needed information into the interest formula.
$P = \$500$; $r = 9\%$; $t = 4$ months
$(I = p\ r\ t)$
$I = \$500 \times 9\% \times 4$ months

Step 2: The interest rate needs to be converted to a decimal.
$I = \$500 \times .09 \times 4$ months

Step 3: Time, in the interest formula, needs to be in terms of years since the money is being loaned for 4 months. The time would be $\frac{1}{3}$ of a year since 4 months is $\frac{1}{3}$ of a 12 months (a year).

$$I = \$500 \times .09 \times \frac{1}{3}$$

Step 4: Work the problem.

$I = 45 \times \frac{1}{3}$

$I = \frac{45}{3}$

I = $15 (if necessary, round to the nearest cent)

Finding Interest in terms of years:

I = $400 × 6% × 24 days

Convert the interest to decimal. 6% = .06

Since the time needs to be in terms of years divide by 360. $\frac{24}{360} = \frac{1}{15}$ of a year

$I = \$400 \times .06 \times \frac{1}{15}$

$I = 24 \times \frac{1}{15}$

$I = \frac{24}{15}$

I = $1.60

1. **Find the interest to the nearest cent.**

p = $600; r = 19%; t = 30 days

p = $500; r = 11%; t = 90 days

p = $700; r = 8%; t = 4 months

p = $7,500; r = 13%; t = 60 days

p = $5,000; r = $6\frac{3}{4}$%; t = 1 year

p = $350; r = $1\frac{1}{2}$%; t = 6 months

2. **Find the simple interest charge and total loan amount for the following loans.**

$12,000 at $10\frac{1}{2}$%	$20,000 at 15%	$9,500 at $7\frac{1}{4}$%	$30,500 at 11%
Interest:	Interest:	Interest:	Interest:
Total:	Total:	Total:	Total:

3. **Complete the savings account withdrawal slip.**
Use your name and the current date. Make up a 6 digit account number.
Write the withdrawal for $12,917.02.

Wooden Nickel Savings and Loan
Pine Cove Branch
Savings Account Withdrawal

Date ____________

Pay to the order of ________________________________ $ ____________

______________________________________ Dollars

Account Number _______________ ____________________
Signature

4 **Complete the checkbook ledger.**

Date	Check #	Transaction	Amount of Check	Deposit	Balance
					$2,505.10
7-4-18	650	Baxter's Toys	$12.89		
7-5-18	651	Books and More	$29.50		
7-5-18		Payroll Check		$1,212.00	
7-5-18	652	Pet Haven	$15.18		
7-7-18	653	World Trader	$157.90		
7-12-18		Payroll Check		$1,212.00	

5 **Find the missing numbers.**

$$\begin{array}{r} 305,?01 \\ -1?5,549 \\ \hline 130,15? \end{array} \qquad \begin{array}{r} 79?,393 \\ -753,3?5 \\ \hline ?7,008 \end{array} \qquad \begin{array}{r} 199,?20 \\ -177,94? \\ \hline 21,8?3 \end{array} \qquad \begin{array}{r} 45,?00 \\ -2?,219 \\ \hline 21,8?1 \end{array}$$

$$\begin{array}{r} ???,??? \\ -96,651 \\ \hline 100,382 \end{array} \qquad \begin{array}{r} ???,??? \\ -534,506 \\ \hline 366,898 \end{array} \qquad \begin{array}{r} ?,??? \\ -4,886 \\ \hline 2,118 \end{array} \qquad \begin{array}{r} ??,??? \\ -64,909 \\ \hline 3,671 \end{array}$$

6 **Compare with the correct sign. (>, <, =)**

$\frac{1}{3}$ ______ $\frac{30}{90}$ $\frac{7}{8}$ ______ $\frac{7}{9}$ $\frac{3}{5}$ ______ $\frac{4}{7}$ $\frac{8}{9}$ ______ $\frac{9}{10}$

$\frac{1}{6}$ ______ $\frac{1}{9}$ $\frac{9}{12}$ ______ $\frac{4}{7}$ $\frac{3}{4}$ ______ $\frac{7}{12}$ $\frac{2}{9}$ ______ $\frac{3}{11}$

7 **A circle graph shows how much of Mike and Robin's monthly salary is spent each month on items such as rent, clothing, groceries, tithing, and other household necessities.**

The sum of the pie pieces should always total 100 when using percents. We have shown percents (%) on this pie graph, so the numbers should total 100%.
15% + 10% + 13% + 12% + 30% + 10% + 10% = 100%

If the family income is $3,250.00 a month, how much money do they spend in each category? Complete the table below. The first one has been done for you.

Monthly Income

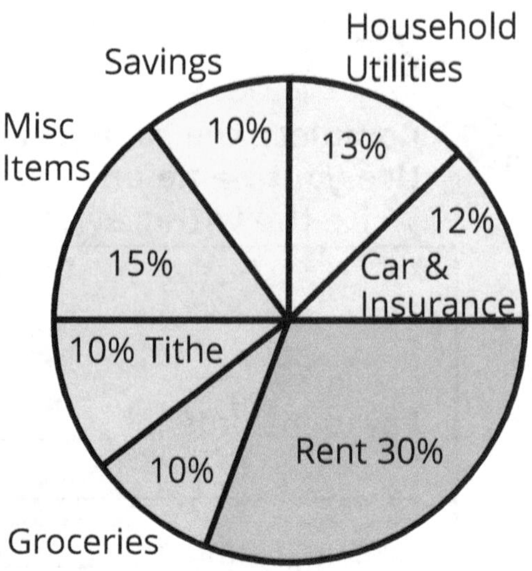

Category	Percentage	Total Amount Spent
rent	30 % (0.30)	($3,250.00 × 0.30) = $975.00
groceries	10%	
tithe	10%	
misc.	15%	
savings	10%	
utilities	13%	
car and insurance	12%	

Installment Buying

Kimberly has been saving her money to purchase a car. After several years of saving, on her 16th birthday, Kimberly and her father went to the local car dealership to purchase a new car. The total price of the car was $17,898.00. Kimberly saved $12,000.00 on her own but will need to borrow the remaining $5,898.00 to purchase the car.

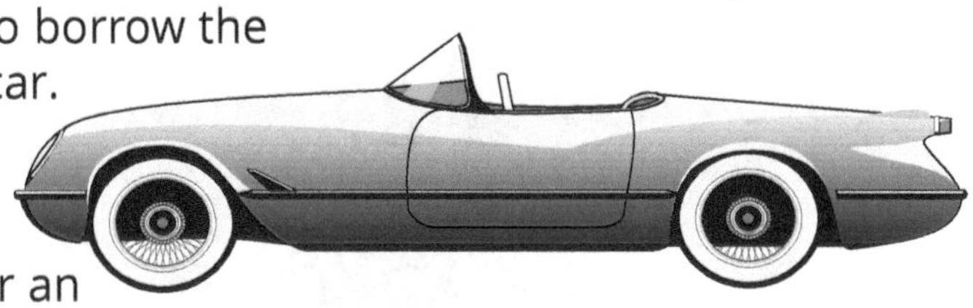

Large items, like cars, as usually purchased through **Installment buying**. Installment buying is when you pay for an item over a period of time through a series of set payments. Below are listed several important facts about installment buying:

1. The customer is charged a **finance charge** (interest paid on the amount of the purchase) for the use of the payment plan. Department store credit cards usually charge between 18% and 21% per year ($1\frac{1}{2}$% - $1\frac{3}{4}$% per month) for installment buying on their credit card. Banks are currently charging between 11% and 14% for new car loans.
2. Credit cards may be paid off monthly to avoid paying any finance charges. This is equivalent to borrowing money from the store for 30 days at no charge.
3. Most stores and credit cards have a minimum amount that must be paid each month. Consumer loans, loans from banks, have set payments that must be made each month.
4. Installment buying is a type of compounding interest. Interest is calculated each month based on the outstanding balance (principal and unpaid interest).
   Look at this chart. It shows a sample department store credit card finance charge and payment schedule.

This chart is an example of **compounding interest**.

Month	*Balance*	*Interest $1\frac{1}{2}$%*	*Payment*	*New Balance*
January	$1,380.00	$20.70	$200.00	$1,200.70
February	$1,200.70	$18.00	$200.00	$1,018.70
March	$1,018.70	$15.00	$200.00	$833.70
April	$833.70	$12.51	$200.00	$646.21
May	$646.21	$9.69	$200.00	$455.90
June	$455.90	$6.84	$200.00	$266.74
July	$266.74	$3.94	$200.00	$70.68
August	$70.68	$1.06	$71.74	$0.00

1 **Complete the chart.**

Month	Balance	Interest $1\frac{1}{2}\%$	Payment	New Balance
January	$1,000.00	$15.00	$300.00	
February			$300.00	
March	$425.73		$300.00	
April				$0.00

2 **Complete the table.**

Interest	Principal	Interest Rate	Time
	$18,000	10%	1 year
	$1,000	11%	3 months
	$7,000	8%	6 months
	$5,000	12%	1 year
	$9,500	$6\frac{1}{2}\%$	$\frac{1}{2}$ year

3 **Adam needs to get a loan for $15,000.00 to buy supplies for his business. Find out how much the interest will be for each of the interest rates listed.** Then answer the questions below.

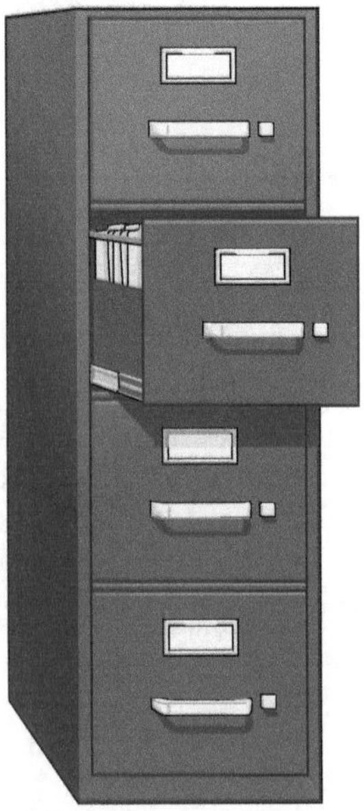

Interest	*Principal*	*Interest*	*Rate Time*
	$15,000	10%	1 year
	$15,000	9%	1 year
	$15,000	8%	1 year
	$15,000	7%	1 year
	$15,000	6%	1 year

Adam will pay the least amount of interest if he gets the loan with a (an) ________ interest rate.

Adam will pay the greatest amount of interest if he gets the loan with a (an) ________ interest rate.

The difference in interest between a 10% interest rate and a 6% interest rate is $________ .

The difference in interest between a 9% interest rate and an 8% interest rate is $________ .

4 **If each person puts 10% of their income in savings every week, how much will they have saved in a week? In a year?**
Round the numbers to the nearest cent.

Weekly Income	Weekly Savings	Yearly Savings
$1,299.00		
$565.00		
$2,900.00		
$3,012.00		

5 **Complete the Binary Place Value Chart.**

Binary Place Value Chart — **Base 10 Equivalent**

(64) 2^6	(32) 2^5	(16) 2^4	(8) 2^3	(4) 2^2	(2) 2^1	(1) 2^0		
1	0	0	1	0	0	0	=	
							=	15
	1	0	0	0	1	0	=	
							=	23
1	1	0	1	0	0	1	=	
							=	43

6 **Add or subtract.** Write the answer in lowest terms.

$\frac{6}{12} + \frac{1}{6}$ $\frac{4}{10} + \frac{1}{7}$ $\frac{6}{12} + \frac{2}{5}$ $\frac{3}{15} + \frac{2}{7}$

$\frac{3}{8} - \frac{1}{7}$ $\frac{9}{12} - \frac{2}{5}$ $\frac{15}{18} - \frac{2}{9}$ $\frac{12}{13} - \frac{1}{2}$

7 **Find the quotient.** Write the answer in lowest terms.

$6\frac{1}{4} \div 1\frac{2}{3} =$ $5\frac{1}{4} \div 1\frac{1}{2} =$ $\frac{3}{4} \div 1\frac{1}{4} =$

$11 \div 2\frac{1}{2} =$ $6\frac{1}{6} \div \frac{1}{6} =$ $2 \div 1\frac{1}{4} =$

Comparison Buying

Joe decided to purchase a new video camera. He went down to the local camera store and purchased one of the first cameras he saw at a price of $698.00. Two weeks later, Joe saw the exact same camera at another store for only $525.00. That is a $173.00 difference.

To help avoid such a situation, Joe should have only bought a new camera after he had compared several store's prices on the same camera.

This is called **comparison buying**.

When comparison shopping, there are certain things you must consider.

1. Make sure you purchase an item that performs all the functions you need but not those which are unnecessary.
2. Beware of salespeople who attempt to "up a sale" by getting you to purchase a more expensive item. Often, these more expensive items are completely unnecessary. Only purchase the item or accessories that you need.
3. Make sure you compare "apples to apples." This means to look for the exact same item at each store you shop. Remember, you are shopping to find the best deal possible on the desired item.
4. Ask about return policies of the store where you are purchasing an item. If purchasing an expensive item such as a camera, TV, refrigerator, computer, etc. ask about warranties or guarantees on the merchandise.
5. Use consumer magazines to research the item you want to purchase, especially if you are making a major purchase such as a car. These magazines conduct tests on a variety of different goods and services. They can tell you the best quality items, any problems you may encounter, and what type of customer service is available through different companies.

(1) **Circle the product that is the least expensive.**

1. 134.12 at 10% discount	128.19	140.00 at 15% off
2. 5 for $1.00	25 cents	0.35 at 10% off
3. 2 for 99 cents	80 cents at 20% off	3 for $1.20
4. 7 for $9.00	$1.35	2 for $2.50

2 **Steve bought a bike on the installment plan. He pays $25.00 a month.** Complete the table.

Month	Balance	Interest 1%	Payment	New Balance
1st month	$150.00	+ $1.50	– $25.00	$126.50
2nd month	$126.50			
3rd month				
4th month				
5th month				
6th month				
7th month				

3 **Find the interest paid to each bank patron.**

Deposit	Interest Rate Per Year	Time	Amount of Interest
$3,000.00	4%	1 year	
$2,500.00	5%	6 months	
$2,000.00	6%	6 months	
$1,800.00	4%	90 days	

4 **Find each missing number.**

$\frac{4}{8} = \frac{20}{n}$

$\frac{6}{18} = \frac{n}{72}$

$\frac{9}{11} = \frac{n}{220}$

$\frac{25}{7} = \frac{n}{49}$

$\frac{200}{300} = \frac{40}{n}$

$\frac{1{,}000}{n} = \frac{20}{90}$

5 **Write the name of each figure on the line provided.**

____

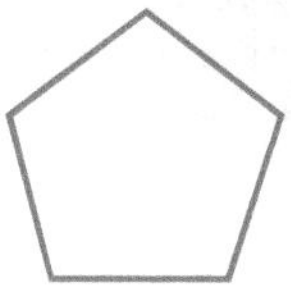
____

____

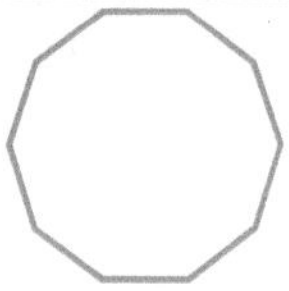
____

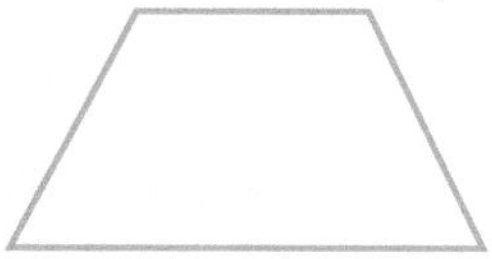
____

____

(6) **Write the numbers below in standard form. Find them in the puzzle and shade them. If the correct blocks are shaded, it will form a picture.**
You may use your calculator for this activity.

10^2 = ______ 2^5 = ______ 9^5 = ______

5^6 = ______ 10^4 = ______ 13^3 = ______

7^3 = ______ 11^2 = ______ 9^6 = ______

3^4 = ______ 12^2 = ______ 6^5 = ______

2^9 = ______ 2^{12} = ______ 3^5 = ______

10^5 = ______ 4^7 = ______ 6^7 = ______

2^8 = ______ 3^3 = ______ 9^2 = ______

2^{10} = ______ 3^2 = ______ 9^3 = ______

3,908	7,776	23	100,000	423,900
81	144	10,000	2,197	243
121	59,049	32	15,625	16,384
343	531,441	512	4,096	279,936
34,977	100	256	27	322,000
54,732	9	1,024	81	456
134,778	645	729	325	900

And you shall love the Lord your God with all your heart and all your soul and with all your might.
Deuteronomy 6: 5

(7) **Complete the crossword puzzle. The decimal point will occupy one space.**

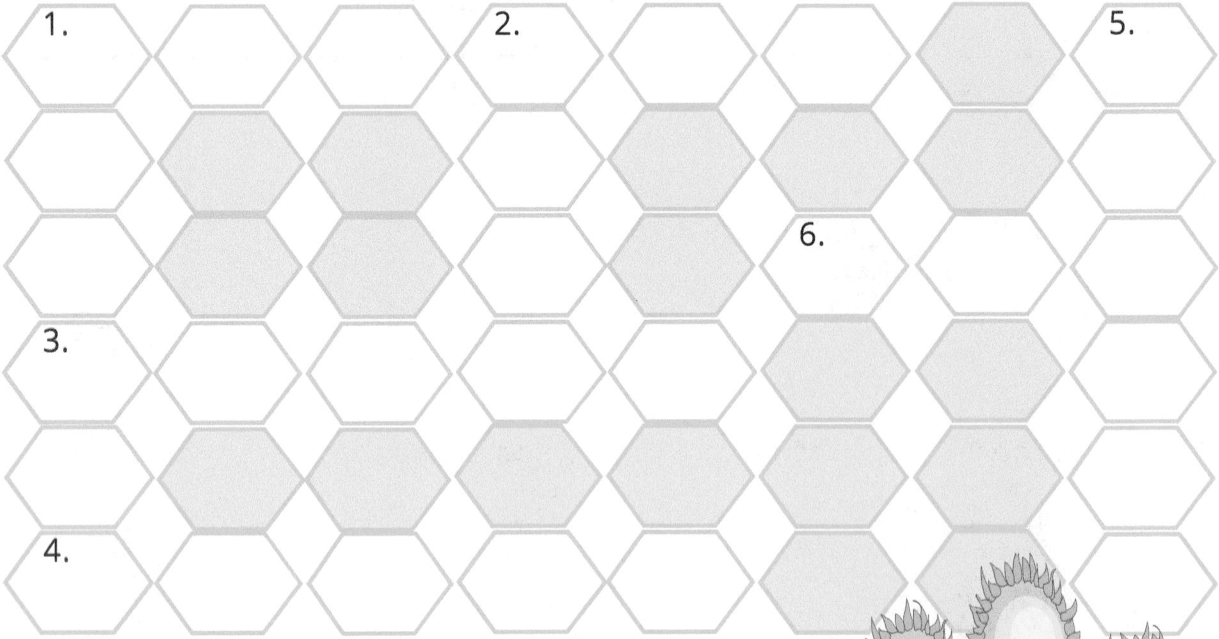

<u>Across</u>
1. $5.87 \times 2.8 =$
3. $24.11 \times 2 =$
4. $3.21 \times 3.1 =$
6. $3.4 \times 2 =$

<u>Down</u>
1. $3.19 \times 6.1 =$
2. $2.1 \times 2.2 =$
5. $63.2 \times 8.2 =$

Finding Average Expenses

When you make a budget it is easy to plan how much you will spend on your fixed expenses such as rent and car payment. However, there are many expenses like telephone, food, entertainment and electricity that are hard to predict.
These expenses are called variable expenses. People often plan these monthly expenses by keeping track of their bills for several months. Then they find an average monthly expense.

Look at the examples below.

	Jan	*Feb*	*Mar*	*Apr*	*May*	*June*	*Total*	*Avg*
Food	$105	$125	$97	$133	$140	$107	$825	$138
Electricity	$150	$175	$145	$160	$130	$155	$915	$153

The average cost for food is $138.00 a month. The average cost for electricity is $153.00 a month. Using these numbers, it will be easier to project an accurate budget.

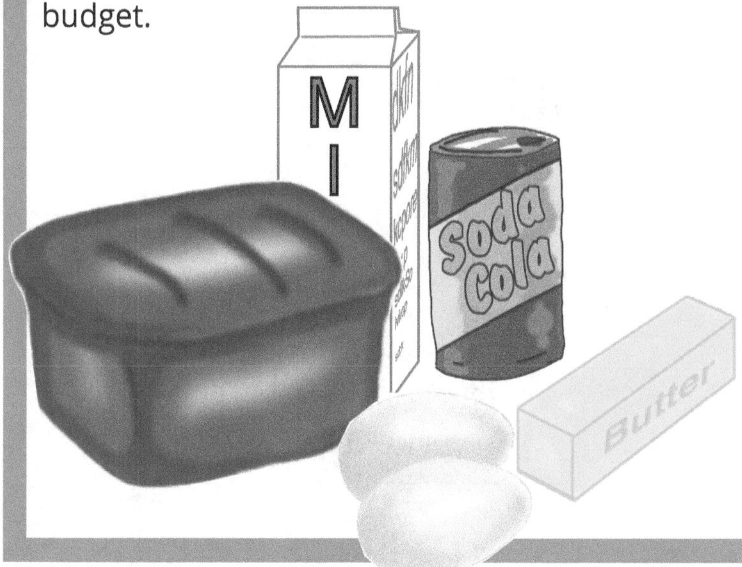

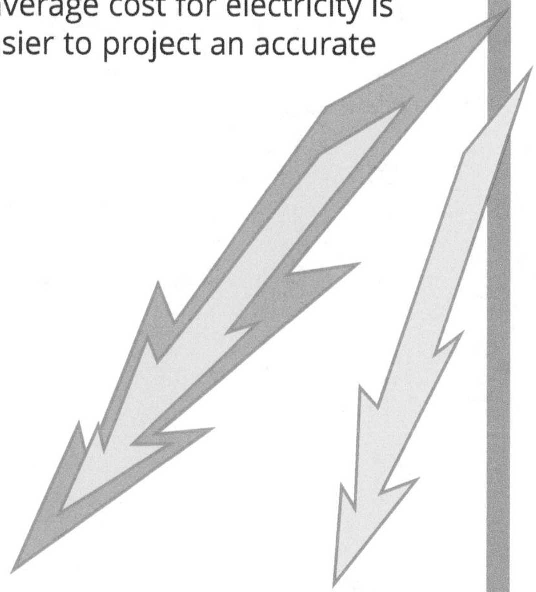

1 **Complete the table.**

	Jan	Feb	Mar	Apr	May	June	Total	Average
Water	$48	$52	$47	$49	$54	$57		
Clothes	$130	$120	$20	$65	$100	$75		

2 **Circle the best deal.**

1. 10 for $2	4 for $1	Pay 50 cents for two and get one free.
2. $6.99	$8 with 20% off	$10 with 40% off
3. $25 with 10% off	2 for $40	$21.00
4. buy 1 for $12 and get 1 free	$10 with 30% off	$7 with 15% off

3 **Renee bought a television on the installment plan. She pays $75.00 a month.** Complete the table.

Month	Balance	Interest 1%	Payment	New Balance
1st month	$250.00	$2.50	$75.00	$177.50
2nd month	$177.50			
3rd month				
4th month				

4 **Find the interest to the nearest cent.**

p = $500; r = 12%; t = 30 days

____

p = $800; r = $7\frac{1}{2}$%; t = 1 year

____

p = $700; r = $5\frac{1}{4}$%; t = 3 months

____

p = $1,500; r = 15%; t = 6 months

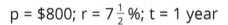

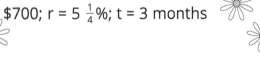

____

5 **Who am I?**

I have three digits that are all the same.
The product of my digits is 729.
The sum of my digits is 27.
Who Am I? ________________

Who am I?

I am a prime number between 2 and 20.
Both of my digits are the same.
Who am I? ________________

6 **Find the surface area of the box.**

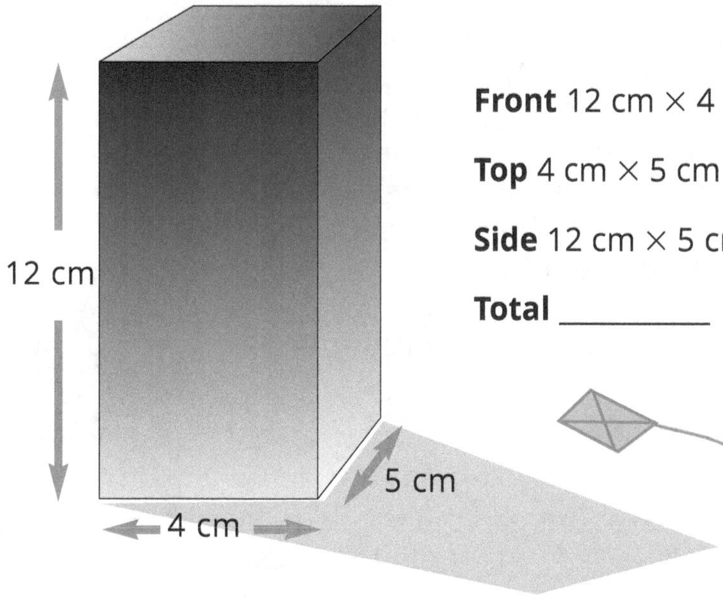

Front 12 cm × 4 cm = __________ × 2 = __________

Top 4 cm × 5 cm = __________ × 2 = __________

Side 12 cm × 5 cm = __________ × 2 = __________

Total __________

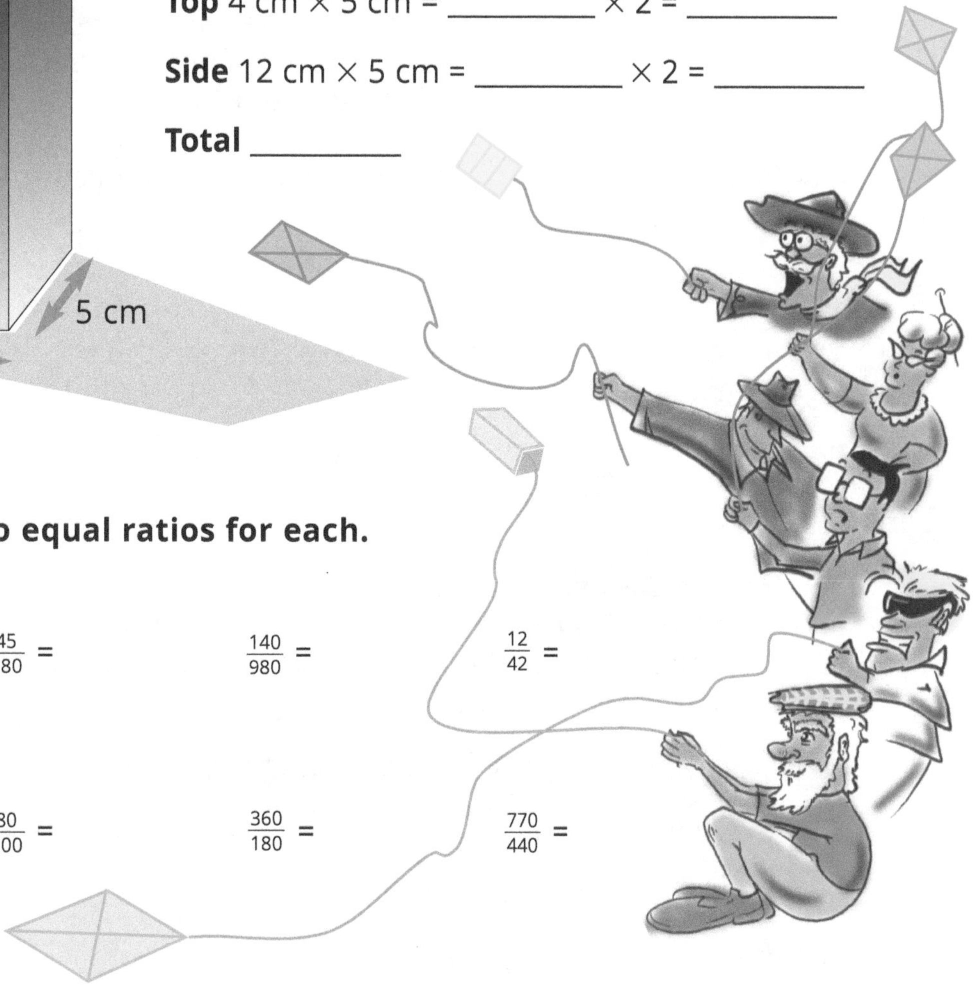

7 **Divide. Write two equal ratios for each.**

$\frac{40}{60} =$ $\frac{45}{180} =$ $\frac{140}{980} =$ $\frac{12}{42} =$

$\frac{100}{300} =$ $\frac{80}{100} =$ $\frac{360}{180} =$ $\frac{770}{440} =$

Using Correct Operation

It is sometimes difficult to decide which operation (+, –, ×, ÷) to use in a story problem. The table below shows you key words that signal each operation.

+	How many in all? Find the total. **Add.**
–	How many more? Compare. Take away. **Subtract.**
×	Finding the total of equal sets. **Multiply.**
÷	Distribute evenly into a given number of sets. Distribute into sets of a given size. **Divide.**
? ? ?	James sold 8 boxes of candy on Monday, 5 boxes of candy on Tuesday, 9 boxes of candy on Wednesday, and 11 boxes on Friday. How many boxes of candy did James sell in all?

UNDERSTAND: You know how many boxes James sold each day.
You need to find out the total amount sold.

PLAN: You want to know the TOTAL amount, so you need to ADD.
$8 + 5 + 9 + 11 =$

WORK: $8 + 5 + 9 + 11 = 33$

ANSWER/CHECK: The answer is 33 boxes. Reread the problem and check to see that this answer makes sense. Is 33 a realistic answer to the question? Yes.

(1) **Solve.**

Mr. Haney's class conducted a survey to find out what type of food their classmates liked the best. The results were: 12 Italian, 10 Mexican, and 6 Chinese.
Using these results, answer the question. Underline the key words that help you decide what operation to use.

1. How many more people liked Italian than Chinese?
2. If everyone votes, how many students are in the class in all?
3. How many more people like Mexican than Chinese?
4. What is the total number of people who like both Mexican and Italian?

2 **Tina's gasoline bills range from \$11.00 a week to \$35.00 a week. Look at her gasoline expenses for a two month period and find an average weekly gasoline expenditure.**

Week 1: \$12.50	Week 2: \$11.75	Week 3: \$13.00	Week 4: \$32.50
Week 5: \$17.50	Week 6: \$11.00	Week 7: \$35.00	Week 8: \$22.50

Average weekly expenditure. ______________

3 **When Pamela goes grocery shopping, she wants the best value for her money. She looks at different brands of a similar product and compares the prices per ounce to find the best value. Look at the products below and find the price per ounce for each product. (Round to the nearest cent.) Then circle the least expensive item.**

Folsom's Egg Noodles
12 ounces for \$1.79
Price per ounce ______

Marilyn's Homemade Noodles
1 pound and 6 oz for \$2.29
Price per ounce ______

Swift's Egg Noodles
2 pounds for \$2.99
Price per ounce ______

Silk Pudding
12 ounces for \$1.99
Price per ounce ______

Mini-Paks of Pudding
4 - 4 ounce cups for \$3.59
Price per ounce ______

Choco Pudding
1 pound for \$2.49
Price per ounce ______

4 **Find the missing numbers for the fraction wheel. Use cross products to solve.**

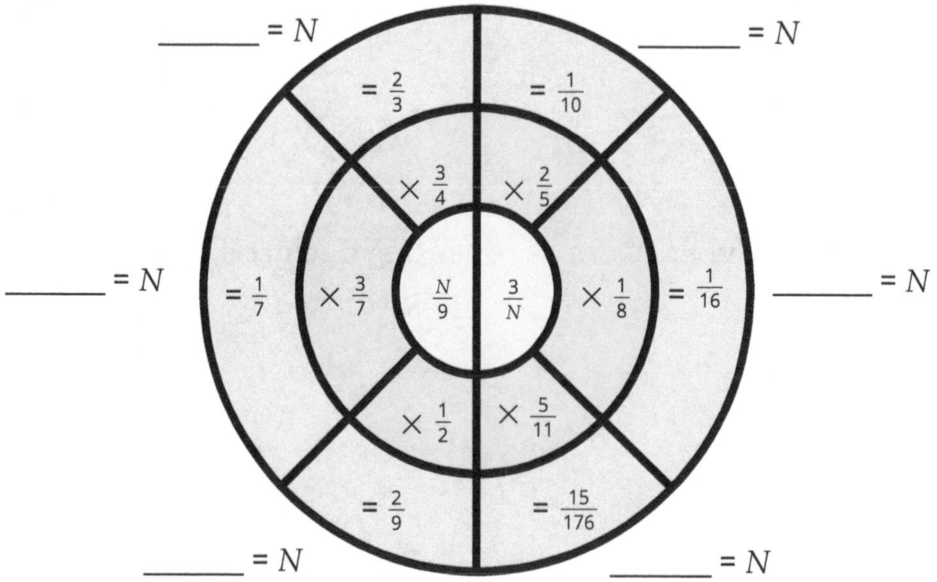

Example:

$$\frac{N}{14} \times \frac{2}{3} = \frac{4}{7}$$

$$\frac{2N}{42} = \frac{4}{7}$$

$$14N = 168$$

$$\frac{14N}{14} = \frac{168}{14}$$

N = 12

5 **Find the difference.**

$$\begin{array}{r} 895,701 \\ -173,549 \\ \hline \end{array} \quad \begin{array}{r} 987,363 \\ -793,385 \\ \hline \end{array} \quad \begin{array}{r} 79,800 \\ -74,947 \\ \hline \end{array} \quad \begin{array}{r} 95,091 \\ -73,219 \\ \hline \end{array}$$

$$\begin{array}{r} 147,865 \\ -93,621 \\ \hline \end{array} \quad \begin{array}{r} 298,484 \\ -134,806 \\ \hline \end{array} \quad \begin{array}{r} 8,484 \\ -4,806 \\ \hline \end{array} \quad \begin{array}{r} 78,484 \\ -64,806 \\ \hline \end{array}$$

6 **Find the sum or difference. Make sure the answer is in simplest form.**

$\frac{7}{8} + \frac{1}{9} =$ ______ $\frac{1}{9} + \frac{1}{6} =$ ______ $\frac{6}{9} + \frac{1}{3} =$ ______

$\frac{8}{10} - \frac{1}{20} =$ ______ $\frac{6}{7} - \frac{4}{21} =$ ______ $\frac{6}{11} - \frac{1}{5} =$ ______

7 **Divide these fractions. Add zeros in the dividend until the quotient is zero.**

$\frac{1}{2} =$ ______ $\frac{5}{8} =$ ______ $\frac{9}{10} =$ ______

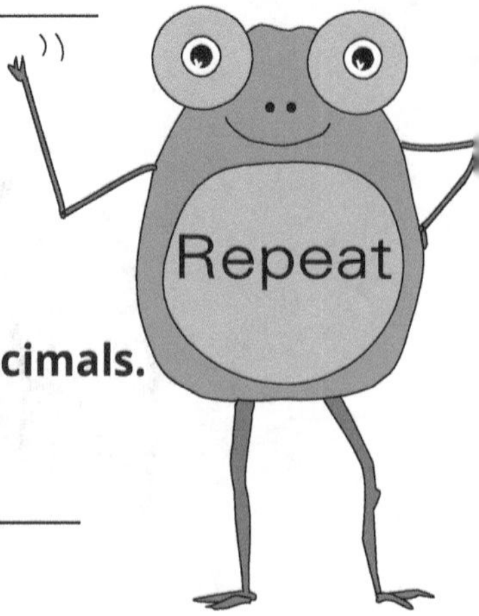

Divide these fractions. Write the answers as repeating decimals.

$\frac{2}{3} =$ ______ $\frac{9}{11} =$ ______ $\frac{7}{9} =$ ______

Traveler's Checks and Money Orders

Traveler's Checks Many people who travel are able to use the same credit cards and ATM debit cards that they use on a daily basis. But there can be some situations or emergencies where another form of funds can be needed. Traveler's checks can be purchased at many banks in different amounts, such as $10, $20, $50, and $100. The bank requires that you pay a small fee, usually around 1% of the total amount of the traveler's checks, for providing the service.

The advantage of traveler's checks over cash is that if your traveler's checks are lost or stolen, you call an 800 number and give them the serial number of your checks and receive new traveler's checks in less than 24 hours.

Travel Cards Travel cards are a preloaded ATM/credit card that has securities similar to a traveler's check. There is typically a charge for issuing the card and there can be charges for making cash withdrawals at ATMs.

Gift Cards Gift cards and gift checks are available for giving as gifts on special occasions. Like traveler's checks they are purchased for a specific amount. Some must be used at a particular business but others can be used at many different establishments. There can be a fee for the purchase of these cards and the value can decay if it is not used within a specific period of time. Occasionally, these are issued as a rebate on a purchased item or for a refund on something that has been returned.

Money Orders Some businesses require payment through money orders instead of personal checks. A money order is a type of check that is written by a cashier at a bank, grocery or convenience store. You tell the cashier how much you want the money order to be made out for. Then give them that much money, plus a small service charge. It is wise to shop around since the price for money orders can vary. The institution where you bought the money order will keep a copy of the money order you purchased.

(1) **Practice.**

1. Andrew wants to buy a German clock for $37.00. Below are the traveler's checks that he has in his wallet. Circle the gift check/checks he should use to make the purchase so that he gets the least amount of change back.

3 - $50	2 - $100's	2 - $20's	1 - $10

2. Andrew eats lunch at a small cafe. His total bill is $7.49.
Circle the gift check / checks he should use to make the purchase so that he gets the least amount of change back.

3 - $50	2 - $100's	2 - $20's	1 - $10

3. One Stop, a convenience store, offers money orders for fifty cents each. Samuel needs to buy money orders for $19.99 and $27.50. How much will he owe the cashier?

4. The Miller Family is going to Florida on vacation and they want to purchase a $450.00 travel card from a bank. If the bank charges a 1.5 % fee for the travel card, how much money will they need in all?

(2) **Read each word problem and decide what operation you would use to solve the problem. Write the operation on the line provided.** You do not need to work the problems.

1. John and Ralph have 450 pounds of rock to distribute between 9 lots. How many pounds of rock will be delivered to each lot? ____________________
2. Sean is packing tent poles for a group camping trip. If each tent uses 2 poles, and there are 27 tents, how many poles should Sean pack? ________________
3. At the craft sale, Tammi made $245.00. What will her profit be after she pays $35.99 for booth rental? ____________________
4. Look at the money earned at the car wash in each category. What was the total profit for the car wash? ____________________
   a. vacuum only - $15.00
   b. wash and wax - $30.00
   c. wash only - $20.00
   d. vacuum, wash and wax - $45.00

(3) **Jeannie kept a record of all of the gifts she bought in 2018. Use this information to find the average amount of money she spent each month on gifts.**

Month	Purchase #1	Purchase #2	Purchase #3	Total Purchases
January	$19.99			
February	$5.79	$10.99		
March				
April				
May	$20.13	$4.88		
June				
July	$14.90	$8.14		
August	$12.90			
September				
October	$32.44			
November	$19.24	$39.00		
December	$22.13	$45.00	$32.99	

What was Jeannie's average monthly expenditure for gifts in 2018?

4 **Shade the prime numbers. If the correct blocks are shaded, the shaded blocks will form a letter.**

2	4	8	9	12	19
10	3	14	15	23	16
22	26	5	41	27	33
34	35	73	7	40	42
44	89	45	46	11	50
97	52	54	56	58	13

What letter did the shaded boxes form? _____

5 **Divide.**

$2.8\overline{)14.56}$ $5.3\overline{)12.561}$ $2.5\overline{)2.975}$

$1.9\overline{)9.291}$ $0.35\overline{)3.122}$ $4.3\overline{)5.418}$

6 **Give the liquid measures as gallons, quarts, and pints.**

12 quarts
______ pints ______ gallons

32 pints
______ gallons ______ quarts

25 quarts
______ gallons ______ pints

24 pints
______ gallons ______ quarts

64 pints
______ gallons ______ quarts

20 gallons
______ quarts ______ pints

7 **Find the quotient.**

$3.01\overline{)159.53}$ $51.2\overline{)7,884.8}$ $4.07\overline{)256.41}$

$1.71\overline{)155.61}$ $11.2\overline{)212.8}$ $5.97\overline{)650.73}$

1 **Do these additions and subtractions and compare.** 8 pts.

7 – 1 = ________	7 + (-1) = ________
11 – (-4) = ________	11 + 4 = ________
(-8) – 7 = ________	(-8) + (-7) = ________
(-9) – (-2) = ________	(-9) + 2 = ________

2 **Find these points on the grid below and connect them in the order given.** 19 pts.

1. (0, -4)	11. (-2, 3)
2. (2, -3)	12. (-3, 4)
3. (3, -2)	13. (-4, 4)
4. (4, -1)	14. (-5, 3)
5. (5, 2)	15. (-5, 2)
6. (5, 3)	16. (-4, -1)
7. (4, 4)	17. (-3, -2)
8. (3, 4)	18. (-2, -3)
9. (2, 3)	19. (0, -4)
10. (0, 2)	STOP

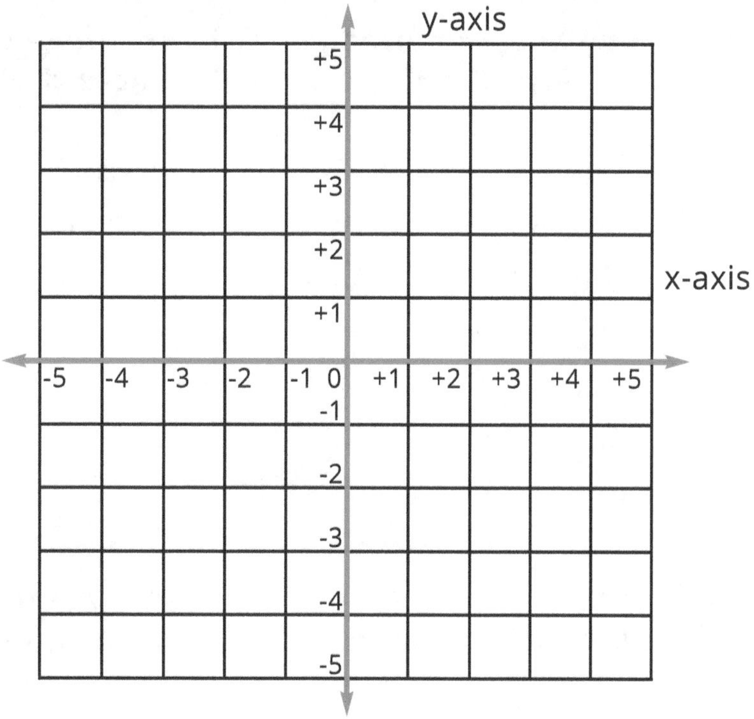

3 **Find the product.**

(+9) × (-8) = ________

(-4) × (-7) = ________

9 × 3 = ________

(+12) × (-4) = ________

(-7) × (-7) = ________

Find the quotient. 10 pts.

18 ÷ (-2) = ________

(-72) ÷ (+9) = ________

(-36) ÷ (+9) = ________

(-45) ÷ (-5) = ________

12 ÷ 2 = ________

4 **Solve.** 8 pts.

George has a balance of $149.13 in his savings account.
What is his balance after he deposits $15.50?

Maureen has a balance of $315.65 in her savings account.
What is the balance after she withdrawals $12.75?

If Suzanne gets paid 179.00 a week and she wants to save 10 percent of her income.
How much should she save a week?

Donald gets paid $240.00 a week, and he puts 15 percent of his income in savings.
In one year (52 weeks), how much will he have saved?

total points 78

⑤ **Complete the table.** 5 pts.

Interest	Principal	Rate	Time
	$1,000	4%	1 years
	$700	12%	3 months ($\frac{1}{4}$)
	$312	$7\frac{1}{2}$% (0.075)	1 year
	$10,000	10%	6 months ($\frac{1}{2}$)
	$3,000	8%	6 months ($\frac{1}{2}$)

⑥ **Amy bought a used guitar on the installment plan. She pays $20.00 a month. Complete the table.** 19 pts.

Month	*Balance*	*Interest 1%*	*Payment*	*New Balance*
1st month	$100.00	+ $1.00	– $20.00	$81.00
2nd month	$81.00			
3rd month				
4th month				
5th month				
6th month				

⑦ **Peter found the same t-shirt at three different stores. Find the discounted price for each store. Circle the lowest price.** 3 pts.

Clothing World	$19.99	10% discount	______
Discounts Galore	16.99	5% discount	______
Gallow's Sports	$18.99	20% discount	______

⑧ **Complete the catalog order form.** 6 pts.

Order #1			
Item	Quantity	Price per item	Total Cost
Tennis Racquet	10	$13.99 ea	
Tennis Balls (case)	10	$15.99 ea	
Racquetball Racquet	15	$15.50 ea	
Total			
6% sales tax			
Shipping		$10.00	10.00
Grand Total			